She's Crazy! About Me!

D. ALBERT LEE

ASPIRE
PUBLISHING HUB LLC.

ISBN
978-1-960758-20-0 (Paperback)
978-1-960758-21-7 (eBook)

SHE'S CRAZY! ABOUT ME!

D. ALBERT LEE

TABLE OF CONTENTS

Chapter 1   Flowers in Her Hair.. 1

Chapter 2   Who's the Crazy One? 17

Chapter 3   Sex on the Mountain 33

Chapter 4   Lady Godiva.. 44

Chapter 5   Don't Make Her Mad! 56

Chapter 6   Carl! 68

Chapter 7   Dilemma!.. 72

Chapter 8   I love you…I love you not!.. 83

Chapter 9   The Demons Return... 95

Chapter 10   Pain Makes it Easier to Let Go! 113

Chapter 11   Spiritual Awakening!.. 119

Chapter 12   Donnte 144

Chapter 13   The Beginning of Trouble....................................... 150

Chapter 14   Bubbles & Sherman's... 164

Chapter 15   The Fight.. 177

Chapter 16   She's Got My Back!...183

Chapter 17   Courtroom #7 194

Chapter 18   Magnificent.. 207

Chapter 19   The Decision 220

Chapter 20   Goodbye Burg 226

Chapter 21   On the Train 243

Chapter 22   The Other Woman 252

Chapter 23   Meet the Carvers 272

Chapter 24   Fun with the Family 285

Chapter 25   The Game 294

Chapter 26   St Louis or Malibu....................................... 306

Chapter 27   I Love You, Daddy..318

Chapter 28   The Diary... 329

CHAPTER 1

Flowers in Her Hair

It was the month of April when I met her! It was the second Sunday of the month on a beautiful afternoon. The gorgeous, beautiful sky was lit up by an awesomely brilliant sun. The temperature was in the mid-70s and a gentle breeze was blowing the newly formed leaves on the branches in the trees. White clouds were the only thing that interrupted the expansive and continual blueness of the sky. There couldn't have been a more perfect day to meet the most perfect specimen of a woman that I had met in quite a while!

When she came into my life I had not intended to get involved with her or any woman for that matter, because my priorities were elsewhere. Women always seem to divert me from the narrow path that led to financial success and placed me on the wide road to financial ruin. I don't blame them for it because it isn't their fault. It's just one of the many defects of character that I had discovered about myself. Women were an addiction to me! I knew that about myself, but I had yet to discover the solution to that dilemma. I had yet to discover the secret of combining a successful business venture with the successful physical relationship with a woman. But Diana changed all of that with just a short ride in my van, a heavenly smile, silky seductive legs, and sweet conversation.

I had just exited a Narcotics Anonymous meeting at The Onala Club when I saw her. I was totally blown away by her beauty. For a split second, I forgot where my van was parked.

The Onala Club is a recovery club, non-alcoholic, open to anyone seeking recovery from drugs, alcohol, or other substances. Its doors are almost always open. It also welcomes groups like, Gamblers Anonymous, Over Eaters Anonymous and others.

She was with several friends of mine whom I had met through my affiliation with Narcotics Anonymous. Phil, Carl and Danny. They had also come out of the Onala Club after attending an AA meeting.

My van was parked in the rear parking lot and I was moving toward it when I heard my friend Phil called out to me. "Hey Donn!"

I turned to greet him but when I saw her walking with him; my eyes were fixed on her and not him. She was absolutely beautiful! Her smile was warm, genuine and radiant. It was eclipsed only by the sun itself! With it, she captured me. I no longer saw Phil, Danny and Carl who just happen to be walking beside her. I saw only of how the light of the sun played with the surface of her light brown skin in just the right way to cause me to be mesmerized by her perfectly fitted pink and yellow flowered sundress which accented her every curve. I watched her move towards me as if in slow motion and I surveyed every inch of her from the pink ribbon that tied back her lovely hair to her pink and yellow painted toenails. When my eyes returned to meet hers again it was obvious to me that she approved of my approval of her.

"Wassup brotha'?" Phil said as he greeted me with a complicated handshake that only black men understand.

"Wassup Phil?" I said as we finished the handshake with a chest bump and a hug. "Wassup Carl? Wassup Danny?"

"Wassup!"

"Wassup!"

"We're headed to the AA anniversary meeting over on Allegheny and Beech. Can we get a ride with you?" Phil asked.

"Sure. C'mon. I'm going that way."

"Thanks brotha'!" Phil said.

Phil and I walked ahead while she walked behind us with Danny and Carl. I glanced back to her because she had the type of beauty that couldn't and wouldn't be ignored! I made eye contact with her and she held it for a second or two and then she looked away shyly. I returned my attention to the conversation with Phil but my mind stayed on her. I was tempted at least 20 times to look back again but I controlled the urge with small talk with Phil. When we got into the van Phil took control of the front seat and she scooted into the back and sat in the seat directly behind me. I adjusted my rearview mirror so that I could see her in the corner of it. Just as I had suspected, she was watching me. Our eyes met again through the mirror. She quickly diverted her eyes as a shy girl would but in the next instant she bravely stared wantonly into my eyes. The quick-change caught me off guard. It startled me and at the same time it aroused my curiosity as well as my desire. I broke the stare, composed myself and began the conversation with Phil again as I drove out of the parking lot and up Carson Street to the West End Bridge.

Just before we began to cross the bridge she leaned over to Phil and whispered something into his ear. He looked at me and smiled then he got up and switched seats with her. She sat, crossed her shapely legs, hiked up her dress just above the knee, winked at me and then she spoke.

"So Donn, are you married?"

"No."

"Ever?"

"Yes."

"Did you leave her or did she leave you?"

I gave her a look of curiosity before I spoke.

"A little of both!"

"Was she cheating on you?"

"No, not really. Not with a man at least..."

"Oh, she turned lesbian on you, huh?"

"Where's all this coming from? I'm supposed to be the one asking the questions."

I reached the other side of the bridge. She shifted in her seat and adjusted her dress again. This time she showed more of her shapely thighs.

"Well..., ask!" She smiled. "Ask anything you want!"

"What's your name?"

"Diana."

She crossed her legs the opposite way and deliberately hiked her dress up to where I could almost see heaven and she made sure that I was watching before she settled back in her seat again.

The van swerved! My eyes were not fixed on the road anymore because I was distracted for a moment, but I was able to straighten the van before I lost control. She chuckled again and shifted once more, but this time I only looked out of the corner of my eye and kept my focus on the road.

She chuckled again. "You'd better keep looking that way!" She pointed out of the front window.

"Then you need to stop distracting me!"

"How am I distracting you?" She said playfully.

I took a quick look into her eyes. "You know exactly what I'm talking about!"

"Oh. You mean," She turned towards me and rubbed her hands across the bare part of her thighs, "... with these ol' things?" She then tugged at the hem of her dress and pulled it down about a quarter of an inch!

"Yes! With those 'fine' things!" I looked back into her eyes again.

She was smiling with great pride as she took hold of my stare with her own. "Thank you! They are kinda nice, aren't they?"

I wanted to say, 'yes, but I need to see the rest before I can make an intelligent assessment!', but I didn't. I just said, "Yes they are."

I noticed how quiet the three guys in the back were. They were all smiling at me. Phil broke out into a hearty belly laugh. Danny laughed right along with Phil, but Carl tried to hide his laughter behind his hands.

His face was asymmetrical because of a thick scar that started at the corner of his mouth and ended just below his ear. It prevented him from having balance when he talked or laughed. He had been cut viciously by a knife or some other very sharp object. I was curious to know how he received it but I didn't ask. He never spoke of it and no one else mentioned it, so neither did I.

My attention returned back to Diana. She was utterly beautiful. Her jet black hair was naturally wavy and lengthy. When she reached behind her neck and pulled it across her shoulder it fell into the crevice of her breasts. Her eyes, almost as dark as her hair, were pools that beckoned me to come and swim in them. Her lips were small but not thin! Luscious, but not large!

She and I began to talk and I asked her an assortment of questions and I answered many of hers. When we reached the church on Allegheny, Phil, Danny, and Carl exited the van and thanked me for the ride. Diana stayed.

"You guys go on ahead. I'll be there in a minute." She spoke through the open window. They walked on and then she turned her attention back to me.

For the next 20 minutes we sat in the van and talked. She was a tease and talked a lot about the power that women have over men because of sex. I learned that her favorite subject was sex! It was also mine, but I preferred doing it than talking about it. To meet a woman who was as beautiful as she was and who was obsessed with sex as I was, was rare! I seriously didn't want to let her get away!

"Donn, why don't you come in?" She asked. "I really want to hear more about your views on who is on top in the battle of the sexes!"

"I'd love to Diana, but I have to get to my meeting. I'm committed, I'm the chairman today but if not for that I would not let you out of my sight!" That brought a gigantic smile.

"I understand. Well I'll call you later after I get home and then we can talk some more. Okay?"

"Sure!" I said. "I'll be waiting!"

"You'd better be!" She said with a smile. "I should be home about 10 PM. I'm going to spend some time with my sponsor but I'll call you when I get home. I promise! Bye-bye!"

"Bye!"

I waited for her to call until 11 PM but the phone never rang. I finally accepted that she had either forgotten, changed her mind or lost my number. I had her number but I decided not to call her. I was anxious to talk to her but I didn't want to appear to be. By 11:30 PM I had showered and went to bed. Sleep came quickly.

The phone rang releasing me from my sleep. It was 1:00 AM. I answered it not knowing who would be calling me at that hour. I was surprised to discover that it was Diana.

"Hi Donn! I bet that you thought that I had forgotten you, didn't you? No, I didn't forget! Who can forget a sexy man like you?" I felt her smiling.

"Why are you calling me so late? It's one o'clock in the morning!" I didn't bother to sit up or turn the light on. I was all right with the conversation ending in a minute or two allowing me to return to sleep, but it didn't happen that way. She knew how to charm a man, even a man upset to be awakened at one in the morning!

"I'm sorry to be calling you so late Donn, but I've been out with my sponsor all evening. We went to a midnight candlelight meeting. I'm sorry, can you forgive me? Do you want me to hang up? I can call you back in the morning." Her voice pleaded with me. "Hold on a minute, please?"

"Okay." She put the phone down and the second or two later she picked it back up.

"Thanks for waiting. I had to get out of that dress! When I'm home I like to walk around in my underwear. It's a lot more comfortable, don't you agree?"

"I haven't seen you in your underwear, but I think that if I did, I wouldn't be too comfortable!" I could feel my pulse quicken.

"I wonder why?" I heard her chuckle under her breath. "You want me to describe my underwear to you?" Before I could answer, she continued. "Well, they're pink with lace all around the edges. There really tight and really hug me where they should. They really feel good on me. They make me feel pretty and if you were here I'd like to rub your hands all over them!"

"If I were there, well,... I'll tell you that when I get there!" Again, the quickening.

"So, you don't want me to hang up?"

"No. We can talk for a while." I cleared my throat. "You've been on my mind too. I thought you had forgotten me." The room was still dark but it didn't seem so dark anymore with her sexy voice in my ear.

"You didn't call me?" She asked.

For a minute there was excitement in her voice. She waited for me to say yes.

"No!" I spoke.

Her excitement waned.

There was an awkward silence for a moment or two until I said. "I wanted to. I started to several times but I didn't want to seem overanxious."

Overanxious? So that means that you were anxious, doesn't it?"

"Yes! Very!"

I felt her excitement return. "So you were anxious?"

"Yes, and I still am."

"Anxious by definition one, or two?"

She asked as a test to see how astute I was. Luckily for me I had spent a lot of time in dictionaries.

"By both!" I said. "But mostly by number two. I was worried that I wouldn't hear from you but it was because of my eagerness to get to know you, that earnest desire, that futuristic wishing for what I wanted to do that overshadowed everything else!"

"Touché'! You're good. You know just the right thing to say. Are you good in 'other' things too?"

"Yes. Are you?"

(Short and sweet. Keep it short and sweet.) Those were my thoughts.

"Baby, I'm good at EVERYTHING that I do!" She fired back.

"Really?"

"Really!"

"How do I know that? You might we just talking trash to see where I'm coming from."

"Sweetheart, when you get your chance to find out how good I am,... And you will get your chance,... And soon, don't disappoint me because I'm not the forgiving type!"

"There's never been any disappointment here, and never will be!" I sat up in bed before I continued. "I like the way that you said 'soon', but that could mean anything. It could mean tonight, tomorrow, next week, next month. How soon is soon?"

"Soon." She chuckled again and I imagined her with her hand over her mouth attempting to stifle it. I also brought up a mental picture of her standing in her pink panties. It was a picture that caused my best friend, 'Big Al' to react.

We continued our conversation for the next two hours. We talked and bantered back and forth skirting the subject of sex without actually mentioning it. I had to work in the morning so 'soon' wasn't going to be that night. If not for that, I would have found my way over to her house and spent the night butt-naked with her in bed, but instead once I hung up the phone I made my way to my shower with Big Al leading the way. The cold water did me good and I easily fell asleep thinking about all of the things that I was going to do once I got my hands on her. There was no way that she would be disappointed, frustrated or upset when I finish with her. She would understand what true satisfaction was!

Soon wasn't to be the next night either! Or the next! We spent the days apart and the nights talking on the phone. Usually she would call me around 1 AM and we would talk until about three. Each night the conversation always turned to sex regardless of how it started. As time passed we didn't skirt the subject anymore but we went straight to it and expressed our desires, our wants, our likes and dislikes. We discovered that we had a lot in common and it seemed that mentally and emotionally we were compatible when it came to the subject of sex. All that was left was to find out if that compatibility carried over into the physical.

Our first time together after our initial meeting was unforgettable. If I live to be one thousand years old, I will never forget it! I invited her to a noon NA meeting that I regularly attended in Mount Oliver. With excitement she agreed to go with me. She gave me her address and I gave her a time when I would pick her up.

I didn't think that she ever attended any NA meetings because she never spoke of NA. She attended AA meetings regularly because she considered herself an alcoholic. She also spoke of her lack of friends. I had plenty friends, male and female, black and white so I decided to share some of mine with her. I would like to say that my reason for taking her to an NA meeting was purely altruistic but that would not be the truth. The truth of the matter was that she was one of the prettiest women that I had met since being back in Pittsburgh and I wanted to flaunt her and show her off to all of my NA friends. What I didn't know was that the day held several surprises for me!

When I looked at her address and realized that the street that she lived on was in the projects in the Hill District, I should have known right then and there that there was a problem. She had no children, and she had no physical defects that she spoke of or that I could see, so why did she live alone in the projects? She didn't seem to be mentally challenged so I was unable to figure it out. I dismissed it from my mind and drove the distance to her building.

She lived in one of the three-story apartment buildings that stood across the street from the regular townhouse housing units on Burrows Street. There were two buildings that faced each other and between them was a grassy park area approximately 50 feet wide that stretched the distance of the buildings. Each building was at least 200 feet long with three entrance doors. Six apartments were serviced by each door. Diana's was the last and she lived on the third floor. I parked on the street and walked to her entrance and up the steps to her door.

The hallway was lit by a stream of light that filtered through the unwashed single window at the front of each hallway landing. There was a light fixture on the ceiling of each floor, but they were turned off or the bulbs were blown out. I expected to see graffiti in various forms adorning the walls of the hallways and stair landings, but I was pleasantly disappointed. The hallway walls were graffiti free and for the most part clean. Not at all what I had expected.

I knocked on her door. She opened it and I received the shock of my life! It was a glaring signal that warned me that this woman wasn't playing with a full deck. It was almost impossible to tell that she was the same woman that I had met just a few days earlier. I had to take a double take and I'm sure that my eyes were bulging out of my head. She still had that beautiful smile, and that beautiful flawless light Brown skin, but now she possessed floor-length hair! I am a man who loves a woman with a plethora of hair and Diana had an abundance, long and naturally wavy, but suddenly, her hair dragged the floor when she walked. The word 'colorful' doesn't begin to describe it. There were shades of colors that you couldn't find in a rainbow! The mixture had no pattern, no style, no rhyme or reason. It made absolutely no sense at all. There were strands of blue, green, black, orange, purple, yellow, red and blonde. Extensions were tied in knots to her hair. There were flowers placed here and there, some with the torn stems visibly showing. The flowers weren't cut flowers that were trimmed and displayed at a flower shop. They were not clipped or cut at the ends but were frayed because they had been ripped from their roots. They were placed here and there as if it were all just an afterthought.

The outfit that she wore brought to mind an Indian squaw. A buckskin jacket with tassels hanging from the chest, arms, collar, and bottom. Underneath, she wore a bright red long-sleeved blouse trimmed in gold. Below, she wore a pair of worn and faded bell-bottoms jeans. Denim patches were on the knees probably to cover holes. There were bright yellow and pink daisy patches sewn all over the jeans. On her feet she wore red plastic go-go boots. She looked horrible. Her fashion statement was a cross between a 1960s flower child and Pocahontas on crack!

What happened to that beautiful, witty, intelligent, graceful and sexy woman that I had met only a few days earlier? Who was this nut that had taken over her body and obviously her mind?

Diana was a beautiful young woman in her early 20s. She had been an athlete in high school and still possessed that tight athletic muscular body with smooth skin and a face so beautiful that it would make a man forget where he lived! She had classically beautiful Nubian features. The type of woman that turned every head everywhere that she went. She had all of that but there obviously was a problem in the penthouse that my trained, roving and woman watching eyes had missed! I wanted to walk away and leave her standing there but I didn't. I was obligated and committed so I reluctantly took her hand, kissed her softly on the cheek and let her out of the building. What I thought was going to be an exhilarating and thoroughly enjoyable experience was already turning into a nightmare.

At the meeting I was totally embarrassed to be seen with her. I had taken her to a meeting that I attended regularly and everyone there knew me. They also knew that I had brought people, male and female, to meetings to introduce them to Narcotics Anonymous, or to help them continue in their recovery, so I prayed that this time they would think the same of my relationship with Diana. But it wasn't to be. No one who knew me was fooled at all! I also assumed that because she was an alcoholic that she wasn't known in the rooms of Narcotics Anonymous, but I was wrong about that too!

We arrived at the meeting just before it started and all eyes were upon us. Diana strolled through the door ahead of me. Her hair bounced and smacked the floor with each athletic step that she took. She seemed to be oblivious to the stares and giggles that were coming our way. They bounced off of her without having any effect, but at the same time, they pierced and penetrated me like a thousand tiny arrows. I felt nauseous, uneasy and under a microscope!

Darla, my closest female friend, spotted me from across the room and began to approach. Darla was as straight-forward and honest as the day is long. It was one of the things that drew me to her. I needed and welcomed friendships built on honesty. I needed people in my life who would honestly tell me what they thought. Darla was that type of friend. But, there were times when I really didn't want to hear it and that time was now, but she was coming my way and I couldn't escape!

Diana had ventured across the room and was being greeted by several people. From the looks of it, they already knew each other.

"Hi Donn!" Darla greeted me with a hug and a kiss on the cheek.

"Hi Darla!" It's good to see you again." I said. I waited for the bomb to drop and it did but it just wasn't the one that I had expected.

"So, what's up with you and Diana?" Darla asked.

"What? You know her?"

"Sure. She used to come here all the time before I met you. I know her well!

I was once her sponsor."

"Wow! That's odd!" I was genuinely shocked. "She never mentioned NA at all. Just AA."

"Well, that's probably because there are things that she might want to forget." Darla's look told me that there was a story to tell but the proper time was later. "We'll talk later!" She said.

The meeting was about to start, and we took seats at the table set in the middle of the room. Diana sat on one side of me, and Darla on the other. A quick look at the faces around the table told me that everyone there knew her story except me. I was dying to know what it was.

After the meeting Darla and I went outside while Diana was busy talking with a few guys that she obviously knew. We stood at the edge of the parking lot close to the sidewalk and away from the building.

"So, what's up with you and Diana?" Darla gave me the stern motherly look that demand the truth, the whole truth and nothing but the truth!

"Well, I… ah... We're just friends…" It felt like a lie.

She scrunched her eyebrows in a dubious way waiting for the entire truth. "Just friends?"

"Yeah, so far!" I then confessed that my intentions went far beyond, 'one addict helping another'. She smiled her usual friendly smile. The Inquisition had ended before it began with my confession.

"I know it's more than just friendship. I know you Donn! You have brought many people to the meetings, even some females, but it's always been about recovery. This is different! You look different! You're embarrassed and if it was only about recovery it wouldn't matter to you how she looked, would it?" The stern motherly look was back.

"No. You're right but we haven't done anything yet!" I began feel like a little boy caught by his mother with his hand still in the cookie jar, but trying to explain by stating that he hadn't touched the cookies, yet! I tried to rationalize and justify but she just looked at me with that look that made me feel guilty as hell! After she had broken me down, she began to tell me what she knew about Diana.

Diana was well-known in the rooms of Narcotics Anonymous. She had attended faithfully for about a year and then she just stopped coming. She had earned the reputation of being an NA whore.

It was shocking news to me because I had no idea that she ever attended NA. Whenever she and I spoke of recovery she always referred to AA meetings, sponsors, and groups. She told me that she had used cocaine but alcohol was her problem, her addiction as well as her drug of choice. I accepted it without question. I had no reason to doubt her. As far as the label of NA whore was concerned, that didn't shock me because men can be cruel to a woman's reputation if she is sexually active and especially if sex is her favorite subject. Maybe she slept around, and maybe she didn't, I didn't know but she had acquired the reputation. Most of our nighttime conversations centered on the subject of sex and almost always the subject was brought up by her. She constantly talked of sex which is why I overlooked the obvious signs of mental instability. I only saw what I wanted to see because I was thinking of the little head and not the big one!

Darla went on to tell me that Diana had gone from one guy to the next and then the next without being concerned of what she was doing to friendships. Guys, who were close friends before they met Diana, had become estranged and weren't speaking anymore while she moved on to the next guy. Some had even become adversaries. Darla was trying to warn me of what was about to happen, what I was about to get into, but my mind was set on having sex with Diana. I heard every word that Darla said but the message was lost as Diana approached us.

Even through her crazy outfit and her ridiculously long and colorful hair, I still saw her beauty and I desired her even more. She threw her arms around me and kissed me full on the mouth, French style! I returned the kiss and lost any semblance of resolve that was left. As we kissed I knew it was for show and I knew that all of her former lovers were now outside watching. I knew that the kiss wasn't for me but I accepted it wholeheartedly and returned it. It ended abruptly and without taking her hands off of me, she moved to my side and her left hand slid smoothly around my waist while her right hand caressed my shoulder and then my cheek and came to rest on my chest. It was a smooth move! A move that had been perfected by practice. As she did it, she looked across the parking lot at the men gathered together just outside of the building entrance. She winked. I knew that I was being used but I really didn't care. They were all one night stands but I intended for it to be different with me. I was going to rock her world and caused her to come back for more and more!

From the looks that the guys gave me, I knew who she had been with and who she had not. The ones that she had been with had very different looks than the ones that had never tasted of her sweetness. I was so hypnotized by the thought of getting into her tight pants that nothing that was said or done mattered.

I pulled the van from the parking lot leaving most of the members standing motionless watching us. I had survived what I thought would be the worst experience of my life and I had come out of it okay. During the drive back to her place I asked the questions and she willingly provided the answers. She explained why she hadn't mentioned Narcotics Anonymous and her lovers and it all sounded plausible, especially after she said that none of them turned her on as much as I did. They only got one chance because as she put it, "they failed to supply and satisfy! I know it will be different with you Donn!"

She looked horrible and beautiful all at the same time. I hadn't noticed until then but she had taken all of the flowers out of her hair.

"Why did you take the flowers out of your hair?" I asked her.

It was a little bit too much." She replied. "Don't you think?"

I really didn't want to answer that question but I did anyway and I answered it honestly. "Yes I agree. They were too much!" What I didn't say was 'and so is that ridiculous hair and outfit'! Maybe she heard me thinking.

She said. "What do you think about the hair?"

I had learned a long time ago not to tell a woman how you truly feel until after you've gotten what you wanted, but I didn't want to lie even if it meant there would be no getting what I wanted, so I said. "Honestly Diana, I think the hair should go along with the flowers. You've got beautiful hair! That's one thing that attracted me to you when I first saw you. Your hair is gorgeous! Absolutely gorgeous! You don't need anything in it at all!"

I waited for her reaction. At first, she sat silently contemplating what I had said and then she smiled at me and began taking the knots out that tied her hair to the extensions.

"I like you Donn. I knew you were different. Anyone else would have said what they thought I wanted to hear just so they could get into my panties, but you're honest. I like an honest man! I get turned on by honesty!" She hesitated and looked at her outfit. "What do you think of this outfit?"

"Get rid of it!" I didn't hesitate to answer that question. "It's ridiculous!"

"You really think I should?"

"Yes!"

"Okay!" She took off the vest and threw it on the back seat. After she finished untying the hair, she balled it all up and threw it back there too. She started finger combing her hair and again became the Diana that I had originally met.

"What about the pants?"

"They've got to go too!"

"Okay." She said. She began to unbuttoned them. "Right now?" She toyed with me. She wasn't about to take off her pants right there in the Van, or was she?

"Sure... Why not?" I said. I waited and watched.

"Now Donn, do you really think that I'm going to take off my pants right here?"

"No. But if you did, I wouldn't try to stop you!" Devilishly I grinned at her.

After she unbuttoned the button, she quickly zipped the zipper down and then right back up again. It caught my attention if by nothing else but the sound alone. She reared back laughing.

"Don't worry Donn. You'll get your chance to see everything you're dying to see!"

"When?" I asked. My breath was getting away from me and I could feel my pulse quickening again as my heartbeat faster.

"Soon!" She teased and she rebutted her button. "Very soon!"

But soon wasn't soon enough. We sat in the van on the street outside of her apartment building talking. I couldn't keep my eyes off of her. I turned my seat to face hers so that I could keep a constant watch. She knew that she was getting to me so she turned up the fire. When she spoke she used her sweet, charming sexy voice that quickly melted away any reasonable thoughts that might have caused me to wake up out of the euphoric stupor that she had me in. If that weren't enough, she turned her seat to face me, open her legs until her knees were about 10 inches apart and began a slow, sensual rubbing of her inner thighs with both hands.

"When I get horny my thighs get hot! It always happens like that!" She moaned.

"Really?" I swallow hard. My eyes did not move from the spot where they were affixed.

"Yeah, I'm serious. You don't believe me, do you? Here, Feel!"

She took my right hand and placed it on her left thigh slightly below her 'goodies'. She was right! It was hot, very hot!

"Feel it? Rub your hands around. I'm hot all over down there!" She taunted me but I did just as she instructed and felt the heat. She placed her hands over her goodies to prevent me from venturing there. "See?"

"Yes." The heat from her thighs found its way through my hands up my arms and had begun taking over my whole body. In a matter of a few quick minutes she turned me from a strong, viral man to a quivering bowl of Jell-O. Then just as quickly as she started her game, she stopped it. She brushed my hand away, reached back to the back seat and retrieved her hair and her Pocahontas vest. She had lost all of the effects of the heat instantly then announced that she was ready to go.

(Well, two can play this game!) I thought. (She wants me to beg, but it won't be happening tonight!)(Maybe tomorrow, but not tonight!)

I walked her to her door, took her in my arms and kissed her passionately, then I ripped my lips from hers while her eyes were still closed. I said my goodbyes and walked down the stairs. She stood in the doorway watching as I descended the stairs. She didn't expect that especially after she had me panting like a winded dog, but I refuse to beg! As much as I wanted to, I absolutely refuse to do it. If I had, she would be running everything from that day on. My libido screamed for satisfaction and my loins burned with fire, but I didn't give in. When I turned on the landing, I looked up and observed her watching me. Just for a quick moment her knees became unsteady, and she reached out for the railing. I smiled with satisfaction. I exited the building with a smile on my face, but problems in my pants.

I got into my van and drove home. Big Al protested the entire time. He rose up several times and each time he threatened to rip a hole straight through my pants, but I didn't give into him either.

About 20 minutes later I arrived home. Big Al was still protesting and was determined to have his way. The only thing that would calm him down when he became crazy was sex, self gratification or a cold shower. I chose a cold shower!

Before I entered my door I could hear the phone ringing. I answered it and it was Diana. She didn't say much but she did say that she wanted to make sure that I got home safely. I knew that wasn't the real reason and I thanked her for her concern. The conversation was dead and dry and she didn't mention sex at all. She wanted me to bring it up but of course I didn't do it. A few moments of silence and then she said.

"Don't you have anything to say to me?"

"Yes I do!"

"What?"

"Goodnight Diana. I'll talk to you in the morning."

She didn't say anything else. She was angry and she quickly hung up the phone. I took my shower then went to bed second-guessing myself but managed to fall asleep.

CHAPTER 2

Who's the Crazy One?

The phone rang and woke me up. It was one o'clock and she had given in. I smiled as I reached for it and placed the receiver to my ear.

I didn't have to ask who it was because I knew it was Diana. "What's up Diana?"

"I'm horny Donn! I need you! Please come over,... Please?"

The words were shocking and sweetness to my ears but even through the shock I responded quickly. "I'll be right over!"

"Hurry up, okay?"

"Okay!"

She hung up and in a matter of minutes I was up and dressed and running out of the building. Big Al was wide awake again and ready and leading the way. Twenty minutes later I parked the van on Burrows Street and jumped out. I ran up the steps and down the walkway to her building. I bounded up the steps two at a time and stood panting outside of her door. I knocked and waited for her to swing the door open wide inviting me in. I imagined her standing in a black sexy negligee that showed plenty of smooth silky skin without actually revealing the secret places. She was smiling, happy that I had come so quickly. The lights were low and sweet incense was burning slowly. The aroma filled the far recesses of my senses and the stereo played Marvin Gaye's Sexual Healing.

Then the door opened but not as I had seen in my vision. Diana had the chain on the door and opened it only enough for her to peek out over the taut chain that prevented my entrance. She looked surprised to see me.

"What are you doing here? Do you know what time it is?"

She seemed genuinely shocked, but of course I thought she was playing a little game of cat and mouse with me, so I played along. "Sure, I know what time it is! It's time for love!" I grinned. "Open the door, Diana!"

Her expression changed. "I'm not opening the door. You'd better go home Donn! You're starting to scare me! What are you doing here?"

"You called me! You said you wanted me to come over! What's up?" My excitement was at its peak, and I was ready for anything.

"I didn't call you! What's wrong with you? Are you crazy? Go home!"

She slammed the door in my face. I heard the dead bolt side back into place, but I still thought that she was playing, so I knocked again. Several minutes later she slid the dead bolt back and opened the door. The chain was still in place.

"What's going on?" I asked. "Are you going to let me in or what?"

"No! Go home!" She tried to close the door again, but I put my foot in the way.

"Wait a minute! You made me come all the way over here and now you aren't going to let me in? What's up with you?"

The game that she was playing wasn't any type of sex game that I've ever played before. She was serious about not calling me, but I knew that she did.

"I didn't call you!"

"You did call me!"

"No, I didn't!"

"Yes, you did! This is crazy! Are you going to let me in or what?" I repeated. I had become frustrated.

She didn't respond but she tried to push the door closed again but couldn't because my foot was still there.

"Donn, please?" She begged. The look she gave me was serious. She was really scared so I removed my foot. She slammed the door again and the dead bolt went back in place. I stood dumbfounded. I almost knocked again but I decided not to. After looking at the outside of the closed door for a few seconds, I left.

I went back to the van and sat behind the wheel trying to figure her out. What she did just didn't make any sense at all. It was ludicrous, almost laughable, but the joke was on me, and I wasn't laughing. Neither was big Al. I drove home completely disgusted with myself. My sexual frustration had now risen to a brand-new level. As I entered my place, I could hear the phone ringing off the hook.

(Now who could that be? Duh!!!!)

"Hello." I said flatly.

"Donn? Why haven't you left yet? I've been waiting for you. Aren't you coming?" Innocence and sincerity oozed from her words.

"What the hell is wrong with you Diana? I just left your house because you wouldn't let me in!"

She was calm but I was furious. She was serene and I was agitated.

"You weren't here." She was calm, too calm! "I've been sitting here wondering why you haven't shown up. I've been calling you for the last 20 minutes. If you aren't coming, then tell me and I'll call someone else!"

I couldn't let that happen. Big Al would never forgive me.

"Okay! Okay! Give me 20 minutes. I'll be right here!"

I drove back wondering what the hell was wrong with me. I couldn't have been 'whipped' because I hadn't gotten that far yet, but nevertheless I was on my way back again. I was mentally kicking myself for going through the insanity, but I had convinced myself that it would all be worth it.

I parked again and started for her building. This time I walked at a normal pace, and I climbed the stairs and again stood outside of her door. I collected my thoughts and took a deep breath before I knocked.

She opened the door, but the chain was still there! I should've walked away right then and there and never looked back but… I could have saved myself a lot of anguish and conflict but… The truth of the matter was that I was not in control! Big Al was running the show and he had a one-track mind, no conscience, and no shame! He overruled any decision that my intelligence and common sense produced.

The look on her face told me that I was in for more of the same. Yes, I should have walked away but I stood there like a fool and endured, still hoping that I would be rewarded with a slice of Diana and sweet chocolate pie! But the words that spewed from her mouth were the same as before and the door did the same thing as it had done before. This time when it slammed shut, I didn't try to convince her to open it. I just turned and walked away and left the building.

As I came out, I noticed several people sitting around the doorway of the building across the way. They were drinking, smoking, talking, and laughing. They were having a good time at two in the morning. They were still sitting out as if it were two in the afternoon. They were looking in my direction while they laughed, and I felt that they were laughing at me. I had heard the laughter the first time that I was there, but the laughter didn't pierce in the same way as it did the second time. They may not have been laughing at me, but I felt so ridiculous and stupid that it sunk in as if they were. They had seen me come and go, come again and now I was going again. They looked in my direction and their eyes followed me as I walked to my Van, again!

I stepped into my van and slammed the door feeling like a complete fool. I drove off angrily because I was upset and frustrated. I vowed to remove all traces of thought of Diana from my head and my life. There was nothing on this earth that would ever be able to change my mind! I was totally done with her!

I didn't want to find my phone ringing when I got home again so I decided to call her and put an end to the insanity right away. I stopped at a phone booth before I left the area, and I called her. As the phone rang, I prepared the words that I was going to say. I intended to tell her to find some other fool because this one wasn't fooling around with her anymore.

She answered. "Donn? Is that you?"

"Yes, it's me!" I tried to sound cold, angry, and calloused. "Diana I..."

"Oh baby, I'm so sorry. I don't know what came over me. Please come back. I promise I'll make it up to you! Please?" She begged.

Just that quickly, just as easily as her words rolled from her lips, all of my mental preparations to end this fiasco vanished and my steadfast, ironclad resolve dissolved leaving me once again a prisoner to my own lust.

"I'll be right there!" I said it so quickly that it startled both of us.

"Really?"

"Yeah, but Diana?" I tried to salvage my pride.

"Yes baby?"

"Don't play with me! I'm coming back but don't..."

"Baby, I promise I'll let you in and I promise you get everything that you want!"

"All right!" I said sternly.

"I'll be waiting." She purred. Her voice was syrupy sweet and promised of great and wonderfully delicious things to come.

I drove back to her building and parked again. As I walked back to her building the people across the way were still sitting out and still laughing as they followed me with their eyes. I looked away and climbed the stairs for the third time. I asked myself, who's the crazy one? I knew that there was something mentally wrong with her, but I kept going back. I thought that I was fairly sane, but I was the one they kept going back, so who was the crazy one? Really? I put the thought out of my head and knocked hard on the door. I didn't have to wait long. The door swung open widely immediately. There was no chain restraining it this time.

(Thank you Lord).

She leaped out and took me into her arms and began kissing my face. Over and over again she apologized for what she had done and begged my forgiveness. I told her that it was okay even though it wasn't. She kept apologizing and kissing me.

"Let's go inside." I spoke. I wanted to make sure that I made it through the door this time!

Inside, Marvin Gaye wasn't singing, and the lights were about as dim as the noon-day sun in mid-July. But I was inside! She was smiling and wearing the smallest, skimpiest, tightest, pinkish Teddy that I had ever seen! It was just that her body filled it out so well and removed any possibility of a wrinkle or creases anywhere. She turned completely around very slowly in order that I might see it from every angle.

"You like?" She asked. "What do you think?" Her smile was electrifying. Her body was magnificent! She placed her right hand upon her hip and her left hand behind her head and posed for me.

(Magnificent!) I thought.

Maybe I said it. I'm not sure but as soon as the thought hit my mind, she smiled and said, "Thank you!" Leaving me to wonder if I had just thought it or had actually spoken it. Maybe she was reacting to the satisfied and pleased look that I had displayed on my face.

She was absolutely beautiful! She knew it and flaunted it. The flowers and all of the crazy clothes were gone. Her beauty was shining through.

A lump formed in my throat, and I swallowed hard. I had been married to a very beautiful woman and I have had relationships with several gorgeous women, a model, a dancer, athletes, an actor and a bodybuilder so being in the presence of a very beautiful woman was nothing to me, but that night as she made the metamorphosis from batty to beautiful, it simply took my breath away and for a fleeting moment I was speechless.

"I... I... I think you're the most beautiful woman that I have ever seen!"

At that moment I meant every word. I knew that her body was impressive, but I had no idea just how flawless and magnificent it was. I just couldn't take my eyes off of her and she loved it. She approved of my approval of her, and it showed with the radiance of her skin as she gave me smiling eye contact that said I would soon have the opportunity to explore every inch of it!

"You want some coffee baby?" Her smile was still radiant. I nodded and she turned and began to sashay toward the kitchen. I watched her movements without blinking. "Sit down!" She said as she took a quick glance at me to make sure that I was still watching her.

She had a coffee pot sitting on a small table by her kitchen door. The cord was plugged in through the doorway, around the corner of the wall that separated the living room from the kitchen. She poured a cup for me and shoveled two heaping spoonsful of sugar into it followed by the same amount of non-dairy creamer. She brought it to me and placed it on the coffee table in front of me on a coaster. She handed me a napkin and then she leaned over and kissed me.

The coffee was strong! Extraordinarily strong! At least twice as strong as I'm used to it being, but I sipped it anyway. I wasn't going to do anything to set her off, at least not before I got what I came for! She told me that she kept a hot pot of coffee available at all times. Coffee was her other addiction. She drank it religiously.

"Are you comfortable baby?" She asked.

"Yeah, I'm fine... considering!" My eyes focused on her breasts that were about to burst free from their restraints.

"Considering what?"

"Considering the fact that I'm looking at you and I see the outline of every curve, dimple, and that you've got and I'm burning up inside. I'm ready to attack you!"

I wasn't just saying it, I meant every word. I saw everything that she had through that flimsy, translucent material. What I couldn't see clearly, my imagination saw for me.

"Baby, I want you to attack me but not just yet. Before I give you what's inside of this..." She rubbed her hands across the length of her Teddy. "... I'm going to dance for you. Okay?"

"Sure!"

I sat back and sipped the hot, syrupy sweet, ridiculously strong coffee and prepared myself for the treat. She apologized again for her earlier behavior and then she kissed me again. The radio was playing 'Ice, Ice Baby' and she started to sway her hips to the music. It was enchanting. Her movements were perfect, fluid, and above all, sexy! She moved like a goddess with angelic perfection and rhythm. I fell into a trance as I watched. I don't think I blinked once. Everything was perfect until she opened her mouth to sing along.

Her voice penetrated me like a thousand sharp fingernails scraping viciously across a giant chock board. It was so awful that my head began to ache. Her voice didn't fit her at all! I had to do a double take to be assured that it was actually her. It was! Her voice was so different from her feminine speaking voice. It was deep and masculine. So much so that it would have made Barry White envious.

"Ice, ice baby... Dum dum dum dum da da dum dum! Ice, ice baby... Dum dum dum dum da da dum dum!

(Oh my God! I can't stand it!) I heard the thought scream in my head.

"DIANA!" I yelled to her, but she didn't hear me. She just kept singing and dancing.

"Ice, ice baby... Dum dum dum dum da da dum dum!" A hip, a very curvaceous hip, popped out at me. She turned her back towards me and began to grind her hips, pushing her behind in my direction.

"DIANA!" I yelled again. Her hips were swaying, and her feet were moving expertly to the beat, but she still didn't hear me. She was lost in her own world.

"DIANA!" I screamed this time. It was so loud that I'm sure that the people sitting across the way heard me, but Diana kept right on dancing, singing, and driving me crazy. She was oblivious to my voice. She wasn't even looking my way. She was so into dancing that she had forgotten that I was even there! I got up and grabbed her by the shoulders and spun her around. "DIANA!"

She looked into my eyes. "Couldn't keep your hands off me, could you?" She looked so innocent, so sexy and so pure, so normal as if there was absolutely nothing wrong with her, but of course, there was!

She had mood swings unlike any other woman that I had known. She could flip this way, then flip that way without even knowing that she did. But I was willing to overlook that. I could live with the fact that her elevator didn't go all the way to the top floor, just as long as she treated me to the pleasures and sweetness of her impressive body. I could even handle her baritone rendition of Ice Ice Baby! Well,... Maybe not that!

I pulled her close to me and began to sway with her. I put my hands on her pink Teddy covered ass. She grinned at me and then put her hands on my ass. We moved that way for a minute or two enjoying the pleasure that we gave and received. Then suddenly, without warning she snapped at me.

"Get your hands off of my ass!"

"What?"

"Get your hands off my ass! NOW!"

"But...but...!"

"But nothing! That's my ass and you can't touch it unless I tell you to! NOBODY touches my ass without my permission! Now get your hands OFF!"

The entire time that she spent ordering me to remove my hands from her ass, she never took her hands off of mine. I took my hands away and placed them at the small of her back and rubbed softly and slowly. I tried hard to forget that this woman was psycho and just concentrate on what was to come. We danced in silence. I stared into her eyes wondering what she was thinking. I hadn't a clue!

"Okay!" Ever so sweetly she said it. "You can do it now!"

I wasn't sure if she meant that I could put my hands back on her ass, or if this was my cue to take her to bed. I was almost afraid to ask. I didn't have to.

"Put your hands back on my ass!"

I did, but the effect that I had been working to achieve was no longer there. The rhythm of romance had been broken. I had planned to romance her, toy with her, tease and then sweep her off of her feet. I wanted her to experience how I played the game of love, but her cooperation wasn't there. Maybe she just wasn't ready for that type of involvement. Maybe she was just used to calling a guy and having sex with him and that was it. Maybe no one had ever romanced her because she was just too difficult to deal with. Whatever the situation had been in the past, I wanted to surpass it and make her experience with me, as great as I had planned for mine to be with her, but I wasn't sure if I wanted to go through all that I probably would have to go through to get there. If judging from what I had already been through to get where I was at that time was any indication of what I had to endure, then I'd just settle for a night of sex! If sex was all that was going to happen, then I'd live with that!

Ice ice baby finally finished playing and I couldn't have been happier! She and I were still clutching each other's ass; our bodies were pressed tightly up against each other as we gazed into each other's eyes. I was still thinking of making this a romantic encounter even though the mood was blown, but when the next song begins play, I found new hope! Rick James and Teena Marie began to sing Fire and Desire. I slid my right hand up the small of her back and caressed. She trembled slightly as my fingers probed. My left hand stayed where it was, touching a little bit of the Teddy and a little bit of naked butt flesh. My left hand squeezed as my right hand caressed. Diana began to breathe just a bit harder, and her pulse picked up a little. I leaned in slowly and kissed her. She responded by allowing me to enter her mouth with my tongue.

"Mmmm!" She purred. "I like that!"

She pulled her lips away just long enough to speak and then she replanted them on mine. She reached around with one hand and found Big Al and rubbed him through my pants. He was already trying to bust loose from his Fruit of the Loom prison and her touch just made him strain that much harder. She continued to rub as Rick and Teena sang. I prayed that she wouldn't try to sing along with them. She squeezed him and I moaned. She giggled.

"What do you call him?" She asked.

"Huh?" I heard and understood but the pleasure was rising, and I became lost, hearing but not hearing.

She squeezed again. "Him! What do you call him? I know you gave him a name!"

"Big Al!" I said. My voice was extremely low, but she still heard me. She continued to gently squeeze him. He didn't protest one bit! I'd like to say that he was so compliant that he was like putty in her hands, but the truth of it was that he was more like case hardened steel!

"I understand the big part, but where does Al come from? I thought you name was Donn?"

"My name is Donn. Al is my middle name." As I spoke my left hand began to travel from her ass along the curve of her hip and straight to the soft hairy flesh that stood at the entrance of her body. I made circular motions, lightly touching her through the Teddy material. She gave her approval. She didn't order me off as she had done earlier when I touched her ass. Her eyes closed momentarily, and her breathing accelerated. She opened her eyes again.

"Now... I.,... I... under... stand!"

I continued to rub her. She tried to talk while at the same time feeling her pleasure thermometer rise.

"A...A Al is your mid...middle na...name, and he's in the mid...middle!" She stammered.

Just from my touch she was beginning to boil. She tried to hide it, pretending that everything was fine, but I could feel the trembling in her body that didn't lie. She was hot-blooded. I knew that once she was turned completely on, it wouldn't take a lot of work and time to satisfy her. I didn't have a problem with that. If it took a few minutes, or all night, I was prepared for it. I was ready and eager to do the job and do it completely.

"Diana?"

"Yes?"

Her eyes were closed again, and she squeezed me hard and long.

"What do you call her?" My finger, the middle one, pressed and slid between the folds of her lips.

"Jennifer!"

"Is that your middle name?"

"No. No, it's n...not!"

She let go of Big Al and wrapped her arms around my neck, holding on for dear life as she began to shutter more and more.

(My God! She's going to come!)

She laid her head on my shoulder. Her eyes were closed but her mouth was open.

"Oooo baby! Right there, right there!" She moaned and spread her legs as much as she could. I was diddling her, and she was about to come! I remembered in the Van when she took my hand and placed it on her thigh to feel the heat. She was hot, but nothing like this! She was ablaze with heat and the material that covered her was soaking wet. I kept my finger moving with her rhythm. Her hot breath was on my neck, and it was causing me to sweat.

"Oooo! Ooooo! Baby, what are you doing to me? This can't be happening!" She breathed into my ear.

"It's happening!"

"Oooo! Aaaah! It feels sooooo gooooood! Oh my God! Oh my God!"

She squeezed my neck and her knees buckled just seconds afterward. I tighten my grip around her waist with my free hand to keep her from falling and I sped up my assault with the other. It was just seconds later that she came for the first time but because she had never experienced an orgasm that way, she was very afraid.

"No! Please stop!" She begged. I ignored her protests. It wasn't what she really wanted. She hung onto my neck and tried to stand but her legs just wouldn't hold her. Then she came and collapsed. I picked her up and sat on the sofa with her lying in my lap. It took her a while to catch her breath but when she did, she started to cry, and I held her close.

"I'm okay! I'm okay!" She said between tears. "It's just that I haven't felt like that in a long, long time!"

She began to compose herself. She laid herself back on my shoulder and her arms went tenderly around my neck.

"Jennifer!" She spoke.

"What?"

"Jennifer! I call her Jennifer!"

"Yeah, I know. You already told me."

"Oh. I did? Really? I must have forgotten."

"I wonder why?" I was smiling with pride when I said it.

She blushed and started to speak but changed her mind.

"You said her name is Jennifer but that's not your middle name." I spoke.

"Oh! I guess I did say that. I'm kind of messed up right now. You understand?" She gave me a smile of satisfaction.

"I understand. I'm kind of messed up too, but in a separate way!"

"Don't worry baby. Mama's gonna take care of you."

"Word?"

"Word!"

We started laughing. It put me at ease, and I relaxed.

"Jennifer is the name that I wish I had." She began. "I've always liked it, so I named my pussy Jennifer!"

"I guess that makes sense." It made about as much sense as naming my penis Big Al! In reality, it all was pretty silly and narcissistic.

"Donn?"

"Yes?"

"I want Big Al and Jennifer to get to know each other really well! I want them to become best friends!"

"I'm with you on that, sweetheart! I think we should introduce them right now!"

"That's fine , except for one thing!"

"What's that?"

"I haven't met him yet! I want to meet him first!"

"Well, take him out and introduce yourself! Do what you do!" I prayed that her introduction was what I wanted it to be.

She slid off my lap and knelt on the floor in front of me and began to undo my pants. After undoing my belt, button, and zipper, she freed him which allowed me to breathe a little better. She sat staring and smiling while I waited to see what her next move might be. I knew what I wanted her to do. I hoped that maybe our thoughts would collide. With one hand wrapped around him, she kissed him on the 'fore-head.'

"Hey Big Al! You're kinda cute! I see you have a couple of friends with you! Hey guys!" She kissed them too. She kept talking and between sentences, she lightly kissed him but that was it. I was expecting more, much more! I waited, expecting her to begin but she just kept on talking as if he could really hear her.

"Diana? What are you doing?"

"I'm getting to know Big Al. What does it look like?"

She went right back to it. Tension had begun to grow, and I felt the mood begin to change. I didn't like it. I came for satisfaction and all that she was giving me with frustration. I thought that maybe if I began to massage her breasts, she would return to the hot-blooded nymph that she was a few moments ago, but that didn't happen either.

I reached out and squeezed one of them. Immediately she slapped my hand away with her free hand, but she never let go of Big Al.

"What the hell are you doing?" I was totally flabbergasted.

"Don't touch me until I tell you to!" She ordered. Her look was strange, evil, and psychotic! "I told you before that nobody touches me unless I give them permission!"

"Now I need permission to touch you? Are you crazy?"

She let go of Big Al and viciously slapped him. My eyes crossed with the pain.

"DON'T YOU EVER CALL ME CRAZY! I'M NOT A CRAZY!" she yelled at the top of her voice.

My eyes were crossed and then my ears began to ring. She got up stomping around the room and yelling! "I'M NOT CRAZY! I'M NOT CRAZY!'

But of course, she was! I put big Al away. He was beginning to lose his desire anyway which made it easier to stuff him back inside of Le Prison de Fruit of the Loom!

In a nanosecond she had gone from sweet, innocent, baby doll sex kitten to vicious, get your hands off me, psycho nut! I threw my hands up in disgust and headed for the door. I had enough! She was just too much for me! I began to understand why guys spent only one night with her. I wondered how many had left, just as I was leaving, without even taking her to bed.

"Please don't go!" She begged.

I turned to her and saw her drop to her knees.

"What are you doing Diana? Get up off your knees!"

"No! Not until you promise me that you won't leave!" Her hands went together as if she were praying. She began to scoot across the floor on her knees begging me to stay. "Please Donn! Please don't leave me. I'll give you what you want. I'm ready! Let's go to bed right now. Please?"

She grabbed my leg and began kissing my knee. Her mouth was wide, and I could feel her tongue sloshing back and forth across my knee cap. I pushed her off but not before she had slobbered all over my knee and wet up my pants. I knew that I should have left right then and there, and I knew she was nuts, but you guessed it, I stayed!

There was no lovemaking that night, but we did have sex! Passionate sex, crazy sex! She led me into the bedroom and laid back on the bed reaching out, beckoning me to come to her. She didn't take off the Teddy and when I began to take it off, she stopped me and said.

"No! Don't take it off! Rip it off! Treat me like a whore!"

I did and she loved it. By sunrise both of us were satisfied and completely happy that I stayed. We showered together that morning before I left, and we ate breakfast which was an experience I never want to repeat. Diana was great in the bedroom but lousy in the kitchen.

In the shower was the first time that I had seen her completely naked and standing. She was a beautiful specimen of a woman, and I didn't really appreciate the full extent of her beauty until I saw her naked in the shower. Diana's body was the tightest and most flawless body that I ever remembered seeing. Her skin was taut, smooth and blemish free. Her breasts stood at attention and had the perfect D-cup roundness. Her hips were not large but perfectly contoured and in proportion to each other. Even her feet were objects of perfection. Her toes were perfect, and her nails were the exact color that nails should be. They were taken care of as well as some women took care of their hands and fingers.

I marveled at her. She loved it when I stared at her body. Unlike other women who would hide their breasts or cover their sex with her hands in embarrassment, she stood unashamed and proud of what she had. Believe me, I took my time! She did a spin, first fast and then slow and I watched with bated breath. She turned her back to me and bent all the way over showing me the incredible rearview. Big Al woke up immediately and took control of my senses.

"Does big Al want to play?" She purred as she looked from between her legs. It amazed me how she could bend like that. Her head was almost touching the floor.

"Yes! He wants to play with Jennifer again!"

"Well, what is he waiting for? An invitation?" She chuckled.

I didn't say a word. I just took a step or two forward until he found what he was looking for. In the shower, she was doubled over and standing, pounding herself against me with complete abandon. I didn't see how she was able to do some of the things that she did. Some things just seemed too physically impossible, but they weren't for her.

After the shower I sat at the kitchen table watching her cook in just her bra, panties, and an apron. I watched as I revisited my earlier theory of why those other guys only spent one night with her. It wasn't necessarily because she was so irrational and unpredictably insane. No! That was only part of it. She was insatiable! They just couldn't keep up with her. They left her nymphomania totally unsatisfied but after the shower session, Jennifer had had enough! What she had done to me, and for me, erased all of the craziness that I had gone through to get there. It was all worthwhile. I better understood the saying that the ends justify the means.

"Diana was an incredible lover. We spent all night in bed without sleep and having sex in every conceivable position. She never let me down. At one point we were on the bed and we're going at it so strong that the mattress began to slide from the box spring until it fell halfway on the floor. I was going to stop just long enough to fix it, but she wouldn't allow it.

"Don't stop! Not now!" She ordered. I was on top, and her legs were wide and pointed skyward. "Don't you dare take it out!"

I didn't. We slid right down the mattress and then off the mattress onto the floor but didn't miss a beat.

I ate breakfast trying desperately to swallow every awful bite. She was no Betty Crocker, not by a long shot! But I did manage to get it all down and when I finished, she asked.

"Was it good? Did you like it?"

I knew that she was referring to the breakfast, but I chose to think about her body and the sex when I answered. "Yes! I loved it! It was delicious!"

"Oh, thank you baby. I know I'm not really good at cooking, but for you I will practice. I'll get better."

I just smiled. What could I say? She was happy and satisfied in more than one way and I wanted to leave her that way. I took her hand and walked towards the door. She put her arm around me and laid her head on my shoulder. Before I opened the door, I kissed her and grabbed two heaping handfuls of her perfectly tight ass.

"From now on, that ass belongs to me! I'll grab it whenever I feel like it! Do you understand?"

"Yes baby!" She purred. "Do whatever you want just as long as you bring him." She rubbed and then squeezed Big Al. "He's all mine, right?"

"All yours baby. All yours!" I kissed her again and walked out of the door. When I stepped out of the doorway of the building, the Sun was up and her neighbors from across the way were still sitting out. The two men had now been joined by a woman. The woman waved at me, and the men gave me a victory sign. I returned it. I saw money go from one hand to another. The guy who received the money held it up and waived.

"Thanks man!" He shouted.

They had bet on my success or failure with Diana. He had bet on me and won.

"You're welcome!" I said in return.

When I got home my phone was ringing. I answered it but never expecting it to be her.

"Hello baby." She said sweetly.

"What's up?"

"Are you going to a meeting today?"

"Yes. I'm probably going to the noon meeting in Mount Washington. I might even keep the store closed and take the day off."

"Can I come over and spend the day with you?" The sound of her voice was still as sweet as honey.

"I was planning to sleep the morning away. I haven't had any sleep, you know?"

"That's fine. I'll come over and we'll sleep together. Well, not 'sleep together,' but we'll go to sleep together. Do you know what I mean? Really sleep? No sex? Okay?"

Before I could respond she continued.

"I'll catch a cab. I'll be right over!" She hung up.

I had the urge to call her right back. But why? I really wanted her to come over. It was just that she made that decision, and I didn't. Male ego! So, I didn't call, I just waited.

45 minutes later she was ringing my doorbell, and I smiled. Last night I was chasing her, now she was chasing me! I smiled and grinned with pride. I went down the steps to open the door for her.

Before I reached the bottom of the stairs I said aloud, "Big Al, you're all that!"

CHAPTER 3

Sex on the Mountain

We spent the entire morning in bed. Most of the time was spent talking and occasionally cat napping. I really intended to sleep but she interrupted my sleep by waking me with desire in her heart, sex on her mind and big Al in her mouth. It was a pleasant way to wake up, but it was shocking because she had previously stated that she didn't give head. It was too personal, she said. It was what a woman does for her man, not just with any guy that she sleeps with. I didn't push the issue because I understood, but she had changed her mind and was doing it willingly and very expertly! Sex wasn't supposed to be on the menu at all, but she managed to slip a side order or two onto my plate and of course, I didn't complain.

She briefly talked about her father but stopped abruptly. He was a good father, she said, up until she turned fourteen. That's when he killed a man and went to prison leaving her alone with a sometimes-abusive mother. She didn't want to detail the circumstances involved in his incarceration, so she stopped speaking of him.

She also took her first drink at the age of fourteen when she started hanging out with older girls 16 and 17. She was well developed and tall for her age, so no one guessed that she was only fourteen. She didn't like the taste of alcohol, but she loved feeling, so she continued until she got used to it. She lost her virginity at the same time to a guy 22 years old. He also turned her onto cocaine, and she liked it, but alcohol was her favorite. Her drug of choice she called it.

I didn't speak about myself because she wanted to talk, and I let her. She said no one really cared enough to want to listen to her story. "They just want to screw me!" She said.

I was content to lay with her up against me with my arms around her listening to her talk. It seemed to work well for both of us.

Darla was at the meeting. When she saw Diana and me together, she scowled. Diana was hooked onto my arm like a clinging vine. I didn't want to go into the meeting that way, but she refused to let go. She wanted everyone to see us together and so they did. Phil and Carl were there but I didn't see Danny. Phil wasn't surprised to see us together because he said that he felt the chemistry when we first met and knowing both of us the way he did, it was inevitable. He told me that he had been with Diana once, but...

"She's a nympho, my brother! A real nymphomaniac!" He bumped his elbow against my arm and added. "I'm sure you know that by now!" He smiled and whispered the way guys do knowing that they have something in common. "But brother man, she was just too much for me. I couldn't keep up!"

"You're right! She is something!" I said. I didn't want to go into a behind-the-back conversation which I felt was coming. Phil was beginning to dig for details, but those details would stay between her and me.

As I looked around the room, I could see that he wasn't the only one who had details on their mind. I had progressed above all of them that had come before me, and curiosity was killing everyone.

How did I do it? What was my secret? Everyone's face seemed ask that variety of questions.

Diana had left me and had found herself in the midst of a small group of women who spoke with her but snuck occasional glances at me. There smiles let me know that Diana wasn't being stingy with details, but the way I saw it, she could do that. Being the man, anything that I might say about it would only sully her reputation, but on the other hand anything that she would say would only accentuate and bolster mine.

"C'mon Donn, give us the scoop brother! Everyone already knows you've been there... Twice at least! We just want to hear it from you!" Phil began to grill me. He was primed and ready to hear details.

When Phil began to speak about Diana, I noticed that Carl became upset. He didn't say it, but it was the look on his face that betrayed him. He managed to find his composure before he spoke.

"Yeah man. Give us the 411!"

"No can do! If you want to know anything you're going to have to ask her." I was firm and unwavering.

Darla came to my rescue just as several other guys showed up with questions in their minds. Questions that didn't require the surface stuff because they already surmised that, but their questions required the deep, dark, dirty answers. They would never get them from me. If they really needed to know they should have performed to satisfaction when they had their turn!

"Hey sweetheart!" Darla hugged me and kissed me on the cheek.

"Hey darlin'!" I hugged back. "You look extremely beautiful today."

"Thank you, sweetheart! You look rather good yourself. I wonder why?"

She and I laughed along with the guys except for Carl who wasn't laughing.

"It shows?"

"Yeah brother. It shows!" Phil replied.

"Donn, I need to talk to you." Darla said. Her mood had changed, and she hooked her arm under my arm and began guiding me through the circle of guys and towards the rear door and the kitchen. "Excuse me fellas." They reluctantly moved from my path. Darla began to speak.

"Donn, you're headed for trouble! Diana isn't stable! She's got problems that you can't solve. Problems that maybe no one can solve! I'm telling you this for your own good," She hesitated and stared at me before she continued. "For your own safety! You need to think about what you're doing."

"But... But..."

"Shut up and listen!" She stopped and looked at me with concerned and caring eyes and then she began again. "I love you, Donn. You're the brother that I've ever had. You're the best male friend that I've ever known and you're very smart. You're always giving me good advice that works, but right now, you're acting like an idiot! It's like you're stupid or something! I know you can see the signs that she's crazy. Don't you?"

"Well..."

"Well, my ass! You see it and you know it!" She looked genuinely concerned, and it caused me to listen a bit more closely. "Donn, you don't know her like I do. She can be fine one minute and totally flipped out the next. When she flips out, your life is in danger! Remember how she was dressed at the last meeting? Do you think that was normal behavior? Well, she does! She thinks it's normal because she's NOT normal! Donn, all I'm saying his watch her. Be careful! She's dangerous! Okay?"

"Okay!"

"I love you."

"I love you too!"

That was all that she said before she gave me a big hug and then went out to the meeting.

Diana was the perfect lady the entire day. She didn't do, say, or wear anything that would cause me to be embarrassed. We talked, laughed, and had a wonderful time together.

I decided to keep the store closed all day and just spend the day doing things that she wanted to do. She had mentioned that she had never been on the Inclined Train because she was always afraid that the cable would break and send her plunging down the side of the mountain to her death. I told her that I had ridden it many, many times without any problems.

The Inclined Train is attached to the side of Mt. Washington and takes you from Carson Street up the side of the mountain to the top of Mt. Washington to Grandview Avenue. It's pulled by cable on tracks similar to railroad tracks. It's a scary ride up the side of the mountain, but it's also the fastest way up. Most people who refuse to ride it are afraid that the cable will break and send them plunging to their death. Instead of starting down on Carson Street, we drove to the top and entered the car there.

"It's a beautiful feeling and once you get over the fear, you'll love it! I'll hold you all the way!" I told her.

She reluctantly agreed. "I trust you baby. If you keep your arms around me, I know I'll be alright."

She was very frightened when we stepped onto the car. She looked down the side of the mountain at the wheelhouse at the bottom and she shivered with fright.

"What if the cable breaks? What if we can't get out and we crash into that building down there?"

"Diana, this thing has gone up and down this mountain for about 100 years and as far as I know it has only crashed once, and that was over 50 years ago!"

I immediately knew that I shouldn't have told her about the crash. When I said it, she tensed up and looked towards the still open door.

"Don't worry baby. They have computers now to check the cable and everything else all the time. If something even looks like it's going bad, they replace it right away. This thing will never fall again, I promise you! It also has special breaks so if anything goes wrong, it stops immediately!"

"Okay, if you say so." She clung to me and only began to relax as the car moved down the track and arrived at the halfway point. Before we reached the bottom she let go of her fears and began to enjoy the ride.

We rode from Grandview Avenue to Carson Street and ran across the street on our way to Rod Woodson's restaurant. We sat, relaxed, and ate a late lunch. We sat in the booth by the window and could see the Incline tracks perfectly clear all the way up the side of the mountain. She watched the cars go up and down and I watched her. I could see the kid in her beginning to come out. She was intrigued by the way the cars travelled, one up and one down in perfect synchronization with each other. She was so excited that she could hardly eat for thinking about the trip back up.

"Baby, I never thought that riding the Incline could be so exciting and so much fun. It was great! It frightened me too but that was a part of the fun now that I look back. I can't wait to go back up!" She reached across the table and grabbed my hand. She squeezed playfully. "I'm horny! Think we can do it on the way back up?" Her eyes were well lit with passion.

"You're kidding, right?" It had never crossed my mind before.

"No! No baby I'm not kidding! I'm serious! Just think of how much fun it would be!"

"We can't do that with people on the car!"

"I know! But if no one is on the car with us, we'll do it. Okay?

I thought about it, and it did sound exciting. I wondered how many couples had tried it, and then I wondered how many of them had been caught. I looked at the cars as they moved along the steep tracks. As one ascended and the other descended at the same rate of speed, the people in the descending car could see into the ascending car until they passed at the halfway point, and then it would be reversed. We would be going up which meant that those coming down might be able to see us. The thought of being seen excited me and frightened me at the same time. The cars passed each other, and I felt an added twinge of excitement and decided to go for it!

Diana sat starry eyes while she waited for my decision and my response. I could feel her pulse as her hand touched mine.

"Okay, but when we get to the top let's get the hell out of there fast! If someone in the other car tells what they saw it might cause us trouble!"

"That's fine but baby, let's do it all the way up. Even if someone sees us, don't stop! All right?"

"You want someone to see us?"

"Yeah. Won't that make it more exciting?"

"Yeah, I guess so! I just never really thought of it, but yeah, I'm down!"

She had my adrenaline flowing already. Just thinking about someone seeing us in the act made my blood pressure rise. I paid for the food, and we rushed out and across the street. We got to the station just in time to board the car. There was no one else on the car so we decided to take the backseat. It was raised to levels higher than the front because of the steepness of the tracks.

As soon as the door closed and the cables began to pull the car up the side of the mountain, Diana dropped her pants and bent over the seat. Big Al, who was already throbbing with excitement, became extremely rigid and ready for his new adventure. Once I released him from his restraints, she reached around and guided him to the place where she wanted him to be. As we slowly climbed the side of the mountain, I could hear the wheels of the car straining against the tracks. I heard the cable stretching and pulling the heavy car up the hill, but above all, I could plainly hear Diana moaning and occasionally crying out as Big Al worked his magic.

The exposure and the high probability of being seen brought much excitement to what we were doing. As the upper car approached and we grew closer to the midway point she became more excited, more animated, and much more vocal. She began to shout at me using foul language and four-letter words and she stared up into the window of the oncoming car. We could see two faces peering through the glass of the window of the car coming down the Hill. They looked to me to be in their mid-thirties. One male, one female. There was no doubt that they had spotted us and that they knew exactly what we were doing. When Diana saw the looks on their faces it raised her excitement to a new level, and she began buck up against me intensifying the rhythm of the strokes. I reached around and cupped both of her breasts in my hands and squeezed while I pushed Big Al deep inside of her.

"Oh baby! I love it!" She shouted. "Don't stop! Don't ever stop!"

The car approached us, and I could see the faces of the man and woman. The woman's face was aghast with horror that registered to the N-th degree. There was no doubt that she had never seen anyone doing what we were doing in public. The man however, had an altogether unusual look. There was an element of shock that played across his face, but his overall look was that of lust... and envy. As the cars were side by side, Diana looked over and waved to them. There was another couple in the back of the car who hadn't seen it until just that moment. Realizing what we were doing, they jumped up over their seats and watched us as we continue to travel up and they continued down.

"Stop!" Diana shouted.

"What? Why?" Big Al was in his glory and of course I didn't want to stop either!

"Hurry! Let's go to the front of the car so that they can see us again!"

I backed off and she hurried down the stairs to the front level holding onto her pants so that she wouldn't trip over them. She reached the spot where she could see the people in the car below and bent over against the glass.

"Hurry! Put it in!"

I did!

All four of the people in the other car were straining at the rear window to see. It became increasingly more difficult as the distance between the two cars increased until finally, they gave up and removed themselves from the window. Diana and I then began to concentrate on each other instead of them. Closer and closer we came to the summit of the mountain, and closer and closer we came to the peak of ecstasy until the car slowed to a tortoise crawl before becoming anchored and stationery in the wheelhouse at the top of the mountain. Diana wanted to keep going. She had almost achieved her climax. I was still a long way off from mine, so I still had a small amount of common sense at hand. She wasn't thinking about anything but coming, but I withdrew, and she became agitated.

"Diana, we've got to get out of here! Pull your pants up!"

"No! Let's finish first!" She was crazy with lust and not paying attention to the consequences.

"No! We've got to go! Now! Those people in the other car are going to tell what they saw and if we don't leave now there's going to be hell to pay. Let's go!"

I returned big Al to his sleeping quarters, although sleep was the last thing on his mind, but slowly he saw it my way and calmed down. Diana reluctantly agreed and got dressed. The doors opened and we exited the car. We passed several people as we climbed the stairs to the exit. They were unaware of what had transpired in the car they were about to enter. I smiled at them and nodded in lieu of speaking. We hurried up the stairs, walked past the operator's booth and towards the door. Just as we approached the exit door the phone rang inside of the booth. Diana and I looked back. We were unable to hear what was being said although we knew that the conversation was about us because the operator listened for a few seconds and then immediately turned to look at us. We hurried out of the door laughing.

"That was fun!" I said as we ran across the street.

"Yeah! We've got to do that again!" Diana was happy and as giddy as a schoolgirl.

My Van was parked just across the street at the corner of the side street a couple of doors from the ice cream parlor that sold some of the best frozen yogurt in town. We stopped in, still laughing and happy that we were able to do what we had done and get away with it. We bought some ice cream and returned to the Van.

Diana sat in her seat and licked her ice cream cone and looked at me. "Donn, I'm still horny. Let's go back to your place. Okay?"

I thought about it, but after what we had just done, I felt that it would be too anti-climactic to just go to bed. We should finish in the same style as we started, with an element of danger, with the chance of being discovered and the excitement of possibly being watched!

"No! We're not going to my place! We're gonna finish right here! Hurry up and eat that ice cream and get your fine ass in the back and get naked!"

She grinned so wide that she showed almost every tooth in her head. She no longer wanted the ice cream, so she threw it out the window! "Oooo! I love it when you order me around!" She stepped between the seats and worked her way to the back and started to get naked. She sat down on the carpeted floor and disappeared behind the seats. "Come on baby! Mama needs her medicine!"

She stayed with me the entire day and most of that time we spent in bed sleeping a little but sexing a lot! Around 11 PM I took her home and kissed her goodnight as she stood in her door. She wanted me to come in, but I refused. I needed sleep! I needed to get back to my world and not spent all of my time chasing my sexual desires.

"I've got to go home Diana! I had a wonderful time with you, but for now it has to end. I'll see you sometime tomorrow." I kissed her again and with my left hand I grabbed a handful of her fine ass! When I broke off the kiss, I looked her in the eye and grabbed the other cheek with my right hand. I didn't say a word, but she knew what I was thinking.

"Yes baby! It's all yours! You can grab it anytime you want to, and I'll never deny you!"

One more kiss, and I started down the steps.

"Thanks Donn! I really had a wonderful time! I haven't laughed that much in a long time or had such a wonderful time with a guy! Thank you, baby!"

I looked up at her and she was glowing. She was so beautiful that I felt my heartbeat faster just from looking at her. "I had a great time too, Diana! We'll do it again soon!"

"Will I see you tomorrow?"

"It sounds like a plan!"

"I'll call you!" She spoke.

I took one last look at her from my position on the stairs and then I continued on down the steps and out of the building.

The people across the way were still sitting out of course. When they saw me come out, they waved, and I waved back.

When I got home, I expected to hear my phone ringing. I expected to answer it and hear her voice on the other end, but I was disappointed. She didn't call. When one o'clock came, I was still awake. I stayed up expecting that familiar one o'clock call but it didn't come. About 1:30 I realized that she wasn't calling so I laid down and went to sleep.

She didn't call me that next day either as she said she would. It was several days before I heard from her again. I thought about her occasionally, but I didn't make any effort to call her. When she finally did call me, it was at one o'clock in the morning again. She wanted me to come over. Of course, she was horny! She didn't offer any explanation as to why she hadn't called me, and I didn't ask. When I answered the phone, she didn't say, 'hi Donn ', but simply said, "Baby I'm horny? Can you come over?"

When I got there, I was half afraid to knock on the door for fear of the same thing happening that had happened before, but I mustered up my courage and I knocked. She opened the door and let me in. She was dressed fairly normal. No crazy outfits but no pink Teddy either! The nightgown that she wore could not hide the curves underneath. It didn't matter what she wore, she was still as sexy as hell! We spent about a half hour talking, playing casino, and drinking coffee before we went to bed.

I could tell there was something different about her. She wasn't her usual jovial self. She seemed to be a bit depressed or preoccupied with something on her mind. During sex she seemed to be more interested in getting hers and not satisfying me. And that became evident when she finally reached her limit and wanted me to stop. But I hadn't achieved mine yet because I spent my energy working to please her. At that point she shut down completely and ordered me to stop. When I didn't, she somehow managed to get her foot onto my chest and with her powerful athletic legs she popped me off of her and sent me flying across the room! She refused to let me mount her again and left me and Big Al totally frustrated. I didn't know what to make of it because she hadn't acted that way before. There was definitely something different about her, but I couldn't put my finger on it.

She jumped up out of bed and went into the living room, made us both coffee and sat down on the couch. I went in and sat down beside her, and we talked for about an hour and a half until she said that she was horny again! Back to the bed we went, but this time when she began to howl like a Wolf and her face transformed from the beautiful to the dreaded ugly face, I did not allow her to send me flying across the room again! I got a good grip on her legs and pinned them back to the bed. She was athletic and very flexible, and she usually loved it when I folded her up like a pretzel, but in that position her strength was greatly diminished, and I could control her. Only then could I finish with the satisfaction for myself as well as for her without being sent airborne.

She soon learned that reaching the pinnacle of ecstasy was not designed to be just a one-time thing, but that she could enjoy it over and over again in the same session. That's when we finally became real lovers, giving and taking and satisfying each other to the max. She began to give herself to me without reservation and I did the same for her.

Several times she told me that she was in love with me, and it usually was after sex. It usually was while we were lying in bed, and I was holding her close. She wasn't in love with me, only with what I did for her.

Everything that we did was based on sex. Most of our conversations were about sex and the ones that didn't start out that way usually ended up that way. We were addicted to sex and without it we probably would not be seeing each other at all.

She thought that she was in love with me because I had taken her to where no man had taken her before! It was about the feeling, lust, desire, and satisfaction. It had nothing to do with love whatsoever.

Weeks passed and our relationship was working out fine. We spent a large amount of our free time together which allowed us to get to know and understand each other a little better. She had mood swings that were unlike any woman that I had ever known. I attributed it to her monthly cycle or PMS, but I quickly realized that it was much more than that. Darla's words began to ring in my ear. Diana was unstable! I needed to understand that, and I needed to be aware!

Before I left around five o'clock in the morning, she began to cry for no reason at all. We were lying in bed spooning with my arms around her and she started to talk about her father, but just as quickly as she started, she stopped. She had done it before which made me really wonder what type of relationship that she actually had with her father. She did mention that he was in prison now because he killed someone, and I wondered why! I wanted to ask her about him but when she began to cry, I thought it best that I just leave that for some other time. I held her while she cried so that she would know that someone did really care about her, not just because of the sex , but because of her!

CHAPTER 4

Lady Godiva

We were on our way to a meeting in Shadyside when I noticed her mood decline and her look of depression surface. She said that she really didn't want to go to a meeting then, but she didn't want me to go without her. As I drove, she said nothing, and I said little. She stared out of the van's passenger window as we headed down Center Avenue towards Shadyside.

We exited the van and began walking towards the church. She didn't say a word but the look on her face told the story. I didn't know exactly what was wrong with her, but I did know that she was slipping into something like a depression. I didn't know what to do so I reached out to take her hand and realized that she had the same thought in mind. We walked towards the church holding hands in silence.

At the meeting she continued with the same look and the same sullen mood. There were about fifty people who had gathered in the main room and after the preliminaries, the meeting was broken down into three circular groups in various parts of the large room. We were just getting started when Diana leaned over to me and whispered in my ear.

"We've got to go!" It was a soft but demanding.

"What's wrong?" I was puzzled. We had just arrived, and the discussion had just started. I wasn't accustomed to disrupting a meeting or leaving before it ended.

"See that lady over there?" She pointed to a white woman in the far circle. "The blonde one in the blue blouse?"

"Yes! I see her. What about her?"

"She's in a plot to kill me! We've got to go!" She began gathering her things.

I looked at the woman again and saw no sign of murder in her eyes. There was nothing there to convince me that what Diana was saying was true. I didn't believe it, but I could see that she did. She got up and walked out disrupting the meeting. I apologized for both of us as I followed her as she cut through the circle.

Outside, she was standing by the Van. She remained quiet and withdrawn. I opened the door and let her in. She sat quietly, looking as if she had lost her best friend.

"What's going on Diana? Please tell me. What's wrong?" I had not seen her look that withdrawn before.

"I didn't want to tell you because I thought you might not believe me."

"Tell me what? What is it that you're afraid of?" I looked into her face, and I could see fear.

She stared out of the window of her door before she spoke. "Sometimes I get really paranoid about being around people, especially white people!" She paused and looked at me. "Especially white women!" She paused again. "Especially... BLONDE white women!"

"Can I ask why?" I said it cautiously. Darla's words rang in my ear. I wanted to know all about it, but I didn't want to alienate her while she was in a vulnerable state of mine.

She looked me in the eye. "Donn, if I tell you the truth, would you promise not to leave me?"

I started to answer but I didn't get the chance.

"Please don't leave me! Everybody leaves me! I can't help the way I am. It's not my fault! Please Donn, you're all I've got left! Please don't leave me!" She was begging and pleading, and I could see that her heart was torn.

"Diana..."

She began to cry. She climbed over the seat and ended up in my lap. The tears were flowing like rain. I held her and she clutched my neck greedily, hungrily as if she were starving for affection.

"Please Donn, don't leave me! I have to tell you the truth. It's not fair to you if I don't, but,... I'm afraid!" She held on tighter and cried harder.

"I won't leave you. I promise!" I said it but did I really mean it? I didn't know. It was too late because the words had gone out and all that I could do was try to adhere to them.

"Really?" She looked up at me.

I was stuck and trapped by my own words. There was nothing left to do but to continue on. "Yes! I promise!"

"I'm going to tell you everything, but I want you to hold me in your arms while I talk, okay?"

"Let's go back to the backseat. There's more room back there." I said. I wanted to get comfortable because if this was going to be something deeper than I could handle, I wanted to be as comfortable as I possibly could be under the circumstances.

We got comfortable on the backseat, and she laid across me and I held her like a small child. It was security and comfort for her. Then she began to speak.

"Donn, I have a mental illness!" She threw it out and waited for my reaction. I didn't react. She hadn't told me anything that I didn't already know, but it was good to hear the words come from her mouth. "That's why I live in Terrace Village." I knew that too. "Sometimes I get really paranoid about people. Right now, I'm paranoid but I still know what's real… well,… I do,… I'm not sure! That's why I really need you right now to tell me what's real and what isn't. I trust you! You wouldn't lie to me, would you? No! Of course, you wouldn't!"

"Diana, what about the blonde lady? What's…"

She cut in before I could finish. "That's what I'm talking about. Donn, do you think she was looking at me funny?"

"No, I don't. When I looked over at her she wasn't even looking our way. She was into whatever they were talking about in their group. What's this about a plot to kill you?"

"It's all in my mind. I know that, but at times it seems so real! And baby, right now that's how I see it!"

"Diana, if you know it's all in your mind, can't you fight it?"

"Yes. But it's hard because it's so real." She rose up and kissed me. "Thanks baby. I'm glad you're in my life. I really need you right now."

She laid back onto my chest. She was getting her courage up. I could feel her breathing and I knew that she was afraid to reveal what she had to say but it was about to come out anyway. She decided to take a chance and reveal her deep dark secrets and she decided to do it with me.

"When I was fourteen, I met this guy. He was a lot older than me, and he knew that I was only fourteen. I was still a virgin, and he knew that too, but he wanted me. He didn't rape me, as everyone said he did. He talked really sweet and charming, and I let him do it. But because I was only fourteen and he was over twenty-one, my mother had him arrested when she found out. By that time, he had turned me onto cocaine, and we were doing coke and having sex all the time. He went to jail for statutory rape. I didn't want him to go because I thought I was in love with him. I didn't want to testify but they made me. All the asked me was whether we had sex or not. I said yes and that was all that they needed to convict him of statutory rape.

"During the trial I found out that he was married to this white girl. Donn, he had been married since he was nineteen and had two kids with her. He told me that I was the only one in his life and I believed him. I loved him! He hurt me! He was just using me! He just wanted my virginity. He preyed on young girls. His wife was only eighteen at the time and she had two kids by him. So, you can see, he had a thing for really young girls. Well anyway, he went to jail, and she was really mad about that. She told me that she was going to get me if it was the last thing that she did.

"Joseph, that's his name, was in jail for almost two years and I had just turned sixteen. I was out at North Park pool with some of my friends and my Aunt Ruby. We were all having fun and a splashing around in the water. I didn't even know that Joseph's wife was there. But she was there and all the time she was watching me, waiting for the right time. She waited until I went up to the deep end and then she ran out and pushed me into the water. She fell in with me and held me under. Donn, she tried to kill me! I could swim but she caught me by surprise and when I hit the water I went under out of breath. I couldn't get away and I couldn't breathe. I was trying to get back to the top to breathe but she was on top of me holding me down. I looked up and all I could see was her evil white face and her blond hair all around her in the water. I could see the sun shining over her head and then it got so bright that I couldn't stand it, so I closed my eyes!"

She began to cry on my chest. I knew from what she had said that she had passed out from the lack of oxygen, and she was dying. She didn't die, and I was dying to know what happened next.

"I… I…(Sniff, sniff) I woke up in the hospital with tubes all in me and my Aunt Ruby was standing there. I saw her but I thought I saw the face of Joseph's wife and I started screaming. Donn, I can't get that image out of my head. Her blond hair! The way it was floating in the water all around her face. It terrified me!"

"Did the woman inside look like her?" I asked.

"No, not really. It's just a hair. It's just the... Blond hair! I don't like it!" She squeezed me and I could feel the tension and fear in her body.

"It's okay baby. Nobody's going to hurt you, not if I have anything to say about it." I meant every word but the only person that was causing her any harm was herself. How could I protect her from herself?

"I take medication for my mental illness, but I haven't taken it in a few days." She confessed. She waited for my reaction, praying that it wouldn't be the one that she was used to getting from men when she revealed the truth.

"Why?"

"Because after a while I feel okay, and I don't need it anymore!" She said it so matter-of-factly that I wondered if she actually believed it.

"What do you mean? You do need it! It's what keeps you together, isn't it?"

The tension in her body grew because she knew the truth but didn't want to face it. She was silent. She didn't want to lie, and she didn't want to tell the truth either.

"Diana, where is your medication now?"

"At home."

I proceeded to explain why the medication was necessary all of the time, even when she was feeling okay and when I had finished, I began to wonder if I had gotten in over my head because she just laid silently on my chest clutching me around the waist.

Then suddenly, without warning, she snapped out of it and said. "Take me home." She rose up and kissed me. "I'm going to take it."

I took her home and she took her medication. She asked me to stay with her and I did. She said that she suffered from schizophrenia, as well as manic depression and had been that way most of her life, but the near-death experience had caused her to become extremely paranoid.

"What does your doctor say? Are you still under a doctor's care?" I prayed that she said yes.

I was sitting on the sofa in her living room, but she was walking around as I spoke. She entered the bathroom and came out with seven bottles of pills with names that I couldn't pronounce. I had no idea what they were, but she did! She sat down and then she held each bottle and read the name as easily as I could read my own name. She tried to explain what it does and why, but she was speaking the language of doctors, pharmacists, and psychologists. It was a language that she knew but it was foreign to me. I didn't understand it and I didn't care to. All that I cared about was if she took the pills, would she get better? The answer was yes. That was all that mattered.

When she finished, she placed all seven bottles on the coffee table and then laid her head in my lap and curled up in the fetal position. I loved it when she laid that way because I knew she felt safe, and it felt good to me too. Almost as quickly as she laid down, she jumped up and startled me and she proceeded to undress.

She peeled off her jeans, unbuttoned her top and took that off too revealing her luscious body wrapped only in Victoria's Secret's powder blue lace panties and bra. Big Al began to wake up. She noticed it and smiled. She shook her finger at me in a scolding third-grade teacher way.

"No, no baby. I'm just getting comfortable." She kept her panties and bra on. "Take off your clothes and get comfortable but leave Big Al in his 'Loom-room'!"

I did as instructed. I adjusted my underwear as I sat back down to give him room to breathe. "False alarm! You can go back to sleep!" I told him.

"Ha ha ha ha ha! You're funny Donn!" She laughed. It was the first time I had seen the smile on her face all evening. It lingered for a few seconds and then faded as she lay back down again. She was like a child curled up in her father's lap to calm and quell her fears. She felt safe and secure and perfectly at ease, and eventually she peacefully drifted off to sleep.

I stayed through the night and watched over her. Occasionally I would slip quietly from under her to use the toilet, or get coffee, or change the music. I sat with her head on my lap watching her, stroking her silky lengths of hair, and allowing her to rest. At one point she turned and woke up Big Al! He began to protest and struggled to free himself from the Loom Room. I thought she was asleep, but she wasn't. She reached into my boxers through the slit and brought him out. She kissed him once with her hand still around him, then she gently laid her cheek against him and fell asleep again with a smile on her face.

The radio was turned to WAMO, and the Quiet Storm was on. The volume was down to just a whisper, and I listened to one slow love song after another as I stroked her hair as she slept. I could also hear the people outside talking and laughing through the open kitchen window. I did get a chance to hear Marvin Gaye's, Sexual Healing, but that night there was to be no sexual healing for me. There was healing, although not sexual, for her, only for her!

After that night I was better equipped to deal with her mood swings. I had learned a lot about her that I didn't understand before. I also knew some of the warning signs that would alert me before she went crashing off of the deep end. I'd love to tell you that I had tamed her and that she was under my control, but that would be as far from the truth as we are from China. Diana was a free spirit and possessed a whirlwind of emotions that were subject to spin off in any given direction at any given time. Most of the time, I didn't know what to expect. She was both exciting and terrifying and she kept me on my toes and kept me guessing all of the time.

Many things that she did excited me and raise my interest in her to a peak. Before I met her, if my phone rang at one o'clock in the morning, it would send a negative shock wave through my body leaving me to believe that it was a tragedy that someone was calling me to inform me of. But now when the phone rang at that time, I woke up smiling. I knew it was her and I knew that she was horny. I knew that both Big Al and I would be satisfied and reap the benefits! But on the other hand, I didn't like it when she would dress up and crazy clothes and wearing her Technicolor floor length hair. She had several wigs, hairpieces, and extensions but most were shorter and less colorful. She had solid color wigs too. There were fairly normal ones, black, brown, and Auburn, but then there were the outrageous ones; blue, orange, blood red, green and purple. In some she looked ridiculous and in others, she looked rather good, but none made her look better than she did in her own natural hair.

She had told me in one of our conversations that she had learned to ride a horse when she was about nine or ten years old. It was one of the things that her father taught her that she remembered vividly. So, I decided to take her horseback riding!

It was early Saturday morning when I called her. She answered immediately because for some reason she knew it was me.

"Hi baby!" I could feel her smiling.

"Hey Diana. What's up?"

"Nothing. I was just sitting here wondering what I was going to do today." She yawned.

I imagined her stretching her body with her arms in the air and at the same time stretching the seams of her favorite pink nightgown. That thought made me smile and made Big Al stir!

"Do you want to go horseback riding today?" I asked as I adjusted myself.

"Really? Are you serious Donn? Of course, I do! That would be great! But where can we go?"

"Schenley Park!"

"Schenley Park? I didn't know they had horses out there!"

"Sure, they do. You wanna go?"

"Yes! Yes! Yes! Yes!"

"Okay, I'll be there to get you in about an hour."

"I'll be ready."

When I picked her up, she had one of her floor-length wigs on. It wasn't the Technicolor extensions that she had worn before. It was an actual wig. A blonde one! Of all colors to wear, she wore a blonde wig! After what she had told me, blonde should have been a color that she would never wear, but there she was, looking as white as a Black woman could!

"What's up!" I must have been looking as surprised as I've ever been.

She kissed me. "Don't worry baby, I'm okay. I've got a plan."

"A plan? Fear gripped me. What kind of a plan? Was this plan going to embarrass me to hell and back? Was I going to feel silly as well is embarrassed?

"Wa… what's your plan? I asked almost afraid to hear the answer.

"I'll tell you when it's the right time." She was feeling happy, carefree, and determined to have some fun. I was just afraid!

"When is the right time?"

"Soon!" She hugged me and kissed me. "Come on stop worrying! Let's have some fun!" She ran down the steps and waited in the doorway for me. "Come on!" She yelled. "I'm ready to ride!"

She disappeared out of the door and by the time I got to the doorway she was almost to the Van. She was running and skipping as if she didn't have a care in the world. She was acting a little crazy again but at least this time she wasn't in a gloomy mood.

At the stables I took care of the necessary paperwork and while I did, she pranced around like a prima donna and played in her fake hair flicking it this way and that. The stable master watched her with curiosity but didn't say a word until she was out of earshot.

She became absorbed in the process of getting to know the horse that she was about to mount.

"Is she okay?" He asked.

"Sure!" I said, trying to act as if I didn't know what he meant, but...

She mounted her horse and spread her hair all around. It completely covered her back and spread across the horse's rear. The horse flicked her tail as the hair irritated her. I was getting a vision of a lady on horseback with long blond hair, and I was trying to figure out who she was when he said.

"Who is that woman that..."

Before he finished the question it came to me.

"Lady Godiva! Oh no!"

"Yeah, that's her! Lady Godiva! Wasn't she the one that road naked through the streets?" He said and he was pleased with himself that he had figured it out.

(No! She wouldn't!) I thought. But, knowing Diana, it was exactly the kind of thing that she would do.

"See you later!" I hurried and mounted my horse and took off up the trail after her.

"Remember don't try to leave the park because they won't go!" He shouted.

I waved a hand of acknowledgement and rode on.

Diana was smiling and whistling when I rode up beside her. Her look was mischievous as if she were about to do something dastardly and I hoped and prayed that it wasn't what I was thinking.

"Diana, what are you going to do?" My words were in the form of a question, but they really didn't require an answer.

"You'll see!" She blew me a kiss through smiling lips and then she coaxed her horse into a trot and pulled away from me and disappeared over the next rise. I distinctly heard her laugh as she went out of sight. I took the rise and rounded the next bend. She stopped, dismounted, stripped naked, re-mounted, spread the blond hair across the horse's rear and rode off laughing! Her clothes, she left scattered across the trail. I gathered them up and followed her. She was having the time of her life, but I was concerned about the police. Someone had to worry,... She wasn't!

"Diana! Put your clothes back on!" I shouted as I rode towards her.

"No way! This is fun! Weeeeeeee!" Her hair, her blonde wig was blowing in the wind. Her naked body was visible to everyone that could see. I rode hard trying to catch her but carrying her clothes and trying to control the horse was just too much. There were bike trails and jogging trails that ran parallel to us. People were stopping to watch. Some were amused, some were shocked, and still others seem to be disinterested. She was making a spectacle of herself riding naked through the park like a woman possessed. She road naked and free, unconcerned about being caught. Unconcerned with the consequences! She wasn't worried at all, she left that to me!

She reined her horse in and stopped about a half a mile from the stable. She was laughing hysterically. For that moment she was Lady Godiva and she reveled in the pleasure of it. She hopped down from her horse without using the stirrups.

"Gimme my clothes." Her face was lit with the fire of excitement. I threw her the bundle, and she began to dress. "That was incredible! I've never felt so alive and free in my entire life!"

I wondered what was next! What crazy thing was she now thinking of? In what direction was her mind about to go? I didn't have to wait long for the answer.

"Come on!" She spoke.

She began walking up the side of the hill leading to her horse by the reins. I followed and passed between several trees before coming to the top and the clearing with a giant oak tree amid the knoll. The branches reached out at least fifteen feet in all directions giving shade to most of the area. There were people sitting under the tree in all of the choice places. It was because of the horse that we were not welcomed, but all of that changed when the clouds rolled in, and the thunder and lightning began to crack the sky and disturb the peace of the hilltop. The shade and shelter were under the giant oak but the people under it, as well as those sitting on the edge of the knoll, decided to run for shelter under one of the pavilions down the hill, leaving us alone under the oak. The sky lit up with streaks of white light. The lightning snaked across the heavens and then crashes of thunder boomed like enormously bass drums. The horses stiffened each time but didn't try to run. Diana and I stroked their snouts to calm them. The rain began to fall slowly at first and then heavily and violently. We were sheltered under the branches and sat down with our backs against the tree trunk.

I think we're stuck here for a while." I spoke.

"Yeah, but it feels good." She replied.

"I love the rain. I always have, especially when it's summer rain."

"What's on your mind?" She saw my face staring out to where the rain fell just beyond the tree.

"Let's go out in it and have some fun getting soaking wet!" I said.

"I've got a better idea. Let's get naked and make love in it!"

"Are you serious?"

"You want me, don't you?"

"Sure!"

"You want to rip my clothes off and screw me, don't you?" (Screw wasn't the word that she used, but you understand.) "You want to throw me down, then bend me in half like a pretzel and screw me until I beg you to stop, don't you?"

"Yes!"

"So do it!" She ordered. "Out in the rain!"

I picked her up, threw her over my shoulder like a sack of potatoes and walked out into the rain. I laid her down on the rain-soaked grass and began to undress her. She did the same to me. Minutes later we were naked and locked together on the grass as the rain pelted down on us. I had forgotten all about the police, or anyone else that might happen along. Big Al was in charge, and he had no conscience, and no shame! Nothing matters anymore. All that mattered was having her beneath me with a blanket of rain above.

It was pure animal passion. No love, no tenderness, no foreplay. Just primal instinct! Love had absolutely nothing to do with it. It was driven by passion and fueled by lust. Most of the things that we did together had that same driving force. Sex was at the center of just about everything that we did. If not at the center, it was very nearby!

The rain ceased before we did. The sky began to clear and the only rain still falling was what had been trapped by the leaves and branches of the big oak tree, but it was just as calm as if sitting in the eye of a hurricane. Clouds rolled in again and began to release their moisture. We dressed in our soaking wet clothes and lay still in the grass side by side allowing the rain to pelt us with soothing blows over and over again. The rain didn't let up for quite some time, but it didn't matter to us. It was the first time I had made love in the rain, and according to her, it was her first time also. It was a wonderful experience, and I enjoyed every second of it. I looked at her and she was smiling with her eyes closed and her blond wig detached and, on the ground, exposing her own crown of glory. She was happy and that made me extremely happy.

I looked at the horses under the tree and they were looking at us as if they knew exactly what we had done. The female neighed throwing her head back and then returned her gaze on me. The mail looked right straight in my eye, and I could have sworn that he winked. I closed my eyes and let the rain beat upon me. Diana curled up next to me and my arm instinctively went around her as we lay silently together enjoying the moment.

CHAPTER 5

Don't Make Her Mad!

It was 1:05 AM when my phone began to ring. It had been over a week since lady Godiva appeared in Schenley Park, and five days since I had heard from Diana, but I knew it was her because she's the only one who calls me at one o'clock in the morning! I also knew what was on her mind because it was always the same!

"Hello Diana!" I said.

She didn't hesitate to get to the exact nature of her call.

"Hi baby! I'm horny! Can you come over?"

My response shocked her and I could hardly believe it myself.

"No! I have to get up early. I've got a building downtown that I have to work on!"

Aside from the resale shop that I operated; I also was the proprietor and only employee of a small window cleaning business. Every other Saturday I cleaned the windows of a five-story downtown office building. Each visit I tackled one complete floor along with the lobby, Main entrance and exit doors. I had six hours to complete the task beginning at 6 AM and I had to be out by noon when the maintenance man went home. I didn't have time to drive to her house and back at one in the morning. I needed my rest.

"Please baby?" She pleaded.

"No!" I said firmly. I had to force myself to think with the big head and not the little one. "I can't. Not tonight."

I had been doing that particular building for over a year. It paid very well, and the checks always came on time, and I wasn't about to lose it over having midnight sex with Diana!

When she spoke again her attitude had changed. In a flash she went from soft sexual begging to sexual blackmail.

"Well, then…" I heard her suck her teeth. "If you won't come, I'll just call someone else!"

"Okay!" I said. "Go ahead. Do what you have to do. I'll talk to you later!"

I was just about to hang up when she said. "Wait! What if I come over there?"

"No Diana! I've got to get up early."

"You don't have to come and get me. I'll catch a cab. We'll just do it once and then we'll go to sleep, okay?" She pleaded again.

Who was she trying to fool? From the very first time that she experienced multiple orgasms, she was never satisfied with just one, but I gave in. I wanted her just as much as she wanted me.

"Okay, but I can't take you home until after I finish my job."

"That's fine. I'll just sleep until you get back. I'll be right over."

"Hurry up!"

"I will."

"Bye!"

"Donn?"

"Yes?"

"Do you have any whipped cream?"

"Yes. Why?"

"Mmmmm! Never mind! Bye!"

I awoke at 5 AM to the sound of my screaming alarm clock. That's what it sounded like after only an hour and a half of sleep. Diana had arrived at my place at 1:30 and kept me busy until 3:30. Understand me, I'm not complaining, not in the least because what she does to me on a consistent basis is always worth the lack of sleep. The can of whipped cream was gone and so was a quarter jar of honey!

She was sleeping serenely and I eased out of bed gently trying not to disturb her, but I must have because she stretched and opened her eyes just as I stood up.

"Morning babe!" She purred. Her voice was as sweet as she was beautiful.

I leaned over and kissed her. She responded with her tongue. I started towards the bathroom when she spoke again.

"Baby? You know I'm falling in love with you!" She purred so sweetly.

I stopped short. I turned to see her smiling at me with stars in her eyes. She didn't love me! It was all about sex. I told her so and I expected a debate.

"You're not falling in love with me. It's just that we have really great sex, that's all it is!"

She pondered my statement. "Yeah, you're probably right." The change was sudden. It was the way that she was. Sometimes I couldn't tell if she was for real or just playing with me. This was one of those times. "But," she added, "I know that you're in love with me!"

"What makes you think that?" I did care great deal for her, but I wasn't in love with her.

I was standing in the bathroom doorway as naked as the day I was born. She looked me over and made reference to a speck of honey that was oozing from my navel.

"C'mere! Let me lick it off! C'mere!"

(She's insatiable! I've created a monster!) I thought.

"I've got to get ready for work Diana. Now answer my question."

"Okay! Okay! Don't get your panties all bunched up!"

"I don't wear panties!" I was annoyed by her flippant comment but she brushed it off like a soft feather from her shoulder and continued unperturbed.

"I know that! If you did, I wouldn't be with you. It's just an expression, that's all!"

"Are you going to answer my question?"

"Okay!" She paused and then she spoke. "I know you're in love with me by the way that you work me!" She said it without emotion.

"No. That's not true. I'm just taking care of business! Right now, you're my business. I'm here to make you happy. I know how it feels to be unfulfilled, I don't like it and I never want to leave you that way. You take care of me, and I take care of you!"

"No baby. It's more than just that." Her emotions were returning to her voice. "Sometimes you're like a wild man, an animal, a man possessed! When you're like that it's like you're trying to drive me through the bed, and I like it! But then there are other times when you are very tender but still passionate, loving, gentle and slow. The way you move tells me that you're trying to find every spot inside of me that you can and when you get to those special places, you know it immediately and you stay there for my pleasure, not just yours. You're not selfish at all. And then there's the way you kiss me and the way you look at me when you're holding me, the way you gently rub your fingers over my skin! It's like I'm some kinda goddess or something! It blows my mind the way you treat me! That's why I know you're in love with me!" She sat up and pulled the covers up over her naked breasts. Why? I don't know. There was just the two of us there and I was still butt naked in the doorway. But, I was learning that figuring her out was next to impossible so I just went with the flow.

"I don't agree with you! You're dead wrong! You've got it twisted!" I walked back to the bed. "I do what I do because that's just the way I'm built. Just because I give you more and treat you better than those other guys that you've been with, don't think it's because I'm in love with you. I'm not! I treat you the way I do because I really enjoy you and I enjoy being with you and I love the way that you satisfy me. You're freaky,... Like me... I like that! I'm just giving it to you like you're giving it to me. Love has nothing to do with it! It's purely physical!"

It sounded really good and it was perfectly believable, but she had her own way of looking at things.

"Well Donn, you can say what you want to and you can try to fool yourself but you can't fool me. I know what I feel and I know what I see. You're in love with all of this!" She threw the covers off exposing her nakedness.

"Believe what you want." I was a little irritated but I really didn't know why. "I've got to get ready for work." I left her sitting there in her splendidness and went to take my shower. I stayed in the shower longer than usual because the water just felt so damned good on my skin. When I returned, she was gone.

The bed was made and the room was straightened up. The clothes I had worn were in the hamper and there was a fresh set of socks and underwear lying neatly on the bed along with one of my work uniforms. My boots were neatly placed on the floor beneath it all. My cell phone was on the bed too, which led me to believe that she had used it to call a cab had gone outside to wait. Her clothes were gone which added to my theory.

The smell of breakfast food began to reach me. It brought a smile to my face momentarily, until the memory of the last meal that she had cooked came rushing back to my consciousness. Then panic struck me! She was very good at many things but cooking wasn't one of them. Her meals were total disasters. The last one brought me to my knees in the bathroom, hugging the toilet and praying for the pain to stop.

I dressed and started for the bedroom door thinking that I might get lucky and sneak out of the house before she noticed, but that morning, luck wasn't with me! She was coming up the hallway caring a breakfast tray full of deliciously smelling food. I have to admit that it smelled very good and looked tasty. By looks and smell alone, she received an A+, but I knew that she wanted me to do more than just observe and smell it! She expected me to eat it and there lies the problem. I had to work for six hours straight and I couldn't afford to get sick. She met me just outside of the door.

"Diana, I... I... I'm in a hurry. I don't have time to sit down and eat. I... I've got to get going."

"I know baby. That's why I called The Coronet!" She stood in front of me smiling pleasantly and then she pushed the trade towards me expecting me to take it. That's when my stupidity took over.

"This came from the Coronet? That's why it smells so,... ah,...thanks Baby. That was really thoughtful of you." I knew before I finished that I had messed up.

She gave me one of her evil looks. A look full of disgust and pain. A look of disappointment and hurt.

"HERE!" She pushed the tray into my stomach spilling some of the coffee on the tray. "Here's your breakfast!"

"I'm sorry Diana. I didn't mean to hurt..."

"Well you did! Sometimes you can be so cruel!" Her face twisted in anguish. She was close to tears.

"What can I do to make it up to you?"

She perked up immediately. "Take me with you! Teach me how to clean windows so I can help you."

"Baby, I can't do that. I'll be working on the inside. I can't take you in."

"Why not?"

I didn't like her look. It was deeply disturbing, penetrating an accusing. It was burning a hole in my chest with angry, tense beams of fire. The perkiness that she had only seconds ago had vanished in a flash!

"Because I'm not allowed to. And now isn't the time to try to teach you the art of window cleaning. I have too much work to do and I don't have a lot of time to do it. I'm sorry!"

"You don't trust me, do you? You think I'm going to steal something, don't you? You bastard! You really don't trust me!" Her eyes were full of flame of fire and hatred came up through them and headed directly towards me.

"That's not true Diana. That's not it at all!"

"Yes it is. You don't trust me!"

"If I didn't trust you, you wouldn't be in my house right now!" I reach for her. "Baby, understand, this is business!"

The truth was the truth, but it didn't take root with her. She had her own idea of what   truth was! Her mind was made up.

"You bastard! You ain't no damned good! You don't even trust me! You think I'm gonna steal something!"

She didn't give me a chance to respond. She started breathing heavily and handed me the tray. As soon as I took it, she slapped the bottom upwards spilling everything all over me. The coffee burnt my chest as it soaked through my clothes. There were eggs, grits, butter, syrup and pancakes all over the front of my shirt and face. A strip of bacon had stuck to my forehead. Thank God the grits weren't that hot!

I'm getting the hell out of here!" She stomped down the stairs and out of the door slamming it behind her.

I pulled the bacon from my face and started down the stairs after her. By the time I reached the door and looked out, she was nowhere to be seen. Twilight was breaking, but the sun had yet to rise. I peered through the window of the Coronet hoping that she was there, but she wasn't. It was the only business open at that hour, and only place where she could have sought refuge. I had no idea where she had gone.

I spent the next half hour searching for her. The recessed doorways and spaces between buildings were places where I concentrated my search, but I found her in none of those places. I checked the neighboring streets but that also was to no avail. When I returned to Warrington Avenue, I caught a glimpse of a woman entering the Coronet, but after further inspection it was revealed not to be her. Wherever she was, she didn't want to be found, or she had left the neighborhood and walked down the hill towards town, or the South side.

It was 5:45 AM and I had to get going. My equipment was already loaded in the Van, but I had to clean myself up from the breakfast that I was wearing. I washed my face, changed my shirt and went to work. I was 15 minutes late! The maintenance man, Bobby, was waiting for me.

"You're late!" He said. "You've never been late before. You're usually here when I get here, what's up? You have some chick over last night? Ha ha ha Ha!" He laughed at me as he fumbled for his keys to unlock the door.

"Yeah, some CRAZY chick!"

"Not good Donn. Remember what you told me? Never mix business with pleasure. You'd better take your own advice!" Bobby told me. He was grinning at me the whole time through the locked door.

"Yeah, yeah! Just open the damn door!"

"Hey! Don't get mad at me 'cause you screwed up! Hey! Screwed up! That's funny! Screwed up! Ha ha ha ha!" He unlocked and held the door open as I wheeled my equipment in.

"It's not that funny!" I said.

"Hey?" Bobby shouted. "What's that on your pants? Looks like bacon and eggs. It is! What's the matter Donn? Can't find your mouth? Ha ha ha ha!"

Bobby was a fun-loving guy who laughed at almost anything and in turn made those around him smile and laugh too. His attitude helped others to look at the funny side of things and that was a time I needed to laugh.

"I'd tell you about it, but neither of us would get any work done today."

"A woman,... huh?"

"Yeah!"

"Figures! Well, you know where I'll be if you need me." He locked the front door and I pushed my equipment to the elevator.

"Okay."

I spent the entire time working and I only took short breaks and had a ham sandwich and a Pepsi out of the vending machine for brunch. I finished five minutes early and Bobby was in his office in the basement when I walked in. His feet were up on the desk and he was reared back in his chair talking on the phone. I sat down and waited. He was talking to his wife. She was giving him instructions on what to bring home for dinner.

"That woman is unreal!" He explained as he hung up the phone. "She doesn't even cook anymore! She always wants me to bring home something from Wendy's, or KFC, or Mickey D's. What happened to fried pork chops, fried in butter with collard greens and mashed potatoes? What happened to stake and onions? Stuff like that?"

He pulled a cigarette from a pack on his desk, lit one and blew the smoke out.

"You ever been married Donn?" He asked.

"Yes. It didn't work out."

"She cheated? You cheat?"

"It just wasn't right. We wanted different things."

Bobby was okay to work around but I really wasn't ready to get cozy and let him in on my life's secrets. I liked things the way they were, besides Diana was on my mind and I wanted to find out what was up with her.

"Well my man, don't ever get married again. They all turn on you! It's just the way they are!" He got up and grabbed his keys. "Let's get the hell out of here!"

I drove to Wendy's on Fifth Avenue and got my hands on a triple cheeseburger and biggie fries. I headed up to Terrace Village eating all the way. I knocked on Diana's door but there was no answer. I knocked again, still no answer. Once again I knocked, but I still got the same results. I listened for signs of life from within but I heard nothing. After a few minutes I left. Her neighbors from across the way were sitting out so I crossed over and asked if they had seen her. The guy to the right of me, sitting in a lopsided sheet-metal chair, took a slow path from a Newport and blew the smoke out in my direction. Immediately I didn't like him.

"Yeah, I seen her," the tough looking one sitting next to him in a matching chair said. "She came in early this mornin', runnin' like the cops were after her. Ten minutes later, she ran right back out! Ain't seen her since!"

"Thanks." I began to walk away.

"You know she's crazy!" He added.

It wasn't an accusation, just a statement of fact.

I stopped and faced him. "What makes you say that?"

"Because it's true! You ain't found out yet?"

"You must be pretty damn slow if you ain't!" The Newport smoker said. He laughed and then took another puff. "You better cut her loose 'fore she cuts you all up. She's done it before! The dude can't even piss without sitting down like a woman! She cut it off!"

"Ain't even a man no more!" The first one said.

"What?" The shock of what I just heard hit me. It was hard to believe the truth in it but somehow I knew they weren't lying. All of them, the woman included, nodded their heads in agreement.

"It's true!" The woman said. Her chair also matched the others. "She ain't right in the head. She cut that dude all up and then cut his 'thingy' off and never did a day for it! They put her in the state hospital in Mayview, or Dixmont somewhere and six months later, she was right back here. Never even lost her place or nothin!"

"That's right man! She's crazy as hell! Why you think nobody comes around? As fine as she is? Why you think she ain't got no man? Ain't nobody trying to lose no body parts,... 'specially not THAT part! She's crazy man! Certifiably! You'll find out!"

If you ever make her mad, don't go to sleep around her. You might wake up missin' somethin'!"

They all laughed.

"Thanks for the info." I heard the laughter as I walked away but I didn't see what was so funny.

I knew that Diana wasn't normal. I knew that she had mental problems but until then I didn't know that she was violent. When she smacked the breakfast tray into my face it shows her anger but under the circumstances it was reasonable. It could be considered violent, but reasonable. But what they had told me was the outer extreme. I had never seen the violence in her but until then I had never made her mad! If I believed what they said than I'd better be extremely careful.

I wondered who the guy was that she had castrated. She didn't talk about the men in her life much. I wondered what he had done to make her so mad. Had he cheated on her? Had he insulted her hair? Did he criticize the way she dressed, or did he badmouth her cooking? I instinctively grabbed my crotch and shuddered at the thought of losing Big Al! He was a good friend and had been since I was twelve. He was there for me giving me comfort and pleasure, in good times and in bad. My plan was to take him the grave with me... not to bury him alone!

It was time to find out who Diana really was, or maybe it was time to leave her alone! For the next nine days I called, stop by and tried to locate her but it was all in vain. Her across the way neighbors said she had come and gone within minutes several times in the night within those days. On the ninth day as I was leaving, a car pulled up behind my Van and she stepped out. When she saw me advancing towards her, she leaned back into the car and said something to the male driver. He looked up at me. She started up the walkway and proceeded to walk past me as if I weren't even there.

"Diana! Wait a minute!" I shouted. "What's going on? Don't you think that you owe me an explanation?"

"No!" She spat. "I don't owe you anything!" Her words were loud, harsh and cold.

I almost argued with her about it but I stopped short, thinking that actually she was right. She didn't owe me anything because she wasn't my woman, just my sex partner. There was no commitment established between us. No verbal agreement, no papers. Nothing! She didn't owe me anything and the same was true in reverse.

I wanted to know for myself that she was all right and I could see that she was. I didn't want to continue the crazy relationship that I had with her and I certainly didn't want to lose Big Al! I needed to move on. It was clear that she had so what was the problem? It was my ego! Crushed by seeing her with someone else. I wanted to get rid of her but seeing that she had moved on wasn't to my liking. I wanted to dump her but instead, she dumped me!

"All right, that's cool!" I accepted the decision and said nothing else. I continued towards my Van but she had more to say. She spun on her heel and started back towards me spitting fire.

"What do you mean 'all right that's cool'? Like you just don't care. You had me all to yourself. The first guy in years that I've been true to, but noooo! You wanted to talk about my cooking! You wanted to insult me! Well, you can just kiss my ass! No! I forgot, you've already done that!" She smacked herself on the rear when she said. "Just stay out of my life!"

"Don't worry, I will! And you stay out of mine!"

"Fine!"

She said it and started to back off. Her friend got out of the car and began to approach me. I turned to face him.

"Look man!" He tried to look tough. "Stay away from her. She's mine now! Don't make me get ugly!" His tone was supposed to be intimidating but it didn't affect me in that way at all.

"Too late!" I looked him dead in the eye when I said it.

"What's that mean?" He had a dumb look on his face.

"What does it mean?" I laughed aloud to aggravate him. "I guess that too deep for an idiot like you!"

His eyes flared. He swung at me but I saw it coming and leaned back out of range. I countered with a straight right to the nose that made contact and shattered bone. I pushed my forearm up under his chin and applied pressure.

"You punk! You think you can beat me? You don't know me! You have no idea what I can do to you!" I backed off just long enough to let him swing at me again. When his fist caught nothing but air, I hit him again. This time in the chest and he slammed against my Van with a loud thud. I moved in again to finish him, but he kicked Big Al's twin boys. My eyes went completely out of focus, and I doubled over in pain. He didn't hit me after that and I didn't understand why. When my eyes began to focus on him I could see that he kicked me to get me off of him. He was in just as much pain as I was. The blow to the chest had knocked the wind out of him and blood flowed freely from his nose. As I watched, I wished that I still had the strength to break his jaw too, but I didn't.

Diana came running towards us. She ran past him and came to me.

"Baby, are you all right?"

I couldn't believe she was speaking to me instead of him. It was hard to believe that she was talking to me at all. She was showing genuine concern for me when the guy that she came with was bleeding all over the place and trying his best to suck air.

As the pain began to ease I stood up. He backed away to a safe distance but kept his eyes on me. She put her arm around my waist. I pushed her away.

"You're crazy! Stay away from me!" I shouted.

She didn't reply but she did let go of me and stared at me with cold dead eyes.

"Get away from my Van!" I snapped at the guy. He moved. I hobbled to the driver's door and managed to pull myself into the seat and behind the wheel before I closed the door. Five seconds later my door flew open. It was Diana who stood glaring at me. Her eyes still possess that dead stare. I could feel her brain teeter-tottering between love and hate sanity and insanity. She smiled from one side of her face while the other side refused to cooperate.

"Baby, you're mine until I say you're not!" She said. Her face contorted as if a stroke had occurred. "Don't think that you can get rid of me that easily, because…" Her half smile turned sinister and then disappeared completely, "…YOU CAN'T!"

She slammed the door and walked up the steps and down the walkway to her building. Her stride was fast and furious that she left Mr. Broken Nose struggling to catch up. She didn't try to help him nor did she look back to see if he was following. She just kept going until she disappeared through her doorway.

He stumbled along, blood was still dripping from his nose and he was holding his chest. He looked a complete fool as he followed behind her like a puppy. I wondered if the way I saw him was the same way that others saw me!

I sat in my Van a few more moments just to make sure that I was okay before I drove away. I took a look down the walkway and watched just as Mr. broken nose turned and entered through the building doorway and disappeared. Would she let him in, or have the chain barring his entrance?

The pain steadily eased and proper focus returned to my vision, so I drove away. Big Al and his boys, as well as my ego, were bruised but would be fine shortly. On the other hand, he had a broken nose and sole possession of a mad woman! I think I had the best of that deal!

CHAPTER 6

Carl!

Weeks passed and I heard nothing from her. Often she crossed my mind and I wondered how she was doing, but I refused to call her.

Phil, Carl and Danny and I met at the Onala Club one Saturday morning shortly after Diana and I had stopped seeing each other. We were early for a meeting and decided to shoot a couple games of pool while we waited. Phil and I teamed up against Carl and Danny. We took the low balls in the game eight ball.

Phil broke and sunk the one-ball. His second shot pocketed the two-ball. On his third shot, he missed the five. Carl took a shot at the eleven and didn't come close. He swore and walked back to the far wall and leaned against the rack of cues that was fastened to the wall.

"Wassup' Carl? Something on your mind? You usually shoot better than that!" Danny asked him.

"Nothin' man. Everything's cool!" He replied. He looked at me as I approached the table. I didn't like the way he was looking at me. Sometimes I felt that he didn't like me, or that he had something against me. He never said anything to that effect, but it was just the way he looked my way, especially when I spoke of Diana! I knew he wanted her but maybe he waited too long to make his move. Maybe he envied me because I had her and he didn't.

I chalked my cue and prepared for the shot.

"So, what's up with you and Diana?" Phil asked. "You two on the outs?"

I didn't want to talk about Diana, but now that Phil brought it up, I had no choice.

"Yeah, that woman is crazy! I've tried to make sense of her, but it's too hard to figure her out!" I replied.

I shot the five ball cleanly into the side pocket and chalked my cue again.

"You knew she was unstable from the beginning! Darla told you, I told you, Carl and Danny probably told you too!" Phil exclaimed.

"Naw!" Danny said as he leaned against the wall awaiting my next shot. "He's a grown ass man with two good eyes. I ain't got to tell him nothin'!"

Carl said nothing. He smiled a little but he said nothing.

I shot the six-ball and missed. It was Danny's turn.

"I knew it, but she's so damned fine! I had to have her, and the pussy? It's just so damn good! I lost my mind!" I retreated to a spot on the wall close to where Phil stood.

They all laughed!

"Good pussy will do that to you, my man!" Phil said. "It will make you stupid and act like a damned fool! For instance, there's this one girl, who will remain anonymous, who calls me every now and then. She's married to a guy that has more muscles than Arnold Schwarzenegger! She has six kids but she likes what I do to her and I love what she does to me! I know that her husband will kill me if he found out about us. He would tear me limb from limb, but when she calls me, I don't give a damn about that! All that's on my mind is getting into her pants! I don't care if I have to crawl through a minefield, or go through a burning house with gasoline drawers on, I'm gonna' do it! That's how good that pussy is!"

"Yeah, I know what you mean!" Danny chimed in. He shot the eleven-ball but missed.

"How the hell are you going to beat us when you can't even make one shot?" I asked.

"Man, I mis-qued!"

"Your brain is a mis-que!"

Phil approached the table.

"I'm telling you Donn, if my cell phone rings right now and it is her, I'm gone! That's how good it is. You know what I'm talking about?"

"I understand. I really understand! Now you know why I'm still going through changes with Diana! She's better than that! Her stuff is so good that I know that she's crazy, but it doesn't matter. And get this, I found out that she cut some guy's dick off but that still doesn't stop me from going over there!"

"She cut some guy's dick off? Get out of here!" Phil stopped in the middle of his stroke. "You're kidding, right?"

"No! I'm not kidding! That's what her neighbors told me. It was some guy that she was messing with. She caught him cheating on her!"

I heard the rack of cues on the wall behind me crash to the floor. Carl was leaning up against them and now they were all over the place. His face was crazy with anger. He looked at us, and then stormed out the door.

"What's wrong with him?" Danny asked.

"I don't know. Carl has always acted strange. It's just the way he is. I think he feels a little inadequate because of that scar on his face." Phil said.

"Yeah, you're probably right." I added. "Sometimes he looks at me strange and I don't know why. I wonder what's going on in his head."

"Well, you know he has a thing for Diana!" Danny said.

"Yeah, I know that."

"You've got her and he doesn't. It's just a matter of pure envy!"

"I agree!"

"Danny, you've known him longer than we have. How did he get that scar?" Phil asked. "I've wondered about it but he refuses to talk about it!"

"I've asked him about it once and he wouldn't talk to me either. I just never asked again!" Danny replied. "All I know is that someone cut him. I only found that out through the grapevine."

"Oooo, that's bad! Who was it?"

"I don't know. I never found that out."

"Carl is a cool guy and I really like him, but he's just too closed mouthed about what's going on with him. Right now, he's probably going through something but he won't talk about it. We're his friends and he should be able to talk to us." Phil added.

"I want to find out what's wrong with him. He was going through something, and I know how it feels to go through something by yourself." I said.

"Good. We'll clean up this mess!"

I found Carl leaning against a car in the parking lot. He was puffing on a Newport and blowing smoke out at a furious rate.

"What's bothering you Carl? Do you want to talk about it?" I asked as I approached him.

"No. I don't want to talk about it! I'll be all right!" His eyes glared at me and then softened.

"It's always better to talk to a friend. You know? Get off your chest?"

He looked at me and I could see the anger rise and fall again.

"Thanks Donn, but it's something that I just can't talk about now. I'll be alright. I just need to be alone for a few. I'll see you in the meeting."

"Okay, but I'm here for you if you need me."

"Thanks!"

I left him alone to his thoughts and returned inside. Just before the meeting started, car came inside and sat in the chair next to me and smiled. He looked much better than he did when he was outside, but he still had that look of worry on his face.

"Are you okay now?" I asked.

"Better! Thanks for being my friend."

CHAPTER 7

Dilemma!

At 3:45 am, the phone rang!

"Hello!" I said with a touch of anger in my voice. I didn't like to be wakened up in the middle of a good sleep. I didn't know who it was, but I was thinking that it had to be bad news. Who calls at 3:45 in the morning unless they have bad news! It was bad news but thank God it wasn't the bad news that I thought.

"Hi baby!" I stiffened at the sound of her voice.

"Why are you calling me?" My words were cold, a lot colder than I try to make my heart.

"Baby, I need your help." She spoke.

Her words were slurred in her voice was distant and pathetic. She was high or drunk. She had relapsed and left recovery to go out to satisfy her pleasures.

I sat up in bed. "What's wrong?" My concern overtook my iciness.

She was reaching out to me for help and regardless of how I felt about her, I couldn't turn her away, but I knew that I was headed for trouble.

I wanted to hang up the phone and let her fend for herself. I wanted to let her go on as best as she had been and hope for the best, but I had to remember that recovery is something that I struggled with too. I had times when I just didn't know how to keep it together and I needed help from someone that I trusted and looked up to. I needed to be able to call someone, anyone, even at 3:45 in the morning and know that they would be there for me when I needed them. I didn't know what had transpired or what had led her to go back out and do what she did, but I knew that I couldn't turn her away and return to the comforts of my warm bed when she needed me. I couldn't turn her off because I was angry with her. This was about her life and my feelings had to take a backseat. So, I switched from 'angry jilted boyfriend' mode, to 'one addict helping another' mode and I listened to what she had to say with open ears and an empathetic heart.

"I've fallen off the wagon!" She admitted pathetically.

"Did you call your sponsor?" I tried to remain calm and firm.

"Yeah, but she's away at a convention. I left messages, but I need help now!"

"What about your boyfriend?"

She hesitated for a second and then she said. "He's not my boyfriend! He's the one that I got high with! Please Donn, please come and get me!"

I wanted to say no, but I couldn't. "Where are you?"

On Brushton Avenue."

"Brushton Avenue? What are you doing way out in Homewood?" I got up and turned the light on and began to dress.

"He brought me here. Please Donn, please come! I need you! I've got to get away from here. I'm the only girl here and they are all plotting on me. We're at his friend's house and there are guys all over the place and he's in the kitchen with some of them now. Donn, I heard him talking about making me turn tricks with them! I ain't trickin for nobody! Please come and get me! Please?" She was begging and it affected me.

"Okay. I'm getting dressed. Where on Brushton?"

She seemed surprised that I decided to come and get her. "Are you coming?"

"Yes!"

"Okay, thanks baby. I'm leaving here right now. I'll be walking up Frankstown Avenue."

Diana was athletic. She could walk faster than most people I knew. By the time that I got over there, she would be far beyond where I estimated her to be.

"When you get to Braddock Ave., turn there. I'll be coming up from the expressway."

"Okay baby. Thanks. Donn?"

"Yes?"

"I love you!"

I wasn't going to say it. I refused to say it!

"Diana?"

"Yeah baby?"

"Leave now! I'll be there! Look for my Van! What are you wearing?"

"Don't worry; you'll know me when you see me! Bye-bye."

I started looking for her on Braddock Avenue as soon as I exited the expressway. About a half a mile up Braddock Avenue I saw her. She was right! I recognized her right away. It was the hair! She had just passed the park and was walking fast and at a steady pace. She saw the Van and came running across the street to meet me. She jumped in with tears in her eyes, closed the door, curled up in the seat, and let her tears flow.

"He wanted me to screw all of his friends. He called me a nymphomaniac! He said I was a whore and he tried to pimp me!" She broke down in tears again and between them she spoke about her ordeal.

I listened as I drove her home. I didn't want to get involved with her again so I kept telling myself that I was only doing what anyone in recovery would do when someone reaches out for help. I tried to keep my emotions out of it. I didn't like hearing about the things that she said about him. How he brought drugs and alcohol around her, how she woke up to witness him blowing cocaine smoke in her face, about his plan to pimp her. But what he did with her was really none of my business and I had to remember that. She chose to be with him, and it was her decision so who's to say that it happened the way that she claimed? All I needed to do was to get her home and try to get her connected again with women in recovery.

I poured out the stale coffee that was stagnant in her coffee pot and seemed to have mold growing on it. It was a clear indication that she hadn't been home in days. I made a fresh pot and then went into the bathroom and ran her a Calgon scented oil bath. I helped her get out of her clothes and even though her aroma was pungent and not pleasing to my nose, her sexy body still turned me on. She was totally exhausted from running around, getting high and partying every night. She was weak from the abuse that her body had taken and from the lack of sleep. The drugs and alcohol and the long walk didn't help much either. I picked her up and gently placed her in the midst of the foaming hot water. I began to wash her. Her pitiful eyes were swollen with magnum tears. Seeing her this way caused my heart to swell and I had to look away for my own sanity. She was drawing me in again, pulling me closer that I intended to be. Each time I touched her naked skin a rush of emotions that lay dormant for the past few weeks began to emerge and reawaken. I tried to conceal my feelings, but she was no fool. She saw right through me as easily as looking through a sparkling clean storefront window. I soaked her back and started on her shoulders and neck. She grabbed my hand, pulled it down and pressed it against her breast. I didn't want to move it, but I did.

"Come on baby. Make love to me!" She pleaded.

"No! It's not happening, not tonight. I'm just here to help you."

"Well help me then!" She begged.

"I'm not going to take advantage of you."

"Please, take advantage of me! I want you to take advantage of me!"

I pulled away. She released my hand reluctantly. I had to leave. I couldn't stay with her and control myself. I had been too close, to physically involved. What she needed was a woman to be there with her and not me. She needed recovery and not sex. If I stayed, she would get sex! I called a female friend of mine in recovery and explained the situation. She understood and arrived about 15 minutes later. When she arrived, I left.

I didn't see or hear from Diana for the better part of the week. I assumed that she was doing well and staying in recovery, but I didn't know for sure. My mind tried to tell me that the lack of contact was because she was using again, but I didn't want to accept it.

We met at a meeting in Carrick, and she told me that she had been clean and sober since that day. I was happy for her.

"Hi baby." She said as she saw me coming in through the doorway. "It's good to see you. How do I look? Better? Huh? I've got six days today!"

She hugged me and then stepped back and did a twirl so that I could observe her from every angle.

"You like?"

She always looked good to me and there was something about the way that she wore a light-colored flowery sundress that especially grabbed me.

"Yeah, I like!" I was reluctant to comment any further for fear of starting something up again. She did look better, and I was glad to see her back on track again. In the few minutes that we talked she explained that she hadn't called because her sponsor advised against it. I understood that. She also didn't mention sex, nor did she try to turn me on and that was a first.

She didn't call that night as I thought she might. I was happy for her, but disappointed too. Three days later, I had just closed the store and was going over some paperwork when the phone rang. It was Diana. There was an 8 PM meeting at the Onala Club and she asked if I would take her there. I tried to sidestep the question because I didn't trust myself to be alone with her, but she foiled my plan by revealing that she was already in my neighborhood.

"Where are you?" I asked.

"Just look out of your window! I'm across the street!"

I looked across the street and saw her inside of the pizza shop jumping around and waving.

"I'll be right over." She hung up before I could respond. I watched her run across the street smiling and grinning, and I knew that I was in serious trouble. I let her in, and she kissed me and threw herself down on one of the sofas that had been placed near the front door. She was in an extremely jovial mood.

"Mmmm! This is comfortable! How much is it?"

I locked the door. "The price is on it."

I was working hard to keep my eyes off of her. My mind began to reminisce of times past when her body brought me immense pleasure. She was the type of woman that any man would love to have beside him. She possessed that type of beauty that stopped traffic. The type of beauty that made women envious and jealous, and made men want and desire her! The type that made everyone notice her regardless of who they were or where they came from. She possessed a gorgeous smile, perfectly pearly white teeth, silky smooth skin, hypnotically beautiful dark eyes, and an enchanting and mesmerizing voice and a curvaceous body that demanded attention. She walked with poise and grace but also was playful and funny and extremely silly at times. She was also intelligent, thoughtful, considerate, understanding, respectful and loving. The bottom line was that she was as fine as Japanese silk from head to toe! She possessed all of those qualities and more, but I had to keep in mind that the problem wasn't physical and although she could be emotionally stable at times, she was not well! She was a woman with a severe mental illness that was capable of taking her off of the deep end of reality if left unchecked.

She grabbed the price tag and read it. "It's worth more than that!" She bounced up and down on it and released a sigh of relief and comfort. She closed her eyes while I waited. I felt that she was up to something, and I waited to see what it was. "Look," she continued, "I don't have that much right now, but," she began to rub her inner thighs. "How about this? What if I pay you with...?"

"Stop Diana!"

"I'm just kidding. You get all of this free of charge!"

"We've got to talk." I said.

My eyes were glued to her body. She had me already and she knew it.

"Well, talk!" She crossed her legs and sat up straight.

"Diana, I…"

She cut me off. "Donn, just tell me that you don't want me, and I'll leave you alone. Just say that you haven't been thinking about screwing me and I'll go away. Can you honestly say that?"

I didn't say anything. What could I say?

"I didn't think so. So, stop playing around! You want me and I want you. Let's do it! What's the problem?"

She got up from the sofa and stepped really close to me. She ground her body against mine and gave me a sweet kiss from her luscious lips which melted at me like hot butter. I gave in!

"Let's go!"

We didn't make it to the meeting. The entire evening was spent in bed. After the first round, I found myself right back in the same situation that I had been in before. But I told myself that this time it would be different. I wanted it to be different, but I didn't want to give her up. Deep inside I never did, but it was circumstances that forced it. In the beginning it was all about sex, but then feelings of love and concern showed up and changed everything. I wondered what she was doing when I didn't hear from her. I tried to convince myself that I didn't care what she did or who she did it with, but it was all a lie! It was a form of self-deception, a bout of intense male ego. She had already gotten under my skin and as much as I didn't want to admit it, the truth was that I had developed an attraction for her that went far beyond the physical.

Again, she disappeared for several days without making any contact with me. I thought about her again, but I didn't call. When she finally called me, it was Sunday afternoon. She wanted to come over.

"I'm bored!" She said. "Let's do something!"

"What do you want to do?" I asked. It wasn't 1 AM so I didn't think that she was thinking about sex.

"I don't know. I just want to be with you. Let's go somewhere together. Anywhere!"

"Do you want to see a movie?"

She became excited. "Yes!"

"I'll be over there in an hour. You decide what we're going to see!"

"Okay. Bye! Donn?"

"Yes?"

"I love you!"

"So does my mother! Be ready!"

There was a movie that we wanted to see playing at several theaters in the area but only one had a time in which we didn't have to wait for hours for it to start. That was in the theater at the Miracle Mile Shopping Center in Monroeville. That's where we went. Monroeville is about ten miles from where I lived but it wasn't a problem getting there. It was just off of the expressway.

The movie started and we sat with our popcorn, sodas and a large and overpriced box of Mike and Ike's! After a few minutes Diana became upset and decided to leave. She didn't say anything to me, but I knew that something was wrong. I looked around for blonde, white women but didn't see any in the area that might have caused her to become upset. Then I saw him. He was sitting just a few rows in front of us off to the left. It was Mr. Broken Nose! He had made eye contact with Diana and now he was looking at me. He immediately looked away when our eyes met. His look was more of surprise then fear but he instinctively touched the bandages on his nose.

I found Diana outside leaning against the wall close to the emergency exit door.

"Don't touch me!" She snapped as I approached. "Get away from me!"

(It's starting again!) I thought.

The crazy roller coaster ride was about to begin again. Her words and attitude angered me, and I had the urge to leave her standing right there. If not for the fact that we were so far from town, I would have. When she began to act that way, it was obvious to me that she had stopped taking her medication. I never knew what to expect. I never knew where her mind would take her, Or us!

"Did you stop taking your medication?" I asked, already knowing the truth.

"That's none of your damn business!" She slid down the wall until she sat on the sidewalk. She started crying. I leaned over and touched her shoulder. "DON'T TOUCH ME!" She yelled.

Heads turned throughout the parking lot along the sidewalk as her voice carried through the airwaves. From the looks that I received and the position that she was in with me standing over her that people thought that I had struck her. I backed off. They're accusing looks made me feel very uncomfortable.

Mr. Broken Nose came out of the theater arm in arm with a woman who looked like she was on crack. I didn't notice her when I saw him in the theater. She looked terrible! Thin, sunken jaws and her hair was matted with a baseball cap on trying to hide it. Her skin was dark and greasy and when they approached, I could smell that unique smell that sets crackheads apart from other addicts.

Diana got up immediately when she saw them. Her countenance abruptly changed, and her dead eyes were back. There was only one emotion there. Hatred!

"No Diana!" I shouted. "Don't!" I knew what she was about to do but I didn't know why. If she heard me, there was no sign. She didn't react at all, but she continued to move with the stealth of a cat. I reached out to stop her, but she was too fast. I missed. She had sprung so quickly that no one knew what was happening until it was too late. She backed off just as quickly as she approached leaving his face a bloody mass of torn flesh and fingernail tracks. The next blurred moment, she slapped the girl so hard with the back of her hand that it sent her flying swiftly and violently to the ground. Then, calmly, and as cold as ice, she said.

"Come on baby, let's go home!"

There was no urgency in her tone, no rush to flee the scene, no thought to what the consequences of her actions might be. There was none of that! She was again the Diana that was willing to listen and do what I asked. The change from menacing maniac too timid temptress was so sudden and so complete that it shocked and frightened me.

There's not much to put a scare me. Stray bullets whizzing by my head, a live land mine under my feet, being in the midst of a burning building, lightning striking around me are a few, but that day I added one more thing to my list. The wrath of Diana! She blanked out in an instant and came back just as quickly and functioned as if she had never blanked out at all. It was so natural to her, just like breathing.

We didn't leave as planned. There were consequences to pay for her actions. The mall police detained the four of us until the Monroeville police arrived. They spoke of charging Diana with aggravated assault.

"If you're arresting me, then you'd better arrest him too!" Diana said as she pointed at Mr. Broken Nose.

"What the hell you talking about? You attacked me!" He had a handkerchief in his hand that was red with his blood. He patted his torn face with it.

Diana looked him straight in the eye. "You started this last night! Do you want me to tell them what you did? Or do you want to forget the whole thing? And you, you lowlife tramp!" She fired at the woman who she pimp-slapped to the ground. "You know you don't want me to talk about you, do you?" The girl hung her head. "So, what's it going to be? Are we ALL going to jail or we ALL going home?"

She had everyone mesmerized including the police and me. At that moment if anyone had said that she was mentally ill, you would have not believed it. She had it all together and was at the top of her mental game.

The place was completely quiet. Even the people walking by seemed to have nothing to say. She had provoked everyone to thought.

"Okay, what's it going to be?" One of the officers asked. He then turned his attention to Mr. Broken Nose and his crackhead friend. "Are you pressing charges or not?"

The answer was no, and we left with instructions to take our feud back into the city. "And leave Monroeville to the nice peaceful people that live here!"

We were almost to the section of parking lot where my van was parked when it started again. The two of them were going in the same direction and we're just behind us. Suddenly Diana turned vicious again after Mr. Broken Nose realized that he was out of earshot of police, began to taunt her! I stopped and turned to confront him, but Diana said.

"Let it go baby. He ain't worth it!"

"Yeah punk!" He yelled. "HideHi behind her skirt. You ain't sh.."

Before he could finish, she reached out and grabbed another handful of skin from his already ragged face. He screamed in pain.

"Owww! He grabbed his face. "YOU BITCH!"

That's when I hit him. He took a step or two backwards before his legs failed him and he sat squarely on his ass. He was dazed and because of it I didn't hit him again. I looked in the direction of the police. They had witnessed the entire thing, but they functioned as if they hadn't seen anything. One threw up his hands in disgust as he turned and walked back to his patrol car. I grabbed Diana and pulled her away before she did any more damage. She looked as if she wanted to tear more flesh, but she didn't resist and moved compliantly with me. She didn't argue or try to pull away, but she asked if she could smack the girl again. I said no.

"Please?"

"No! Let's go!"

I didn't care about the girl one way or the other. I was concerned about the police. Enough is enough! We left Monroeville peacefully and quietly. She sat in her seat with the most pleasant and serene look that I had seen on her face in sometime. I could tell that she was reliving the events that transpired and that she was extremely pleased with the results. She held her hand to her face admiring the fragments of skin and blood under her nails.

I turned my attention back to the business of driving, but through my peripheral vision I saw her take a quick glance my way. After she assured herself that I wasn't watching, she placed her fingers in her mouth and licked the blood! My heart thumped in my chest! I couldn't believe what I had seen! My blood raced through my veins and my adrenaline rushed wildly throughout my body. Did I really see what I thought I saw? An element of fear gripped me but at the same moment I felt exhilarated and turned on with sexual energy.

She was right, I couldn't get rid of her that easily! There was something about her craziness that kept me attached. It attracted me and robbed me of my self-control. Watching her taste someone else's blood should've turned me off completely but instead it did the opposite! She continued to lick her fingers. I should have been repulsed but I wasn't. I looked over at her and she looked at me, but she didn't stop licking and sucking her fingers in and out of her mouth. Her eyes pierced mine and what she did no longer seemed cannibalistic but then became sensual and sexual. The way she slowly pushed her fingers into her mouth, wrapping her lips around them and just as gently pulling them out was driving me crazy and she knew it.

She was quietly seducing me as her body screamed for me to have my way with it. The sexual tension was so alive that sparks were flying from me to her and from her to me. I could feel and hear my heart beating. Or was it hers? I definitely heard her breathing and I knew what she was thinking.

I quickly pulled off of the road and parked on the shoulder. She looked at me with questions at first but then with a smile.

"Get your ass in the back and get naked... NOW!" I ordered.

Risky business with Diana, but I took the risk. She made me wait for about 30 seconds and then she squirmed in her seat and sweetly said.

"Okay baby! Whatever you want!" Then she scooted out of the seat and worked her way to the empty space in the back of the van and began to undress!

CHAPTER 8

I love you…I love you not!

"His name is Darren! Not 'Mr. Broken Nose'!" She said.

"Whatever his name is, I want to know what's up with him!" I sat down on her sofa with a cup of her famous, strong, dark coffee in my hand. "Why was he here at your house last night and why are you just telling me about it?"

"Don't get upset baby! I'll tell you everything." She finished putting sugar in her coffee and then she sat down beside me.

"Don't get upset? Why shouldn't I be upset? This is the second time I've had a run-in with him and I'm just finding out his name! What else is there that I should know?"

I was upset and it showed. I didn't like to be in the dark about some potential foe and I didn't like finding out that she was still seeing the creep after he tried to pimp her out to his friends. I wanted to know exactly what was going on.

"He showed up at my door, but I didn't know it was him until I opened it. I didn't have the chain on, and he just pushed his way in. Baby, I didn't want him to come in but there was nothing that I could do.

"He told me that he robbed a white guy on Center Avenue of $2500 and he gave me $100 to let him stay at my place for a few hours. I was okay with that. I told him that he had to leave before midnight, and he agreed. He left but came back about a half an hour later with some cocaine. I didn't let him in. He pushed a bag under my door. When I saw it, it made me feel really funny. You know, when you want to get high, but you know that you shouldn't?" She looked at me with sad eyes. I understood. "I really was angry with him for doing that. He thought that I would smoke it and then I would open the door and he could come in. I took it and flushed it down the toilet. He kept banging on the door trying to get me to open it. I wanted to open it because I really wanted to get high, but I knew what would happen once I did. I knew that I'd be right back where I was before, and I didn't want that. I went to my bedroom and closed the door. I could still hear him banging and talking but I refused to open the door. I was really miserable."

"So why didn't you call the police?"

She was shocked that I had asked such a question.

"You know we don't deal with the cops!"

"Why didn't you call me?"

She hesitated. "I guess I just didn't think about it!"

"Hummm!"

She shot a glance my way, but she didn't respond. She sipped her coffee and continued to tell me what happened. It all sounded good but so did a lot of things that she said. I just couldn't take it at face value. She was very manipulative and at times it was easy for her to manipulate me.

She told me that she had been seeing him for some time before she met me but broke it off because he started using drugs again. She said that she hadn't given him the time of day since then until the day that I foolishly spoke about her cooking. He called her that day, she said, and because she was mad at me, she started seeing him again.

"If you hadn't made me mad, I wouldn't have given him the time of day!"

"So, you're blaming this on me? It's my fault? Is that what you're telling me?"

"No! Not really! I'm just saying that I was mad at you. When I'm mad, I don't think clearly and sometimes I do things that I regret later."

"I understand. I'm the same way, but it still sounds like you're not taking responsibility for your actions. Being mad at me isn't reason to start seeing someone else!"

"You shouldn't have said what you said about my cooking!"

"You're right. I shouldn't have said it and I'm sorry, but you didn't stick around long enough to hear me apologize. You didn't want to hear anything. You just stormed off!"

She leaned up against me in an attempt to soften me up. She knew how to handle me.

"So why did you get high?"

She expected me to continue on about Darren, but I changed the subject. She sat up to look at me. For a moment she was speechless but quickly recovered.

"I guess because I was still mad at you!"

"That's ridiculous and you know it! Nobody can make you get high! No one can make you cheat! Nobody but you! If you didn't want to get high no one could force you. If you really were my woman, nothing or no one could make you cheat! That's the truth! What I said about your cooking made you upset, and again I'm sorry, but you left my house mad and gave relapse an opportunity to take you. Darren called you many times, but you didn't give in to him, so why that time?"

She scooted close to me again and laid her head on my shoulder. "I'm sorry baby! Can you forgive me?"

"There's really nothing to forgive. You're free to do whatever you want. You're not my woman! It's just I need to know what I'm getting into if I'm going to spend time with you. I don't like being at a disadvantage."

She didn't respond to that except in the way that she hugged me. That was her way of saying, 'you're my man, and don't you forget it!'.

She went on to tell me about the woman who was with Darren, alias; Mr. Broken Nose! Her name was Bimini. She was Diana's first cousin. She was strung out on crack and had outstanding warrants pending. Both she and Darren were willing to forget the incident at the theater because of their previous involvements with the law. She explained some things, but others were left unanswered. Still, questions lingered in my head and created new questions. I resigned to the fact that she was going to be herself and that there was nothing that I could do to change that. I didn't try. I stopped worrying about what was to come next and who I would encounter and why. I stopped worrying about who she might be seeing or what she might be doing. I went back to the way it was before amorous feelings came into play. I enjoyed her body when it was my turn!

For the next few months, we continued to see each other. Sex remained the focal point of our relationship although we did spend a lot of time together outside of the bedroom. Several times she disappeared for several days at a time only to call me at one in the morning to tell me that she was horny. There was never an explanation offered as to where she had been, and I never asked.

I hadn't seen her in five or six days but that Saturday evening at closing time she came in and sat in one of the chairs in the front of the store. She sat quietly and waited until the last two customers had left. I locked the door and closed the blinds.

"Donn, I'm horny!" Her words were slow. She didn't look at me, but she looked straight ahead at the window although the blinds had been closed preventing her from seeing out. I could tell that there was something wrong. I believed that she had stopped taking her medicine again. It was the one thing that kept her in touch with reality, but she was losing that contact again.

"Diana, did you stop taking your medication again?"

She got up from the chair, faced me and nodded yes and then attempted to unzip my pants.

"Why Diana? Why do you keep doing that? You need that medication to be okay."

She continued to try to get into my pants, but verbally she didn't respond. I pulled her hands away. I wanted her badly, but not in the condition that she was in. I didn't see that glow in her eyes that told me that she was really ready! I didn't see that fire in her eyes that said, 'I've got to have it, or I'll just die!' I didn't see, nor did I feel, the passion that ignited the lust and desire to grow in me for her. She was mechanical, void of passion, going through the motions, doing it out of habit and not out of need. I stopped her, sat her down and began to talk to her as I had done so many times before.

She spoke of the group of blonde, white women plotting against her life. It was ridiculous I thought. There was no army of any kind out to kill her but in her state of mind without the stabilizing medication, she believed that there was. Usually there wasn't much that I could say or do to change that, but I tried anyway. I wanted her to understand that she needed to get back on her medication. It was a challenging task but what I had in my favor was that she trusted me. She had sought me out and that meant something. I spoke as calmly as I could and she listened, but her focus was still on sex. She wasn't responding as I had hoped that she would and that blank expression on her face continued to tell me how much she wanted me inside of her. I wasn't getting through, and I had to change tactics. I told her that I'd give her all the sex that she wanted but first she'd have to take her medication. That worked. We went to her place, and she took her medication.

The problem I then faced with that she remained in the same state of mind because the medication takes quite some time to start working, but I had promised, so I delivered. When I had finished and she lay beneath me kissing my lips repeatedly, I felt something missing. I didn't feel right about what I had just done. I felt as if I had taken advantage of her. I felt guilty, dirty, and sick. I imagined it was the way a woman feels after having sex with someone when she really didn't want to, when she turned her first trick, or if she had been raped!

I looked into her eyes and knew that I would never let it happen again. She had been temporarily satisfied but her eyes were not afire like they usually were. Her moans were not as passionate nor as loud or as deep from the pit of her. She didn't have that 'ugly face' that was always there before she reached her climax, and I felt no fingernails in my back or thighs squeezing my sides. This time it was different. There was none of that! There was pleasure for both of us, but not as it should have been. Not as it usually was! That 'morning after' feeling engulfed me and caused me to feel embarrassment. She turned one way, and I turned the other and we laid back-to-back in silence. I wanted to talk but I didn't have a clue as to what to say to her. We laid without talking, hugging, or kissing. We were in our separate silent cells praying for time to pass and sleep to come to parole us from the dungeon of misery that we had placed ourselves in. I fell asleep mentally kicking myself for what I had just done.

I heard my name being called by a familiar voice. It was coming from the trees atop a mountain where I stood naked except for a pair argyle socks! The voice called out, 'WAKE UP DONN!' And then it quickly vanished along with every tree around me leaving me shivering in the waist deep snow that suddenly appeared as instantly as the trees disappeared. The coldness took my breath away and I immediately sat up in the bed wide awake. It was just a vivid dream! I struggled to catch my breath.

I looked over to check on Diana trying to be careful not to wake her but saw that she was not asleep. She was sitting with her back against the headboard, her pillow was behind her, her knees were drawn up to her chest, her eyes were wide with fright, her hands were clasped together touching her knees and squeezing the handle of a large butcher knife!

I checked Big Al! He was still there, still attached and still asleep. I jumped out of bed with the covers over my feet causing me to trip and fall. I scrambled to my feet expecting to find her standing over me poised to strike by plunging the blade of the knife deep into my chest, or worse, permanently separating me from Big Al! But thank God, her mind was elsewhere. She hadn't moved from her position on the bed. She rocked forward and backward and made sounds that were of no language familiar to me.

"Diana?" I moved cautiously and dangerously close. Her eyes stayed affixed to wherever mine had taken them. They didn't move, they didn't blink! I reached for the knife but her cat like reflexes easily moved it before I could reach it. She didn't look at me at all but continued to stare off to that place where only she knew. "Diana, please give me the knife!" Just for moment her voice became as clear and as plain as you can imagine. She said, no! Then she went straight back to mumbling. "Please Diana! Give me the knife before you hurt yourself!" That was what I said but what I meant was before you hurt me!

Defiantly she shook her head. I tried several different tactics designed to get to the knife without getting cut or stabbed but they all failed. She just shook her head and moved it as easy out of my reach as taking candy from a baby. A few minutes later she began to speak.

"They're coming!" She was frightened. Her hands began to shake and she white knuckle the knife.

"Who's coming?"

"You know!

"Tell me about them! Please?" I tried to be calm and understanding.

"You know about them! You know who they are!" She continued to stare off into nothingness.

"Where are they now?" I knew then that she was talking about the blonde, white women.

"Outside the door!"

"Diana, there's no one out there!"

"Yes, they are! I can hear them!"

I listened. I heard nothing but faint voices of the people across the way coming through the open kitchen window.

"There's nobody there Diana. I'll prove it to you!" I got up and started walking towards the living room. Before I reached the doorway, she was up. She grabbed me from behind and placed the blade of the knife to my throat.

"Don't go near the door!" She threatened. Her voice was menacing and totally unlike her normal speaking voice.

That really pissed me off! I wanted to snatch her and beat the crap out of her for threatening me that way, but I'm no fool! (Well, maybe I was for messing with her!) I knew that one false move, one slice of that blade and I'd be dead.

"Get that knife away from me!" I snapped at her, but I didn't move. "RIGHT NOW DIANA!"

Maybe it was the tone of my voice and maybe she had a moment of clarity and realized that I wasn't the enemy, but she gently removed the knife and allowed me to take it from her.

"I'm sorry Donn." She apologized. "I don't want to hurt you. You're the only real friend I've got. I'm so sorry!"

"That's okay." I said but it wasn't okay. She could've killed me! I took her gently but firmly by the waist and guided her to the living room and towards the front door. She was afraid but she trusted me, so slowly, step by step, we approached the door. About ten feet away I stopped. I laid the knife down on the coffee table.

"What do you hear?" I asked. "Do you hear voices?"

"Yes. They're out there! I can hear them!" She was trembling and holding onto me for dear life. I moved her away from the door and towards the kitchen.

"Do you still hear them?"

"Yes. There's still there." She stared at the door expecting it to burst open at any second.

"Baby, there's no one outside of that door. What you hear is coming from over there!" I directed her attention to the neighbors who could be seen and heard across the way. "That's what you hear, isn't it?"

She looked out of the window and then back to the door. Again, she looked to the window and back to the door. She began to understand. She nodded her head in agreement, but she wasn't fully convinced.

"Okay. Diana, you need to open the door!" She wasn't at all ready to do that and my words frightened her again.

The knife was on the coffee table, and she tried to get to it, but I stopped her.

"No Diana! You don't need that!"

She began to cry and tried to pull away from me like a child would, but I held her close and promised her that everything would be okay. I told her that she needed to open the door herself and see that there were no blonde, white women out there bonded together to kill her.

"No baby! Please! I don't want to open the door!" She pulled away and flattened herself against the far wall near the kitchen. She was frightened to death.

"Okay, okay." I gave in. "You stay right there. I'll open the door so that you can see. Okay?"

She nodded.

I opened the door slowly. She tensed against the wall then eased a bit when she saw that no one was there.

"See? There's no one there! It's all in your mind. Fight it!"

She looked out of the window and then she walked over to where I was standing in the doorway. She put her arms around me for security and then she looked out. She looked at me.

"You love me, don't you?" Her voice was still that of a scared child. I didn't want to say it. Every fiber of my being screamed, 'deny it', but...

"Yes Diana, I do love you!"

She smiled. "You never said that before, but I've always known that you loved me. You know why? Because you always put up with me. You're always trying to help me. Most guys just want to do it to me so that they can say that they screwed me, but you're different. You really care!" She hugged and kissed me. "I love you too!"

I grabbed her and gave her a long, wet, sloppy kiss with plenty of tongue. My emotions got the best of me.

(So what? Sue me!)

Then things really got ugly.

"Donn?" Her eyes were starry.

"Yes?"

"I want to have your baby!"

My brain went numb. I went into shock. I couldn't believe what I had just heard. That statement brought reality to a terrible screeching halt. The thought of her caring for an infant was terrifying. Preposterous! She barely cared for herself. What would happen to that child when she refused to take her medication? What would happen when she became driven by those uncontrollable desires to have sex with anyone and everyone she chooses? The child would be neglected, maybe even abandoned! What would happen if she suddenly saw the child as an enemy? A blonde, white woman? I shuddered at the thought.

She was not ready for motherhood. How long had that thought played around in her beautiful mind? Had she thought about it for a while? What if she stopped taking her birth-control pills right along with her medication? What if she was already pregnant? I looked at her trying to decipher what was going on in her head.

I asked the obvious question not knowing or even thinking that I would get the reaction that I got. If I had known, I would never have asked.

"Diana, are you pregnant?"

It was too late! I said it and her reaction to let me know that trouble was brewing and coming my way. I was about to feel a portion of the wrath of Diana!

"No! I'm not pregnant! Do I look pregnant?" Her face begins to twist and distort.

"No, but…"

"Then why the hell would you ask me that? Do you think I would deliberately get pregnant without talking to you about it first? Huh???"

Her eyes grew cold and blank. Just a few moments ago she was fearful for her life, now she was looking at me as if she wanted to take mine! She was about as close to rage as I had ever seen her, and I didn't like it.

"Diana, listen to me!"

"NO! You listen to me!" She shouted. "First, you don't trust me, then you insult my cooking, and you think I want to steal from you, and now you think I tricked you into getting me pregnant!"

"Diana, wait a minute!"

"NO! YOU WAIT A MINUTE! YOU BASTARD! YOU WAIT A GOD DAMMED MINUTE!"

She started stomping around the room. She slashed at her lamp that was on the end table by the door. It wobbled from the slight brush of her fingers, but it didn't fall over. I was poised to catch it, but I didn't have to.

"I would never think of tricking you into knocking me up! Oooo! You make me so me! You don't give a damn about me! You don't care about my feelings!" She reached out for me. "Come here!" She grabbed my hand and slapped it to her stomach. "Do I feel pregnant? Huh? You bastard!"

"I'm not going to be too many more of you bastards!" I pulled away.

"Here, kiss me, you bas…" she stopped short of saying it, but she didn't stop short of giving me a piece of her mind. "Kiss me, tell me if I taste pregnant?"

She tried to force me to kiss her, but I pulled away. My anger was rising right along with hers, and I struggled to control it. I didn't want to compete with her in a shouting match, so I shut down. She couldn't hear me anymore anyway. I stopped trying to reason because she was no longer reasonable. I began to search for my opportunity to leave. She continued to rant and rave about what I had said. She called me the most inconsiderate, ungrateful, uncaring stupid man that she ever knew! Earlier, I had been the most considerate and caring, but now I was just the opposite!

"You know something Donn? I don't need you! Get the hell out of my house and never come back!"

I didn't argue with her. I grabbed my keys and took my opportunity to exit. I was so upset that I forgot that I was standing in my boxer shorts. I was about to leave that way but when I realized it, I turned and began walking to the bedroom. She picked up the knife from the coffee table and threatened me with it.

"GET OUT NOW, OR I"LL KILL YOU!" She screamed.

When I turned and looked at her, her face seemed unrecognizable to me. Whoever that was in Diana's body, was no longer anyone that I knew!

"I've got to get my clothes!" I was totally pissed off, but I had the same thought in mind that she had. Leave and never come back! She waved the knife in my direction.

"NO! GET OUT NOW!"

"I told you, don't threaten me!" I started to yell right along with her.

"GET OUT!"

"NOT WITHOUT MY CLOTHES!"

"GET OUT! GET OUT! GET OUT! GET OUT!"

She kept saying it. She yelled over and over and over. I turned towards the bedroom again. She stepped closer to me. I grabbed her and twisted her wrist until the knife fell out. I pushed her down on the sofa, picked up the knife and threw it out of the open kitchen window.

"YOU CRAZY BITCH!" By this time, I had totally lost control right along with her.

"DON"T CALL ME CRAZY!" She shouted. "I'M NOT CRAZY!"

She was sitting on the sofa and began kicking the coffee table as she shouted. She was having a tantrum and her actions negated her words. If she could see herself as I did, kicking the table and punching the air, she would have known that she was insane! She said nothing about me calling her a bitch but went crazy over the word crazy!

"You are crazy! That's why you don't have a man! Nobody wants to deal with you, except me, and I must be crazy too!"

"I'M NOT CRAZY! I'M NOT CRAZY! DON"T CALL ME CRAZY! YOU BASTARD! I'M NOT CRAAAAA-ZZZZY!"

She fell back on the sofa, her feet kicking in the air, her hands punching at nothing at all while she kept screaming at the top of her lungs that she wasn't crazy.

I went into the bedroom, put on my clothes, grab the rest of my things and walked past her and without saying a word. I slammed the door behind me. As I walked down the steps, I could still hear her screaming that she wasn't crazy. I wondered if she even knew that I was gone! The answer to that came just as I exited the main entrance to the building when her clock radios shattered on the ground in front of me.

"You bastard! Don't you ever come back here! I'll kill you! I'll cut off your balls and stick them in your mouth! Do you hear me? You bastard! I HATE YOU! I'll kill you!"

I didn't respond. I kept walking and didn't look back. The people across the way were enjoying the show. One guy stood up and grabbed his crotch mockingly and then the others all laughed.

"Better let her go before you lose em!" He shouted at me. I gave him a wave of agreement and continued on to my Van.

Diana was still going off. I could hear shouting and tearing of her apartment. Every few seconds something would crash and break on the ground behind me.

In my Van I took a deep breath and vowed to leave her alone forever. I was finished. I drove off thinking that I must be crazy to be dealing with her. I must be out of my mind!

CHAPTER 9

The Demons Return

I didn't see her for at least a month after that incident. I didn't call her but she did call me. I hung up without speaking as soon as I knew that it was her. For at least a week, she called me day and night. She didn't limit it to just the usual one o'clock calls. When she did call me at one o'clock or later, I didn't answer at all. There was no doubt that it was her. She finally got the message and stopped calling.

It's strange, but during that week I didn't want to talk to her and hardly thought of her even though she was calling me all of the time, but when the calling stopped, my thoughts of her were constant. I wondered how she was doing. Was she taking her medication? Was she really pregnant? Why had she stopped calling? Was she seeing someone else? Who? Was she drinking and getting high again? Was she still going to recovery meetings? My mind was full of thoughts of her and I had to get relief so I immersed myself into other things that took the focus off of her. My store was the main thing!

The store was doing well. I became well acquainted with the neighborhood and the residents and learned what they desired. I stocked my shelves with the things that they needed and my business began to bloom.

I hadn't been accepted in the neighborhood at first, probably because I hadn't grown up there and because I was the only black businessmen there, but that slowly changed and I became accepted as a legitimate resident and businessman.

My shop was in the Allentown section of Pittsburgh which is on the backside of Mount Washington just before you enter Mt. Oliver.

When I opened the shop, I thought that I would be accepted immediately, but the initial reaction of the people was rejection. That rejection came from potential customers as well as other businessmen. I had become the only black businessmen in the neighborhood and with the exception of the Chinese restaurant, owned and operated by Harry Fong and his wife; every business there was owned and operated by white men or white families. My initial welcoming was shrouded in suspicion, cold stares and mistrust. No one wanted to deal with a black man, not even a light skin one who was the product of a black father and a white mother, like me!

My first weekend in business netted me exactly one customer. It was Harry Fong. He came in on the third day, but before he stepped through my door, I noticed him as he walked past peering in the window. He passed by several times before he made up his mind to enter. He had seen me as I struggled to prepare for my grand opening and I'm sure that he knew the trouble that I was facing. He wanted to welcome me but he was a little afraid of what the other business owners might think of him. Finally he pushed open the door and stepped through to the sound of the bell clanging atop the door.

"Good morning sir!" I said with a smile. I was happy that someone, anyone came in.

"Good morning sir!" He replied. He had no Chinese accent whatsoever and if I had heard him speak before seeing him, I wouldn't have known that he was Chinese at all. His English was better than mine!

"May I help you with something?" I asked.

"No. I just wanted to introduce myself. I'm Harry Fong. My wife and I own the Chinese Garden restaurant across the street."

"Oh." I stepped from behind the counter and offered my hand in friendship. He extended his hand and we shook. "My name is Donn Diamond. It's a pleasure to meet you Mr. Fong."

"And you, Mr. Diamond!" He smiled graciously and he bowed slightly. I bowed in return.

"How long have you been in business here, Mr. Fong?"

"About five years now. You will find that the people here are slow to accept new people." He put an accent on the word 'new'.

"By 'new', you mean,... Different?" I interrupted him.

"Yes! Different! When I came here nobody wanted to come into my restaurant. They did eventually once they got used to me being here. Once they realized that people who live down on the South Side were coming up here to my restaurant, they began to come and have been steady customers since. They will come to you too, but you must be patient. Once you win them over, you will have many loyal customers!"

"Thank you, Mr. Fong. I really appreciate that. I was beginning to feel that I had made a terrible mistake!"

"No mistake! It's just that you are the first Negro to open a business here!" He looked closely at me, and then added. "You are very,..: light… for a Negro!"

"I'd appreciate it if you would refer to me as a black, not Negro!"

"I'm sorry. I meant no disrespect. I didn't mean to offend you."

"I understand. No offense taken. I just prefer Black, and yes, I'm light-skinned because my mother, my birth mother was white! My father was black!"

"Your birth mother?"

"Yes. When I was a baby my mother gave me up for adoption and I was raised by my 'true' mother, Mrs. Donna diamond who was black."

"So you are half white." It wasn't quite a question and his words trailed off into the distance.

"Yes! Maybe they will accept that half!" I said it jokingly in order to lighten the mood.

"Yes, maybe they will, but it's the neg,… Black half that they will have a problem with. But don't give up because if they accepted me they will accept you too!" He smiled again and bowed before he began to leave.

"Thanks again Mr. Fong." I said.

"Call me Harry, Donn. Friends use first names!" He smiled. His smile was genuine and I felt that we were definitely going to become friends.

"Okay Harry!"

He stopped and looked into the glass case in front of him. "Are those wooden skewers for sale?" He asked.

"Yes they are!" I became excited believing that my first sale was about to happen.

He looked closer and saw the price tag. "I'll take them. I'm going to be making some shish kebabs for the sidewalk sale this summer and they will be perfect. Do you have more?"

"As another fact I do. I've got several boxes, 1000 per box. Do you need that many?"

I was hoping that he would take them all. I had bought them with several other items at an auction in the package deal and I really didn't think that they would sell, but I put them out anyway.

"How much for an entire box?" He asked. When I told him he said. "I'll take two boxes!"

"Great! I'll get them for you!"

When I returned with the boxes, Harry Fong was admiring a mini refrigerator that I had planned to keep for the store, but when it was all said and done, I sold and delivered it to him the next day.

Harry Fong was my first customer. Just as he had said, most Allentown people stayed away from me. When business began to pick up, it was due to the people that I had met in Narcotics Anonymous who came from Beltzhoover, Mount Oliver, The South Side, Mount Washington, Carrick and The North Side. Once my friends in NA heard about my store, they came in droves to patronize me. Only then did the Allentown people begin to trickle in.

There were two police officers that visited me on almost a daily basis for a week or two. They bought nothing but spent time jotting down the serial numbers of my electronic items and anything of value with a serial number on it. I knew that they were there because someone had sent them. I didn't know who, but I knew why. When they came in, they spoke as they entered and were very cordial, but not friendly. They went about their business checking out everything that they felt they needed to. That went on for about a couple of weeks before they finally engaged me in conversation.

"Mr. Diamond. I'm Officer Spivey and this is Officer Cramer." He extended his hand and I did the same.

"It's a pleasure to meet you officers. What can I do for you?"

"I'm sure you've been wondering why we come here as often as we do."

"Actually, I stopped wondering after the couple of days. I know that you're just doing your job." I wanted to tell them that I knew that they were checking me out through my inventory, but they already knew that I knew that.

"Let me just say that there are some people here in Allentown that don't want you here. We received a report that you were selling drugs and dealing in stolen goods." Officer Spivey told me.

I replied. "That was my thought but I didn't think that they labeled me as a drug dealer!"

Officer Spivey smiled. "Well, we've done a background check on you, I'm sure you have figured that out by now. We've checked your stock and we've been watching you also. As far as we're concerned, it's nothing personal. We're just doing our job. Whenever we get a report, we have to check it out, but I'm happy to inform you that you've passed with a clean bill."

"I could have told you that, but my word would have meant nothing to you then." I said.

"You're right. But now,… it does! But, whether we believed you or not, wouldn't have made a difference. A complaint was filed and we had to investigate it to its conclusion."

"I understand. Are you at liberty to tell me who made the complaint?"

"Yes. It's public record. Mr. Diagliano and Mr. Warwick."

"Thank you." I didn't know who they were but I was definitely going to find out.

Business picked up greatly after that and friendships grew. My normal business hours are 8 AM to 6 PM but there were days when I stayed open later. Most days, I closed for lunch at 11:45 to attend a noon NA meeting and then I reopened about 1:15 or 1:30.

I attended Narcotics Anonymous meetings regularly. It was a vital part of my life. Most of the friends that I had were recovering addicts who I met through NA. Darla was my best female friend. Then there was Phil, Carl and Danny who was the nucleus of my inner circle support group. Then there was my sponsor, Will. Will and I didn't hang out much but we talked on the phone almost every day. He was a man that I respected above all. That's why I selected him to be my sponsor. I saw the program of NA was working for him and I wanted what he had, so I listened to what he said and did what he said to do regardless of what my brain told me and I found out that it worked for me too. Together they kept me balanced. They listened when I spoke of thoughts and feelings that others outside couldn't understand. When Diana came up in my thoughts, I would call one of them. It was usually Darla or Phil. Danny was elusive and Carl didn't want to hear about Diana. But Diana was not out of my life. As time passed thoughts of her became less frequent. I had all but forgotten her but the same wasn't true for her!

She called at 1 AM! When I heard the phone ringing, I knew it was her and I didn't answer it. About 15 minutes later, she called again. I was tempted to answer but I didn't. Big Al and I both knew what she wanted. He began to protest as I resisted the temptation to pick up the phone. With each ring he grew more rigid in his attempts to persuade me to give in to him, but I kept thinking with the big head. I refused to let him win this time. The phone stopped ringing and I lay in bed in the dark waiting for it to ring again. While I waited, Big Al began talking to me through my thoughts.

(You know Donn; you don't have to be so stubborn! We can just go over there and get what we want and then leave. We don't have to stay!)

"No! It won't go like that and you know it!"

(But, let's give her another chance. I really miss Jennifer!)

"So do I but,… hey! No! It can't happen!"

The phone rang again. Both of us sat up. I wanted to get up and tell her that I'd be right over but I didn't want to go through hell again.

(Aw, c'mon Donn! Give her one more chance. Just this once!)

"No!" I said loudly then I realized that this conversation was just in my head, but I was speaking out loud.

"Great! Now I'm talking to my dick!"

When the phone stopped ringing, I got up and took it off the hook and went to take a cold shower with Big Al leading the way.

The following Friday I went to a meeting at the Onala Club. When I passed through the front door I saw her standing with her back to me in the TV lounge. She was talking to a guy whose eyes were firmly glued to her. I hurried to try to slip by but she turned and saw me just before I was out of her field of vision. She instantly left him and came running over to meet me.

She was wearing one of her floor-length wigs. This one was Auburn and didn't look that bad except for the length. She had on enough makeup to make Tammy Faye Bakker proud, and she had on a faded blue men's dress shirt with tails tied around her stomach. Her blue jeans were almost gray, skintight and ragged. She wore red socks and her sneakers were mismatched. I wasn't sure if the sneakers were a mistake or a new fashion statement!

"Hi baby!" She said cheerfully.

"Hi Diana. How are you?"

"I'm fine! Just fine! Aren't you glad to see me?" She must have forgotten about what happened the last time we were in each other's company, but I hadn't forgotten!

"Actually, I'm surprised, not glad." I tried not to sound cold but the chill reached her anyway.

"Oh!" She looked hurt. I felt bad. I didn't want to hurt her but I didn't want to lead her on either.

"I guess you're here for the meeting."

"Yeah, you too?"

"Yes!" I gave her a hug and smelled the White Diamonds perfume that started my senses to awaken. Involuntarily I gave a sigh of pleasure as I smelled the fragrance and she smiled again.

"So you are glad to see me! I know you're mad at me, but,..." She put her arms around me and kissed me. "You'll get over it!"

I broke the embrace. The meeting was about to start and I didn't want to be late.

"See you upstairs." I said.

"Okay." She replied then she looked at the front of my pants and added. "Hey Big Al! Jennifer misses you!"

"He misses her too!" As soon as I said it I started kicking myself mentally for saying it. I climbed the stairs feeling pretty silly and stupid.

The chairs were arranged in a huge circle, and I found a seat near the front of the room. The meeting was just about to start when she walked through the door. There were at least 15 empty seats around the circle but she chose to sit next to me. Lucky me! I was uncomfortable with it but I didn't say anything. She had the right to sit anywhere she pleased, even if it was next to me! I had the option to move but I didn't. Soon all the seats were filled and I was stuck with her.

Most of the people there knew me. Some of them knew her and knew that we had past history together. They also knew that we were no longer seeing each other. I had talked about our breakup in a prior meeting, but now she was sitting beside me and I began to receive funny looks and disapproving stares. They assumed that we were back together again. I wanted to shout to the room that it wasn't true, but of course I didn't. I silently and humbly waited for the meeting to start.

As the preliminaries finished, the chairman asked everyone to introduce themselves for the sake of the newcomers. Each person introduced themselves in the normal NA fashion.

"Hi, my name is…(so and so)… and I'm an addict!"

When my turn came I said. "Hi, my name is Donn, and I'm grateful recovering addict."

Then came Diana's turn. "Hi, my name is Diana and I'm an alcoholic, I'm an addict, and the doctors say I'm schizophrenic, manic-depressive, bipolar and a bunch of other stuff! But I just have a different way of looking at things than other people do. I'm single and am looking for good man. This guy," she pointed to me, "used to be my boyfriend but he isn't anymore so don't think that just because we're sitting together that we're back together because we're not! We're just friends. So, if anyone is interested, see me after the meeting. Thanks for letting me share!"

I wanted to slide under the table and hide from the embarrassment, but there was no table. I sat in the distress that sometimes comes with being in her presence. There were smiles and laughter and snickers hid behind hands in response to what she said and it added to the uncomfortable feeling that I already had.

I didn't speak at all at the meeting and I prayed that she wouldn't either. God heard and answered my prayer. After the meeting she had no takers on her offer so she asked if I would take her out to dinner. I told her no. She attempted to convince me that it would be advantageous to both of us if I did. I obviously knew what she meant. The temptation was great but I still turned her down. I wanted to have sex with her again and my body yearned for it, Big Al begged for it, but I knew what would happen afterwards and I didn't want to go through that hell again. She then asked me to take her home.

"Don't you have a ride home? How did you get here?"

"Well…" She was searching for a way out. Just then the guy that she was speaking to in the TV room came in. He saw us talking and walked straight over to where we were and spoke to me. "Hi. I'm Bill!" He extended his hand to me. "You must be Donn. Diana has told me about you. It's good to know that she has a friend like you."

I took his hand in mine and shook it. His grip was weak, almost dainty. I wondered who he was and what she had told him about me.

"Hi Bill. You have me at a disadvantage. She's told me nothing about you!"

"Well, that's because we just met a few days ago."

"Oh, that explains it."

"But that didn't stop her from telling me about you!"

I detected a bit of envy in his voice. I didn't blame him for being envious. I wouldn't want to be hearing about her ex either. "When you first walked in and she looked your way, her expression told me everything." He was upset but he fought diligently to hide it.

"Well, I'm going to let you two talked. I've got to go." I hugged Diana again. "Take care of yourself. Nice meeting you Bill."

"You too!"

Diana was speechless and I left quickly before she regained her composure. I silently wished Bill well and return to my Van the same way I came, alone!

The next day she called while I was in the store. She said she needed to talk. Before I could respond she said that she was coming over and she hung up. I called her house immediately but there was no answer. There was nothing that I could do but return to running the store and wait for her to show up. Two hours later, she called again.

"Diana, what's going on with you? Why are you bothering me again?"

"I need to talk to you." She sounded drunk.

"Well, talk." I said. "Are you drinking again?"

"Well, that's what I need to talk to you about."

"I'm listening, but I don't have time for any of your games. I'm very busy."

"Too busy to help a friend?" She threw in the sympathy card and attached to it was the NA fifth tradition card!

"No, I'm not too busy to help a friend but if you really want to help, you would have called me before you got drunk, not after! Have you called your sponsor?"

She didn't answer right away. "No! She's out of town." She finally admitted.

"How do you know she's out of town if you haven't called her?"

There was silence again but this time I didn't wait. "Diana, I've got to get back to work. The store is full of people and I've got to go!"

"Wait! I really need to talk to you!"

"I don't have time. Call your sponsor!" I hung up the phone and went back to work.

At 6 PM she was at the door. I had just locked it when I saw her and I was tempted not to open it but I did. I listened to her story and it was the same as always.

"I'm really sick and tired of going through the same thing with you Diana. Aren't you sick and tired yet? You need to make up your mind. Either you going to do the right thing or you're not. Stop playing games with yourself and with me. I'll help you in any way that I can but only if I know that you're serious about this thing. It's not a joke! This is your life that you're playing with!"

I looked at her pitiful face and continued. "I care about you Diana. I care about you a lot! And yes, I do love you! That's why I go through all of these changes with you. You're a very beautiful, intelligent woman and you do some zany things that keep me laughing, amazed and happy, but you also do things that cause me great concern and they get to be downright dangerous sometimes. When you stop taking your medication you become dangerous to yourself and to everyone around you, including me! You start drinking and taking drugs again and you get into a jam, then you call me to come and bail you out. Each time that you do you put my recovery in jeopardy. If you really want to stay clean and sober, you would call me before,... Not after! You show up at my door expecting me to drop everything for you. Do you know how selfish that is? When I don't accommodate you, you throw a tantrum and act like a spoiled child."

She began to cry but it had no effect on me as it had in the past. It was the sympathy card again. Just an act orchestrated to draw me in. Her hands covered her face as the sounds came out but there were no tears. She looked at me through the spaces between her fingers and quickly closed her eyes when she saw that I was on to her. I almost laughed aloud. It was so comical and juvenile but the tragedy was that I used to fall for it all the time.

"Do you need a ride home? Or is there someone out there waiting for you?"

The fake crying stopped immediately.

"There's nobody waiting for me!" Her level of agitation rose rapidly. "But that's okay. You don't have to go,... OUT OF YOUR WAY to take me home. I thought you might want to see me. You know, have a little fun? Bring Big Al out to play?" She paused. "Don't you want me anymore? Don't you think I'm beautiful? Don't you think I'm sexy?"

"Yes, yes and yes! You're very beautiful and sexy! I'll never stop wanting and desiring you, but I can't keep dealing with you when you're like this!"

She heard the words but the meaning wasn't getting through. She had made up her mind that we were going to have sex, and why not? It usually happened that way in the past. I usually gave in regardless of how she acted or treated me. Why would she think that this time would be any different? But it was.

Big Al loved Jennifer as I loved to Diana but, even he was beginning to understand the danger that she posed for his life and lifestyle. His existence would be cut short, (excuse the pun) if he continued to be around her, so for once, he was in agreement with his nemesis, the big head! For the first time in a long, long time he didn't rise up in her presence.

"Let's go Diana! I'll take you home."

I opened the door and she walked out ahead of me but she turned and started up the street. My Van was parked directly across the street but she went off in another direction. She expected me to call and run after her but I didn't. I stood in front of the store and waited until she disappeared around the corner, and then I went back inside.

That evening I attended in 11 PM candlelight meeting in Carrick. Most of my friends in the South Hills who worked the daylight shift attended this meeting. I had never taken Diana to the meeting, and I had never seen her there but that night she was there with Nona. Nona was a friend of mine who lived on the Hill District not far from Diana. She was also the woman that I called the night that I picked Diana up walking from Homewood. I was grateful that this time Diana didn't wear her 'embarrass me to hell and back' clothes and wig. She looked as normal as the rest of us, as if that was any consolation.

The meeting went well and was very peaceful and spiritual. Diana didn't speak but sat quietly across the table from me alongside Nona. The candlelight illuminated her face and I reflected on our past. I remember the first time that I saw her and how beautiful she was. In the candlelight, her beauty again was evident, but there was a great sadness there also. There was no one else in the room nearly as pretty as she was but also there was no one quite as sad. After the meeting we spoke briefly and waited for Nona to come and get her. I had begun to feel sorry for her for all that she had to go through with the mental illness that she possessed. I wonder how I would handle it if it were me. I wished that she would finally, once and for all, realize that she could not stop taking her medication regardless of how she felt. Feelings came and went, but the illness remained in the same manner as addiction.

Nona returned and asked if I would take Diana home for her. She had an emergency situation that she had to attend to. I didn't want to but I agree. Nona hugged me, thanked me, hugged Diana, and rushed out into the night.

Diana looked at me sadly and said, "I won't cause you any problems, I just want to go home."

I had already agreed to take her home and I should have left it at that but I had to open my big mouth and say. "I want to get something to eat over at Eat N' Park on W. Liberty Ave. Do you want to come, or do you want to go straight home?"

She contemplated what I said for a few seconds and then answered. "I'll go with you."

There were a lot of people who obviously had the same idea as I had. The place was packed and it was almost 1 AM! After a short wait we managed to get a small booth along the front window. She sat quietly and cautiously watching everyone around us. It became clear to me that she hadn't taken her medication and the effects were wearing off. Her paranoia was returning and soon she would be out of control. I regretted the decision that I had made and wished that I had taken her straight home. We ordered our food and I prayed that she would be okay long enough for me to get her home. While we waited for our food to arrive, that familiar dreaded look came across her face. It was too late! She had already crossed the line!

"Diana?"

She didn't respond. She was staring at someone behind me. I would have bet $1000 to a Krispy Kreme doughnut that there was at least one blonde, white woman there. The fact that we were in a restaurant in a white neighborhood filled with mostly white people set the odds high in my favor.

"Diana?" I repeated.

She kept looking past me, frightened by what she saw but afraid to look away. After a moment or two she said. "That lady behind you is in the plot to kill me!"

She pointed and I turned to look. The woman, blonde of course, smiled and waved. I smiled back and gave her a courtesy hello nod of the head. When I turned back to Diana, she was giving me the same frightened look she had given to the woman.

"You're in it too!" She said it loud enough that people in the neighboring booths and tables took notice. She slid back as far as she could into the corner of the booth.

I leaned forward and tried to talk some sense into her but I had never seen her that frightened before, and to top it off, she was now afraid of me! My words were having no effect whatsoever. I was no longer a friend, I had become the enemy!

People who were watching her cringe in the corner of the booth were wondering what was going on. The look on her face told everyone that she was afraid of me.

"Diana, please! Trust me! Nobody's going to do anything to you. I won't let them!" I tried to be as calm and as reassuring as I possibly could. I tried to keep my voice low so everyone couldn't hear what was going on, but she pulled her knees up to her chest and hung onto them with her feet on the seat and said loud enough for people way in the back of the restaurant to hear.

"NO! THEY'RE GOING TO KILL ME! I DON'T WANT TO DIE! I DON'T WANT TO DIE!"

Those that weren't looking before, now were. People had stopped eating and turned their attention on us. The murmurings filled the room and some of it reached my ears intact.

"What's going on?"

"Is someone in trouble?"

"I hope it's not terrorists!"

"It's those black people up front. We should never have let them set up front!"

"I think he hit her!"

"He should be horse whipped for beating her!"

"Where is my cell phone? I'm calling the police!"

"I think she's crazy! She looks schizoid!"

It went on and on as Diana continued to perform for them.

"Diana, no one's going to kill you. No one is going to do anything to you. It's all in your head. You've got to fight it!"

The man in the booth directly behind me tapped me on the shoulder. "Is she okay? Do you need a Doctor? My wife is a doctor. She's in the ladies room. I will get her for you if you want."

"Yes. Thanks."

He stood up and began walking towards the ladies room.

By this time people were figuring out what was going on and some began to gather around to offer help. Some were just there out of curiosity. I was beginning to be concerned because they were getting too close. It showed in the reaction of her body and the look on her face.

"Backup please! I'd appreciate it if you would go back to your seats." I tried to gain control and keep the confusion down.

"What's going on? Is there anything that I can do? I'm the manager." He looked at Diana as he spoke, and he knew immediately that something was wrong.

"Yes! Get these people out of here!" I raised my voice in frustration. He began to tell the people to go back to their seats and they started to move away.

Through the opening in the crowd I saw the man coming who went to get his wife, the doctor. I didn't see his wife at first but I assumed that she was behind him. I turned my attention back to Diana and she continued to deteriorate into her shell, and I prayed that the doctor would be able to help, but, when the doctor came into view, I knew that things were about to go from bad to worse. I jumped up from my seat and tried to stop them before they got to where Diana could see them.

"Let us through!" I heard him say. "She's a doctor! Let us through!"

"Wait! No, wait! I shouted but it was too late. Diana saw her and screamed! She jumped up on the table, stepped across the back of the booth to the next table, and then the next. She leaped as easily as if she were playing hopscotch on the sidewalk. She reached the booth by the door, and she jumped down and ran screaming through the door and down West Liberty Ave. towards the tunnel.

The den of murmurings rose to a fever pitch but this time I didn't pay much attention to it. Everyone was talking about Diana, and trying to figure out why she freaked out, why she acted so strange, so crazy. They didn't know, but I knew! I knew but I couldn't explain. I didn't have the time or the inclination to explain. I had to go and find her before it was too late.

The doctor turned to me for answers but I didn't have time to explain it to her either.

"What's going on?" She asked.

"She's afraid. She schizophrenic and she stopped taking her medication!" I tried to push past to get to the register.

"But she seemed to be afraid of me! I don't understand!"

"It's your hair!" I made it to the counter and paid for the food that never came. They gave me a rain check.

"What about my hair?" She shouted at me through the small crowd of people between us.

"It's blonde!"

"What?"

"IT'S BLONDE!" I ran out the door.

I raced my Van down West Liberty Ave. looking for her. I hoped that she didn't try to find another way. If she didn't stay on the main road I'd never find her. I was getting close to the Liberty Tunnel and as I grew closer my fears increased. Just before I got to the tunnel I saw her running as fast as her legs could carry her.

"Diana!" I yelled as I pulled alongside of her. "Get in! I'll get you home!"

At first look, she didn't recognize me. I yelled at her again but I really didn't think that she would get in after thinking that I had joined the blonde brigade, but she looked again and then pulled on the door handle. It was still locked. I pushed the button to open it and she got in. She closed the door and sat against it watching me. Even though she had gotten into my Van she seemed not to trust me still.

I drove and I talked to her trying to get her to understand that I wasn't her enemy. She said nothing but never took her eyes off of me. We entered the tunnel and almost immediately the she began to freak out again. She opened the door and tried to jump out. I saw her and reached for the handle. I tried to lock the door but it was too late. The door swung open almost touching the side wall of the tunnel. I reached out and grabbed her free arm and held onto it with everything I had. She screamed for me to let go but I knew that if she jumped out or fell out that it would be certain death for her. I tighten my grip and prayed. I struggled to keep the Van going in a straight line as I struggled with her. I managed to get through the tunnel and onto the Liberty Bridge where I pulled over. I snatched the door closed and locked it with the override button. She tried desperately to open the door but she couldn't. She then tried to lower the window but the override controlled that too.

"Please baby! Please let me out! I promise I'll go straight home. Please?" She begged but there was no way I was letting her out until I got her home.

"No Diana! I'll take you home. Nobody is going to hurt you!"

"But you. Baby, you!"

"I love you, Diana. I would never hurt you. Please believe me!"

"But you,... you smiled at her!"

"I was just being polite, that's all!"

"But the other lady that came to the table, she was one of them and you didn't stop her!"

"That was the doctor. I didn't know that she was blonde. I'm sorry! I tried to stop her when I saw her but it was too late. Diana, I love you! Don't you know that?"

She thought for moment but didn't respond.

"Who's been here for you?" I asked.

"You!"

"And who tries to help you all the time?"

"You!"

"And who took you horseback riding in Schenley Park?"

"You!"

"And, who owns Big Al that Jennifer loves so much?" I smiled and I hoped that she would too. She did and that was a good sign.

"YOU!"

"Now tell me, who love you? Who's going to protect you?"

"You! I love you too!" She was beginning to think again.

"C'mere!"

"Promise you won't hurt me?"

"I promise!"

"Word?"

"Word!"

We met in the middle and hugged. She began to cry.

"Come on baby, let me get you home so that you can start taking your medication again."

"Okay."

The ride back to her house was peaceful. She didn't try to jump out and she didn't say anything either. She just looked out of the window and every now and then she looked at me and smile when I looked back, but I could see that she still didn't trust me. She was sliding back into paranoia again. I started driving a little faster.

I parked and unlock the doors. She was smiling a really seriously fake smile. Even a blind man could see how fake it was. As soon as she heard the doors unlock, the smile vanished and she jumped out and ran as fast as she could to her building. Catching her was completely out of the question so I didn't try. She disappeared through the building entrance and I thought of following her to make sure that she was okay, but I knew that she would never open the door. My second thought was to leave. I followed the second.

In my mind I saw her sitting in the middle of the bed, knees pressed against her chest, eyes wide with fright, butcher knife in hand and deathly afraid to go near the door. My heart went out to her and I prayed that God would protect her from the demons in her head and then I drove home.

I couldn't sleep for thinking of her. The image of her suffering would not leave my mind. I called her. It was two o'clock. The phone rang but remained unanswered. I called back 15 minutes later and still didn't get an answer. Again I called with the same results. I then thought of driving back over there, but if she was too afraid to answer the phone and then she would be even more afraid to answer the door. I laid back down trying to rid her from my mind but she wouldn't leave. I couldn't sleep, I couldn't rest so after anguishing for a while I got up and drove over there.

When I arrived there was an ambulance slowly pulling away. They didn't rush, there were no sirens and no flashing lights. There was no emergency. I started up the path to her building and encountered two police officers coming from the direction of her apartment. Several police cars were at the scene and unlike the ambulance, they did have flashing lights on. My heart jumped as I caught an image of her lying in the back of the ambulance still and lifeless. Her neighbors were out milling around and talking. I learned that it actually was her in the back of the ambulance. There was glass on the sidewalk outside of her building and in the grass. There were items that she had thrown out of the window lying there too. Her treasured coffee pot lay smashed next to her toaster. Her kitchen window was completely void of glass and as I looked up, I saw police still in her apartment. Had she jumped out of the window? Was she really dead? Fear gripped me.

One of the guys from across the way was standing in the crowd and I asked him what happened.

"She flipped out again man! She just started tearing up the place! The dude on the second floor got tired of it and called the cops. When they got here, she was in the window acting like she was fighting with someone, but man there was nobody there but her! The cops broke down the door and the white coats took her away in a straitjacket. This ain't the first time, and it won't be the last!"

"So she's alive?"

"Yeah man! She's alive! They're gonna take her out to the Western Psych for a couple weeks and she'll be okay."

"Thanks man." I said. I was relieved that she wasn't dead.

"That bug bit you, didn't it?" He asked.

"What?"

"That bug! That LOVE bug!"

"You know she's crazy, but you hangin in there anyway. It's that love bug!" He returned the smile.

"I guess you're right. The love bug!"

"I gotta give it to you man. You ain't no chump! You got bigger balls than those other guys, but man, you better watch out. Okay?"

"Yeah. Thanks."

"Check out Western Psych in a couple days. She'll be there!" He patted me on the shoulder. Gonna go now. My girls back with the wine!"

Across the way his girl was standing with a bottle in a Brown paper bag. He became ecstatic when he saw it.

"Drinkin wine, po-de-o-de, drinkin wine for sport! Drinking wine, po-de-o-de, gotta have that port!" He spoke it in a sing-song way and then he dashed off.

I left feeling better knowing first that Diana was still alive and also that she would get help and be all right. I then went home and quickly fell asleep.

CHAPTER 10

Pain Makes it Easier to Let Go!

A week later, on Sunday morning, she called me from the hospital. She told me that she was doing better but would have to stay there for at least another week or so. She wanted me to visit her. She said she needed to talk to me. She did sound a lot better, and I was happy that she was getting the help that she needed so I agreed to see her at two o'clock.

"I'm on the seventh floor. Take the elevator to the seventh floor, okay?"

"Okay." At 1:30 I came out of Nona's church on center Avenue. She had invited me to come to church with her after hearing about my fiasco with Diana. She knew that I needed to increase my spiritual contact with God, so she invited me to her church. I accept it and went with her. The church was not far from the YMCA on Center Avenue and closer to Oakland then my place was, so I decided to go directly to the hospital from church. I didn't want to go to the hospital in my suit, but time was of the essence. I had promised Diana that I would be there by two o'clock.

"How did you like my church?" Nona asked as we stood on the steps amongst the crowd of exiting churchgoers.

"I liked it fine." I placed my Kufi on my head as we stepped out.

"I know that you aren't a holy roller, but you know that you need to go to church more often!" Nona said. She spoke to me in her motherly way. She was 10 years older than me and had four children. She knew how to speak the language.

"I know Nona. I will."

"Okay, I'm going to hold you to that!"

"I like your church because most people aren't stuffy! I might come back!"

"Good!" She hugged her me after we walked down the steps. We walked across the street to the parking lot where our vehicles were parked.

"I'm going out to see Diana. Do you want to come with me?"

"No. I'll just be in the way. Tell her that I said hi and that I'm praying for her."

"I'll tell her!"

Nona hugged me again and I kissed her on the cheek.

"I like your Kufi! That red, black, and green pattern is very nice. I like it!"

"Thank you. Well, I've got to go. Take care."

When I got to the hospital, the patients were having their smoke break. They were permitted to smoke only at specific times and only in a particular room. Diana smoked occasionally and that's where she was. I didn't smoke at all, and I didn't want to be in a room full of smokers, so I told her that I'd wait for her in the activities room.

There was an upright piano there and I sat down and started to play. One of the patients, an elderly white gentleman, stood over me as I began to play. He stood so close that he almost touched me and made me a little uncomfortable, but I kept in mind where he was and why. He was in a mental hospital; he was a mental patient. Instead of allowing my anger to flow, I just smiled and said hi.

"Are you a Muslim?" He asked.

"No. I'm not a Muslim." I replied.

"Then why are you wearing that Muslim hat?"

"It's not a Muslim hat." I explained. "It's an African Kufi!"

"It looks like a Muslim hat!"

"Yes, I guess it does a little but it's not about religion, it's about celebrating my African heritage."

I began to explain the difference and he listened and nodded when he understood. As we talked, Diana came into the room and flipped out when she saw us talking. She rushed over as I got up from the piano, grabbed my arm and started pulling me out of the room.

"I didn't bring you here to talk to anyone else! You came to talk to me!"

She started down the hallway past the nurse's station to her room with me in tow.

"I don't want you talking to anyone! You can't trust these people! They're all crazy!" She opened the door to her room and entered still fussing.

Her room was small but well lit and comfortable. There was a soft chair just inside of the door. The bed was just beyond the chair and flat against the side wall. She had a small writing table and a hard wooden chair that matched. A tin mirror hung over the table securely attached to the wall. There was a small reading lamp on the table along with a Gideon's Bible. On the floor next to the table were several books neatly stacked. She had clothes in the far corner. Some were stacked and folded, while others just lay haphazardly on the floor.

I took a seat in the soft chair by the door. She sat cross-legged on the bed, and she didn't stop fussing about what she had seen in the activities room. After the first minute I stopped listening and began to wonder what I was doing there. It was a mistake for me to go. I began to entertain the thought of leaving. I expected her to talk, I expected her to communicate but all I got was a lot of hot air. I expected something different. I expected her to be normal, but she was in a mental hospital because she wasn't normal, and she probably never would be normal. I knew that I had to leave and allow her to heal without any interference from me.

She stopped fussing and began to undress.

"I'm horny! Gimme some!"

She laid back on the bed, spread her legs and waited for me to mount her. Her eyes were begging, her body tempting, but I couldn't do it. It wasn't right! She was sick and in a mental hospital! I thought about the last time I had sex with her and how I felt afterwards knowing that I shouldn't have, and I didn't want that feeling again.

"No Diana! Put your clothes back on!" I got up out of my chair. "I think I'd better leave!"

She jumped up and started putting her clothes back on.

"I'm sorry baby but I just thought that you missed me and wanted me. Wait Donn! Please wait!"

I waited at the door. She fastened her jeans and came to me.

"I'm sorry." She said again. "Before you go would you buy me a pack of cigarettes?"

"No. I told you before that I don't buy cigarettes."

"Well, would you get me some matches?"

I agreed to that and told her I'd be right back.

"There's a gift shop downstairs. You can get them there."

I didn't go to the gift shop but instead I went outside and walked around. I went down to a store on Forbes Avenue and bought her a lighter. I needed time to clear my mind. The walk gave me time to think and reflect on what had just happened. I needed to think about why I was there and why I had brought her back into my life. Things weren't working and hadn't been working in a long time.

I thought about what my sponsor had said when I told him about her. I told him about the changes, the craziness, the good times and the bad. I told him everything! I told him about the pain that I felt being with her and the pain that I felt being without her. I told him that even though I didn't want to be, I was in love with her!

"Even with all of that, I know that she isn't right for me, but I just can't give her up!" I said.

He spoke. "When the pain of being with her is greater than the pain of being without her, you'll let go, but not until then! Just like with the drugs!"

He didn't lecture me; he just gave me the information that I needed. And he was right. This was a different kind of pain than what I felt using cocaine, but pain is pain. Nobody in their right mind likes pain!

I questioned myself about several things. First, was I in my right mind? At times I really didn't know for sure. Why was it so difficult for me to let her go? Even Big Al now agreed that I should. Why did I keep going back? It was painful for me to see her suffer with her demons. It was painful to deal with her erratic behavior, especially when we were out in public, and she embarrassed me over and over again. It was painful to watch her sink deep into depression and feel that the entire world was against her. Sometimes she included me! It was painful because I cared about her, and yes, I loved her! Why did I keep going back? Was it love? Yes! But more than that, it was insanity. Not hers but mine! I kept doing the same thing but expecting a different result. I thought that if she just kept taking her medication that everything would be fine, but that wasn't the complete truth. Even with the medication she displayed erratic behavior and still had times when she became depressed, lethargic, and violent. She didn't stop being mentally ill whenever the medication was in effect. The medication just controlled it to a degree. Some of the crazy things that she did I approved of, and others I didn't. My interpretation determined what was acceptable and what was not, and that wasn't fair. The nude lady Godiva trek through the park was unacceptable, but the sex in the rain afterward was. Who was I to judge? What gave me the right to scrutinize her behavior when mine wasn't exemplary either? I wondered again, who was the crazy one? I wasn't sure of a lot of things but one thing I was sure of was that even if her insanity didn't stop, mine had to! I decided to give her the lighter, leave and not go back.

I returned with a lighter and gave it to her. I had a little speech planned to let her know how felt but I didn't get a chance to speak. Her attitude was cold when she snatched the lighter from my hand and told me to leave. Without saying another word, she turned and walked down the hallway to the recreation room. I got back on the elevator and allowed it to take me back to the ground floor.

I drove the long way home through the Hill district and then into town, and then up Arlington Avenue because I wanted time to think before I got home.

My phone was ringing when I got home. It was Diana! (Who else?) She screamed at me and went on and on about how much of a dog I was for trying to have sex with her in her room. I didn't want to hear it. She was the one that got butt naked, not me! I didn't try to argue with her or try to convince her that she had it backwards. I just hung up! She called right back and foolishly I answered. She continued right where she left off. I put the receiver down and went downstairs to the computer in the store to enter some information. When I finished about 15 minutes later, I went back upstairs and picked up the receiver. She was still yelling and cursing. I hung up the phone again. She called back and I answered hoping that it wasn't her, but it was. She continued her tirade. I hung up again but this time when the line cleared, I took it off the hook. About an hour later, I replace it and it rang right away. As soon as I said hello, she started again. I listened for a minute or two before she hung up on me. I thought that would be the end of it then it rang again about 30 seconds later. Foolishly I picked it up and it was her continuing right where she left off. This time I hung up and left the phone unplugged for the rest of the day.

Her accusation upset me at first because the reality of it was that she was the one who tried to initiate sex, but once I thought about it without emotion and realized that she was in a mental hospital because her reality was distorted, I let it go. I couldn't be angry with her for being sick. Her mental illness wasn't her fault, it was just the hand that she was dealt. She could only play the cards in her hand.

Years ago, I had become addicted to cocaine. Was it my fault? Some say yes, some say no. I really didn't know but it became the way that I was and no power aside from God could change that. I didn't ask to be addicted, and I'm sure she didn't ask to be mentally ill. If she could change it, she would. I needed to be more sympathetic and understanding and keep my level of empathy high.

Through working the twelve steps of Narcotics Anonymous I've learned that there is a vast difference between knowing your problems and addictions and accepting the responsibility and doing something about keeping it under control. She knew that she was mentally ill because she proclaimed it and often times, she would do what was necessary to keep it under control, but many times she would allow it to get out of control because she came to believe that she was no longer ill. She would stop doing the very thing that kept the dark side of her illness at bay. She stopped taking her medication and that brought it crashing down around her. It was a relapse in the same manner as a drug addict or an alcoholic, after being clean and sober for length of time, feels that they can drink and get high. She had to accept that she couldn't manage it alone. The medication was something that she always needed and taking it had to be a daily routine, just as brushing her teeth, showering, and putting on her clothes. She hadn't arrived there yet and until she did, her life and lives of those around her would be in danger. For that reason, I had to separate and distance myself from her. My life was becoming unmanageable again without the drugs and alcohol and I couldn't allow that to continue.

I prayed that she would quickly reach the point of full acceptance, then and only then would her life become as close to normal as it possibly could get.

Until that time came, I had to remove her from my life for my own sanity and for my own safety. I want to help her but there was nothing that I could do. I wanted to be with her but under the present conditions, it was impossible! When I realized and accepted that it made it much easier for me to move on. When I realized that the pain of being with her was always going to be greater than the pain of being without her, I had to let go!

CHAPTER 11

Spiritual Awakening!

Early Monday morning, after my Sunday fiasco with her, I called her counselor and explained my relationship with Diana. I told her what had happened while I was there and about the phone calls. She assured me that the phone calls would stop, and they did.

Diana spent three weeks in the hospital before she was released. I had three weeks of silence before Diana called me again. This time she was out of the hospital and obviously doing much better.

"Hi baby!" She said and I quickly wish that I hadn't answered the phone.

"Hello Diana. What do you want?"

"You know what I want. Can Big Al come out and play?"

"No Diana. Big Al is asleep, and I don't want to wake him!" I lied. He was more awake than I was. She didn't believe me anyway.

"Donn you're lying! I know you better than that. Baby, I really want to talk to you. We need to talk?"

"What do we have to talk about? Diana? Our relationship is over! There's nothing to talk about."

"Yes, there is! We've got plenty to talk about, but first let me apologize for the things that I said and did the last time I saw you. It was really, really wrong. I'm sorry! Can you forgive me?"

She was speaking calmly, and she didn't come off too strongly and it made me take notice. It reminded me of the way we used to talk when we first met. Our conversations were levelheaded, funny, intelligent, and two-sided. It hadn't been that way in a long time and that's probably why I stayed on the line and didn't hang up.

"Exactly what are you apologizing for?" I cautiously asked.

"Well, you know. The incident in my room, my attitude, the phone calls. You know! All of that. I'm better now and I'm sorry!"

"So, what are you going to do now? Are you going to stop taking your medication again?"

I was unimpressed with her apology. It sounded good but what about the next time? There always was a next time.

"I guess I deserved that. I let you down so many times in the past, but Donn, it'll be different this time. I promise."

"What do you mean 'this time'? You don't really think that we're getting back together, do you?"

"Of course, I do! You're my man, I'm your woman! And besides… I'm pregnant!"

I stood up! Big Al laid down!

"WHAT?"

"I'm pregnant! We're going to have a baby!"

"No, WE'RE not!"

"Yes, WE are! I'm so happy!"

I was standing in my bedroom in the dark. I was shocked out of my mind and trying to absorb what she had just said. It was too much for my brain to accept, so I didn't accept it. I thought that this was just another one of her games. Something to use to get me back again, but little did she know that she was playing the wrong tune. It wasn't Sexual Healing; it was Ice Ice baby!

"I don't believe this! I'm going back to sleep."

"Wait baby! Don't you believe me? I'm really pregnant!" She sounded genuinely happy, but I knew that she was a great manipulator, especially when it involves me.

I remembered the conversation that she and I had a while ago when she flipped out because I asked her if she was pregnant. Now, just out of the nut house and in the first few minutes of our conversation since she accused me of attempted rape, she emphatically and joyously tells me that she's pregnant and that WE are going to have a baby. She expected me to be happy about it. If it were true, then it would be the worst possible news that she could give me.

"I don't believe you! Even if I did, why would I be happy about it?"

"Because it's yours! You should be happy!"

"Yeah right! Do you expect me to believe that? With all of the screwing around you've done, how can you say it's mine?"

"Because a woman knows!"

"You're right about one thing. A REAL woman knows! She knows because she's not screwing everyone in sight, but that leaves you out! Diana, I'm going to sleep. Goodnight!"

"Wait Donn! Don't hang up on…"

Click.

I laid the phone down, but I stayed up. I knew the ringing would start again and I was prepared for it. I walked over to the front window and looked out. There was no traffic at all on my street. The trolley was still running but not as often as it did during the day. The bar up the street was still open along with the Coronet restaurant but that was all that there was. I saw a couple staggering across the street to their car. After several failed attempts to get their car started, they finally succeeded and drove off.

Rain began to fall, and I watched it as it fell on the roof of my Van. Immediately I began to think of our time in Schenley Park. It brought a smile to my face that quickly faded when the reality of my present situation came flooding back on me.

Diana pregnant? It couldn't be! It shouldn't be! It can't be! How could it happen? It was something that my mind just couldn't manage. The phone rang again. It startled me as the rain began to pour down. My mind was frozen in time for a few seconds, but the ringing continued for a full 15 minutes before it stopped. It started again just seconds later, and I knew that I wasn't getting back to sleep if I answered it, or even if I took it off the hook. I considered turning the answering machine on but all that would do was to give me a full tape of her messages that I had to erase in the morning. Actually, it wasn't the phone keeping me awake anymore, it was the information that she had placed in my head that wouldn't go away.

I was dressed in my pajama bottoms, so I put the top on, slipped into a rain parka, grabbed an umbrella, slid my feet into my red Air Jordan's and dashed across the street to my Van. Once inside and slightly wet, I eased into the backseat to think. Something about listening to the rain poured down on the roof was soothing and comforting to me. It had always been that way from my childhood when I would climb up into the attic to listen to the rain beat down on the A-frame roof and relax. I no longer cared about the phone and its relentless ringing. It probably still rang at that moment because Diana was persistent!

Thoughts of great magnitude raced through my brain. I imagined all sorts of ridiculous scenarios which all started with a baby coming out of Diana's body. The baby would have my genes, my face, my temperament, intelligence, and common sense, but went left by taking on the characteristics of Diana in her worst state of mind. Or, the child was fine, but Diana continued to do what she does when she refuses or neglects to take her medication. Then the baby would be neglected, abused or dead! I shook my head in an attempt to rid myself of the thoughts, but it didn't work. I began to think of timing. The last time I had sex with Diana was…? I had to figure it out. I needed to know down to the exact day. I had to convince myself that she was lying about being pregnant, or at the very least, prove that I wasn't the father.

I should have asked her how far along in her pregnancy she was when I had her on the phone, but I didn't because I wasn't thinking clearly. I made a mental note to ask her the next time we talked but first I had to trace back to the last time that we were together sexually. It had been approximately 2 months since the last time. I remembered that time. She flipped out on me because I had asked her if she was pregnant. It had been two weeks since the fiasco of the hospital visit that I had experienced. One week before that she entered the hospital. If I recall correctly, it was the same night that she accused me of being a party to the imaginary murder plot by the blonde bombshells. Before that it was just over a month since she and I had been together for the last time. So, by my calculations, which were crude at best, it had been between seven and eight weeks. 7 to 8 weeks wasn't good enough, but it was a start. I wished I could have pinpointed it closer than that, but it was the best that I could do. I hoped that all of the calculations, all of the time thinking of it, all of the anguish would be for naught. What I hoped and prayed for was that she was mistaken or lying about being pregnant!

The rain continued to pour down creating a small river in the middle of the street. The water rushed forcefully down the street covering the trolley tracks and cleaning the dirt from them and the rest of the street at the same time. I moved up to the driver's seat, inserted my key in the ignition and started the van. I wasn't going anywhere but I wanted to hear a little music to soothe my tortured soul.

Gerald Albright version of "So Amazing" began to play. I sat back and adjusted my seat to the extreme relaxed position and listened to Gerald's beautiful sax. The rain continued to beat against the roof and before I knew it, I was fast asleep. When I woke up, the entire disk had played. The van was still running, and the rain was still falling heavily down. I wanted to go back to bed and forget all that I had heard, and I wanted to forget Diana and all that came with her. My bed called out to me, but I had to wait until the rain lightened up.

I put Gerald back on and listened but this time I didn't go to sleep. About a half hour later, the rain finally began to slow down. I snatched my keys, grabbed my umbrella, and dashed back into the building. As I climbed the stairs, I could hear the phone ringing. I couldn't believe that she was still calling. I looked at my watch, it was 3:24 AM. I entered the room and angrily reached for the phone. I was about to give her a piece of my mind, but it stopped ringing. I stopped short and waited with my hand extended for it to start again but it didn't. I laid down and after only a few minutes of fitful unrest, I went to sleep.

The doorbell woke me. Someone was leaning on it, and it rang nonstop. The Sun was up, and the sunlight was streaming through my front window. The rain clouds had moved on as morning broke. It was just after 6 AM and there was no doubt in my mind that it was Diana at my door. I didn't want to answer it, but I needed to get to the bottom of her alleged pregnancy. I went down and opened the door expecting her to be upset, expecting her loudmouth to be cursing me, but she surprised me. She was looking as beautiful as I've ever seen her with no fake hair and no crazy clothes. She had no angry look and no butcher knife in her hand! Instead, she was smiling and in a very good mood. Before she entered, she turned and waved to a guy in a blue Lexus 400 that was parked just ahead of my Van.

"Thanks Bill!" She shouted to him. "I'll call you if I need you!"

It was Bill! The same guy that I had met at the Onala club. He saw me and his look changed. I guess she didn't tell him that he was bringing her to see me.

"Okay!" He waved and began to drive off.

She wasn't really listening or paying attention to him because she was so busy kissing me. She kicked the door close with her foot as she pushed me back inside.

"Baby, I really missed you. Jennifer misses you too! Let's go upstairs!"

I opened my mouth to speak but she had already pushed past me and was taking the stairs two at a time. She was all the way up and out of sight and around the corner before I even placed one foot on the staircase. Upstairs, she laid across my bed in her underwear. She knew how I loved to see her, and she was determined that we were going to let Jennifer and Big Al play together. I wanted to resist, I really did, but Diana was just too beautiful, and Jennifer was so deliciously wrapped in that flimsy soft pink material. I wanted to resist, I really did, but Big Al deserted me and switched sides again. He was looking out for his own selfish interests. He strained in his silk prison and was determined that he wasn't going to lie down and behave. Being outnumbered by Diana, Jennifer and now Big Al too, I had no choice but to surrender. I sat on the side of the bed knowing that I was about to make the biggest mistake of my life, again, but I just didn't have the power to fight!

"Baby? You know you want me! Come on!" She sounded so sexy, and she was absolutely right. I wanted her badly, so badly that I could taste it! Her sense, that natural womanly scent was coming forth and whether it was real or imagined, I inhaled her aroma. As I breathe it in it sent a rush of excitement throughout my body. Diana was no fool, noticing my vibes was not difficult for her. To her I was probably as transparent as a summer breeze. Once Big Al was running things, and he was, I had no control over any emotion. Actually, my control factor was at zero! Big Al had gotten a whiff of Jennifer so his was at 100%!

I began rubbing her thigh just above the knee. I didn't speak because I didn't need to. The communication was perfect without words, but my common sense kept saying that I needed to talk to her instead of proceeding in what I was about to do. But when do I ever listen to common sense? Big Al was selfish, and he had no common sense, and I was listening to him!

We made love. It lasted throughout the morning and into the early afternoon. We didn't talk much at all. I felt the way I did in the beginning when we first became true lovers. I could tell that she was having the same thoughts and feelings that I had. There was something about the way we connected that day that was difficult to explain. It was better than before. It was electric and extremely satisfied in every way. We remained tender, not torrid, and sensuous without being strenuous. She seemed to me to be an entirely different person. Her skin felt softer and silkier. Her kisses were sweeter and more passionate. Her movements were perfectly synchronized with mine. Her moans were coming deep from her soul and her cries of pleasure were accompanied by tears of joy. She was the woman that I longed for. She was the one that I had dreamed about and prayed for. I couldn't remember a time when I was so completely satisfied and at peace with myself. There was something quite different about her. I couldn't put my finger on it, but I definitely knew that something about her had changed! And it was a welcomed, and positive change.

Between each session, she lay curled up in my arms restful and satisfied, peaceful and serene. We were lying that way at 12:30 when she broke the silence.

"Donn?"

"Yes?"

"Do you love me? I mean, do you REALLY love me?"

"Yes, I love you Diana, but…'

"No! Stop!" She interrupted. "No 'buts'! I just need to know that you love me. I know that you don't believe I'm pregnant and I know that you have problems with that, but baby, I really am pregnant, and I know for sure that it's yours!"

The door was opened, so I stepped through it.

"You're right, I don't believe it. You are just late and it's all in your head. You do imagine things, you know!"

"Yeah, I know, but this is real. I'm not imagining it. I know it!"

I expected her to get a little touchy about the remark about her sanity, but she didn't. She handled it very well.

"How can you tell the difference between reality and imagination? How do you figure out which is which and know without a doubt that you're right?" I asked.

"It's easy!" She laughed. "I do it just the same way that you do it!"

"But you can't! You're not the same. Your mind is different. You said so yourself!"

She looked around at me and smiled. "By different, you mean crazy?" She held her smile to let me know that she was not upset.

"No! I didn't say that!"

"But that's what you meant, isn't it? It's okay. I told you on the phone that I'm much better now. I've accepted who I am and what I am. Just like Forrest Gump!"

"Forrest Gump?"

(What did Forrest Gump have to do with this?)

"Yes! Forrest Gump! 'Stupid is as stupid does!' He accepted he was slower than most, but he still lived life and achieved a lot. 'Stupid is as stupid does'… 'Crazy is as crazy does'! I didn't want to accept that I was different. I didn't like it when people called me crazy. It made me feel different and I don't want to feel different. I wanted to be just like everyone else, but I did stupid and crazy things trying to fit in, and it always made trouble for me. The last time I was in the hospital I was forced to face the fact that when I stop doing what I do to keep myself right, then I really am crazy! Crazy is what crazy does! Baby, I'm different. I know it! Now I've accepted it! I have a mental illness that will kill me if I let it, or it will cause me to kill someone else. I have to do everything that I can to keep that from happening." She hesitated a moment and then she decided to tell me what she had never spoken of before.

"Do you remember when I tried to jump out of the van in the tunnel?"

I nodded my head.

"You saved my life. At the time I didn't realize that I would have died if I jumped out. All that I thought was that I had to get away from you. I believed that you were going to kill me! When I looked at you, you weren't you anymore. You were one of them. I saw them, but I didn't see you! I believed that if I jumped out of the van that I would be okay, but the reality was that I would have been killed instantly. Baby, my thoughts start out right but somehow, they get twisted. Once I get paranoid, I see enemies everywhere!"

She stirred and pressed herself against me. Silence permeated the room until she spoke again.

"Donn, I need to tell you something. You may hate me when I tell you because it's really bad!"

I didn't know what she was about to say, and I was a little bit afraid to hear but I waited, and I listened.

"Baby, I don't want you to hate me. I want you to love me. I want you to be with me for the rest of my life, but I have to tell you this even if it means that you may never want to be with me again."

"Do I really need to know this?" I asked.

"Yes! You need to know all about me. You've seen some of my dark side, but this is really bad. It's something I never intended to tell you, but our relationship won't be right if I don't."

I was worried that she was about to tell me something even more sinister than the things that I already knew. Maybe she had killed someone. Maybe she had been pregnant before and had killed the baby. Maybe this, maybe that! My head was spinning with maybes!

"About three years ago I was with this guy. I won't tell you his name, not right now, okay? I'll tell you after I finished."

I nodded.

"Well, he and I lived together in my apartment. He was a really nice guy at the time, and he worked at the Homestead steel plant, and he made a lot of money. He lived with me, and we had plenty of time and money to do things together. I like him a lot. I don't know if I was in love with him, but I knew that I really enjoyed being with him. He wanted to have a son and I thought about it and decided to give him one. I wasn't sure at first, but I decided to do it because he was so good to me. We were saving money to buy a house in Fox Chapel, and we were going to get married!"

I cut in. "Why were you going to marry him if you weren't sure that you loved him?"

"I don't know. He was really nice and treated me good. Most guys that I had dated before him were always just trying to get in my bed and that's all that they wanted. Once I went to bed with them, they changed. But he didn't! He was still good to me! I don't know! Maybe I just wanted something more than what I had."

"I think I understand. It's good to be appreciated. Go on."

There's this restaurant out in Squirrel Hill called Bubbles and Sherman's. It's a really exclusive restaurant and I got a job there. I didn't have to work because I was receiving disability and SSI for my… Problem.

I didn't pay any rent either so money wasn't a problem, but I wanted to work, and he was all for it. Have you ever heard of Bubbles and Sherman's?"

"Yes. I've been past there but I've never been in. It seemed like a place strictly for white people with a lot of money!"

"Black people go there too, but they're rich! You need money to afford a meal there. I loved the job. I loved working for people, and I love the people that I worked with. I met a woman there named Martha. She and I bonded together right away. I was a waitress, and she was the assistant maître d'. I remember the first time that we talked. There was this guy who came in to ask his girlfriend to marry him. Martha asked me to help her set it up. The waiters brought out this big high backed red velvet chair and placed it in the middle of the floor. They also had a pillow made of the same matching material for the guy. The woman sat in the chair and the guy knelt down on the pillow in front of her and proposed while everybody was watching. It was amazing! Fantastic! Martha and I stood with tears in our eyes as we watched. It was like a fairytale, and I dreamed of being proposed to like that!

"Oh! I'm sorry! I'm digressing. Anyway… I worked overtime a lot because they always needed extra help on second shift. Many times I would call my boyfriend let him know to pick me up at eight o'clock instead of four when I usually got off. This day I called him and told him to come and get me at eight, but about an hour later I wasn't feeling good, and I needed to leave. I started having those thoughts about blonde, white woman again. I tried to fight it, but it seemed like every woman in the place was blonde! I tried to call him to come and get me, but he wasn't answering the phone anymore. Martha knew about my problem and so she took me home. Once I got to my building and saw his car parked outside, I felt better just knowing he was there. Just knowing that he would help me through it because I needed to be held! I needed to be comforted and reassured."

"Had you been taking your medication?" I asked.

"Yes, but I wasn't taking it all the time but even when I do, I sometimes get depressed and paranoid, but I can usually handle it and when I can't I just need to be around someone that I trust.

"I walked into the apartment feeling better just because I knew that he was there, but when I opened the door, I heard a woman moaning. At first it scared me because I thought,… you know what I thought! Blonde, white women! But then I realized that she was moaning from pleasure and the sounds were coming from my bedroom. I heard him and I heard the bed. That's when I knew what they were doing! My fear turned to anger, and my anger turned to rage. I went into the kitchen and eased the knife drawer open and took out a butcher knife. I tiptoed to the bedroom door and peeked in. I saw them both in bed. She was on her back with her legs spread wide and he was pounding into her like there was no tomorrow. They were so into it that they didn't even know that I was there. I walked right up to the side of the bed and stood there about a minute. They kept going at it until she sensed my presence. She opened her eyes and screamed! He jumped up and just then I came down with the knife and chopped his dick off! I tried to stab her, but she was too quick. She rolled off of the bed and ran past me and out of the door butt naked! I wanted to kill her, but she was gone. I turned to him. He was screaming like a bitch! I slashed him about ten times before he got smart and ran out too. I slashed him across his face and chest and when he turned to run, I slashed him across his back. I didn't want to stab him because I didn't want to kill him, but I wanted him to suffer. He was bleeding all over the place. I took his dick and flushed it down the toilet. When the cops came, I was sitting on the side of the bed crying. But Donn, I wasn't crying because of what I had done, or even because I was about to go to jail. I was crying because, this may sound crazy, 'crazy is as crazy does', I was crying because I was thinking that I'll never have that dick again!"

I started to laugh, and she looked at me curiously.

"What's so funny?"

"It's just that I know how much you love a good dick!"

"Oh! That IS funny!" She started to laugh along with me.

She went on to tell me what I already knew. Six months in Mayview and not jail. Then she became concerned about me. How was I going to react to what she had just told me?"

"Diana?"

"Yes baby?" Fear gripped her.

"I already knew about that."

"You did? How? I never said anything!"

"The people across the way told me!"

"When did you find out?"

"Months ago!"

"Did you know before that day that I threatened to cut your balls off? The day I flipped out on you in the apartment?"

"Yes! Before that!"

"But you still stayed?"

"Yes. I still stayed."

"Why?"

"I've asked myself that question many times. I'm not sure. You've put me through more changes than any woman ever has, and them, I left alone. But you? I just don't know why I stayed."

She turned to face me. My arms were still around her. Her smile was radiant, and her skin had a fresh new glow. It made me wonder if she really was pregnant.

"I know why!" She said softly.

"What do you know?" I said playfully. "You don't know anything."

"Oh yes I do! I know what's going on right in there." She patted my chest with the palm of her hand. "You're not as hard and cold as you want people to believe. In fact, you're a big teddy bear! That's what you are! A big lovable teddy bear!" She squeezed me. "I love you!"

"I love you too!"

"Baby, do you think you can live with me knowing what I have done?"

"Whoa! Hold on! Who said anything about living together? Where did that come from?"

"Now that I'm pregnant, we've got to live together for the sake of the baby. A baby needs to have both parents, not just one!"

The talk killed my mood, but it was all good because I needed to get back to my senses. The euphoria of this woman always got to me and robbed me of my common sense. I loved the way I felt being with her when she controlled her episodes but her history for the lack of control was sharp and glaringly vivid in my mind. I couldn't allow the one time of relative sanity to overshadow all of the insane times I've shared with her. She was talking about hooking up, living together, and marriage. I wasn't even sure if she was pregnant and if so, who was really the father. What about her new beau, Bill? Where did he fit in? How long had she had been seeing him? What was really going on between them? I needed to return to sanity myself.

"Diana? Do you want to have a real relationship with me?"

"You know I do!"

"Then we've got to get things straight. First tell me about this so-called pregnancy. Tell me why I should believe that you are pregnant and why you believe that I'm the one!" I said it harshly for a reason. I wanted to observe her reaction to see if she would get upset.

"Okay I will! Baby, I didn't have my period last month. I didn't really think too much about it because I miss sometimes because of the medication, but I've never missed two in a row! This time I did! I did a test before I left the hospital, and it was positive!"

"But don't they sometimes positive when they're really negative?"

"Yes, but usually they're right."

"Was that the only test that you took?"

"Uh-huh!"

"So, it could be wrong."

"Yes. There's a possibility, but I know I'm pregnant! I want to be pregnant with your child!"

"Just for the sake of compromise, I'll assume that you're pregnant. I'm not saying that I believe you, but I'm just saying."

She nodded.

"How pregnant are you?"

She didn't take any time to think because she knew. She answered immediately.

"I know exactly to the day because the last time was with you! Seven and a half weeks. That was the last time you and I did it. That was also the last time I had sex!"

"What about Bill?" I fired back at her. "Don't you include him?"

"No! I've never had sex with Bill!"

" Come on Diana. I know you and you're insatiable! You want me to believe that you haven't been to bed with him?"

"Yes, I want you to believe it because it's the truth."

"Come on Diana! Be for real!"

"You're right, I am insatiable. Especially when I'm with you, but Donn, I'm not a whore! Why do you think I always call you? You satisfy me and even though I've got a bad reputation, I'm not a whore! He wanted to have sex with me, but I wouldn't do it. I just didn't feel right about it!"

"Why?"

"Because of you!"

"What do I have to do with it?"

"You're the one! It's always been you! I tried to go back to Darren when I got mad at you, but it wasn't right either. The whole time that we were together I thought about you. I had sex with Darren, if you want to call it that, but I didn't have sex with Bill! I swear it! You were the last one and the last time that we had sex was 7 1/2 weeks ago!"

"So, who is Bill? Why does he know about me?"

"He's a guy I met at AA. He's a sweet guy and all, but he's more like a brother. At least that's how I see him."

"But he wants to be more, right?"

"Uh-huh, but I told him that I don't want him that way, I don't see him that way. I told him about you. I told him how I feel about you. I told him hoping that he would understand, and we could just be friends."

"How did he take it?"

"Okay, I guess. He hasn't tried anything since and he's there when I need him, but I know he's still hoping for more. Do you believe me?" Her eyes were saying, please believe me!

"Yes! I believe you." (Damn! I'm falling again!)

She produced a smile that illuminated the entire room.

"Thanks baby. I need for you to believe in me. I'll never, from this day forth, tell you a lie. Whenever you ask, I'll tell you the truth. I love you baby!" She kissed me. "Let's do it again!"

"No! Wait! I've got another question."

"Shoot!"

"You said you tell me who the guy is!"

"The guy?" She had forgotten about it.

"The guy that you, ah, removed his manhood!"

"Oh." She laughed.

"Do I know him?"

"Yes."

"Who?"

She looked at me. She gave me one of those 'duh' looks that said that if I just thought about it, I would figure it out.

"Remember what I said? I told you that I slashed his face. Who do you know with a big scar on his face? Who do you know that always talks about women, but you never see him with any?"

I thought for a minute. It didn't take long to determine about whom she was talking.

"Carl! Carl Bladen!"

Suddenly, I felt deeply sorry for him. He was a really nice guy, but he lived a lie trying to convince those of us who didn't know his history that he was still the player that he used to be. One night of stupidity and infidelity negated his player status forever. I couldn't imagine how it would be to live without Big Al and never feel that extreme pleasure that fills my brain only through him.

Diana nodded. It was Carl. They seem to be so comfortable in each other's company. I didn't think that if I were the one that had been separated from my manhood by her that I would be comfortable in her presence, but that was me, obviously not him.

"About four months after it happened, he got saved. He came out to Mayview to see me and tell me that he forgave me for what I had done to him. He said that he had found God and was at peace with the world. By that time, I had been through weeks and weeks of therapy, and they experimented on me with different types of drugs trying to find the right combination and I was doing a little better. His visit helped me more than he knew, and I was grateful. It was just at the right time. He asked me to forgive him for what he had done. Forgive him? I had cut his dick off and flushed it down the toilet and he was asking me to forgive him? Anyway, he said that he would help me in any way that he could. At first, I was suspicious. I thought he was planning something, like retaliation or revenge or something. But he was real! After I got out, I could see that he was for real, and it stayed that way for about two years until he left the church. He said he was still a Christian, but he had changed. He stayed in AA and NA, and he didn't drink or get high anymore, but he started getting mean with people and I became afraid that he might begin to think about getting even with me. Every day he thinks about me when he reaches down there and realizes that he can't stand up but has to sit down now! We stopped hanging out and I really only see him at meetings now."

"Does Phil know?" I asked.

"No, I don't think so. This happened before Phil moved here. He's only been here about a year and a half."

"What about Danny?"

"No."

"Darla?"

"Yes."

We talked a little more about her relationship with Bill. I believed what she said about her relationship with him, or the lack of it, but instead of making me feel better it did just the opposite by dropping the pregnancy issue squarely in my lap.

"Diana? You really don't know for sure if you're pregnant, do you? One test can be wrong. Why didn't you test again?"

"I didn't think I needed to, but if you want me to, I will!"

"Yes. I think you should."

Before I could respond any further, she was up and dressing herself.

"I'll go to the drugstore and get one, and we'll know for sure!"

"Get two!"

The tests were positive! Both of them! Diana was pregnant! She was about to become a mother. She was holding the test strips out so that I could see the positive results. She couldn't stop smiling as she read the results, but my heart was sinking. This was not good news to me at all. This was a major complication in my life that would change the direction of all that I was attempting to do.

I sat heavily down on the side of the bed. There was a heaviness within me that caused me to mope like a child. She wanted me to be as happy as she was, but I couldn't be. It just wasn't in me. All that I could think of was the downside, the negative side. I saw her going deep into depression, not taking her medication and the end result was that I was again caught up in the middle of her insanity but this time I just couldn't walk away. There was another life about to be introduced into the world that needed protection from her!

"What's wrong baby?" She asked. "You should be happy, but you look so sad."

I didn't want to tell her what I was thinking but I had to. In the past when I spoke my mind about her illness it usually caused problems, but this time I wasn't sure what to expect. I told her my feelings and why I was apprehensive about the situation. She listened quietly and patiently and above all, very calmly. The baby wasn't the real problem, I said. She was!

"Over and over again, you've always done the same thing and you've always gotten the same results. You've drawn me into your shadowy world because you didn't want to accept that you are who you are. You tell me that you've changed, and I'm supposed to believe that. You told me the exact same thing many times before and you always went back to doing the same thing again. How am I supposed to believe you this time? You're fresh out of the hospital talking good talk. What about three weeks from now when life catches up to you? What then? Are you going to do the same thing? That's what I'm afraid of. This child is in danger, and I don't know how to deal with that!"

At first, she didn't say anything. There was complete silence when I finished speaking. She walked over to the window and looked out.

I had seen her naked from the back many times, but it was like the first time as I watched her silhouetted form against the light coming through the window. The curve of her back, her hips, her buttocks. I wondered how a growing fetus in her womb would affect all that. Would she lose her perfect figure and become like so many women who had children? Would she let herself go? Would she turn into a fat slob? Would I still desire her? While my mind was gone admiring and wondering, she turned from the window and returned to me.

I loved her! I knew it! There was no doubt about it! She was a part of me, and her image was burnt deep within my soul. I was a fish on a line, hooked and couldn't break free. I watched her sit beside me ladylike and cross her legs. There was something different about her this time that wasn't evident in the past.

"Donn," she began. She said 'Donn', not baby. "I don't blame you for feeling the way that you do. You have every right to feel that way. I've acted the same way that I've always acted after telling you that I was going to be different, so you have no reason to believe me, but I have changed! I really have! You will see as time goes by and I'll just have to prove it day by day. This baby means the world to me. I never thought that I could get pregnant, and I never wanted to get pregnant until you came along. With Carl, I was going to do it, but I really didn't want to. I cared a lot about him, and I was going to get pregnant because he wanted a son so badly! It was almost an obsession with him, and I felt obligated.

"Donn, please believe me, I didn't do anything to make it happen. I didn't plan this! It just happened because it's a gift from God! The day that I found out that I was pregnant I laid on my back on my bed in the hospital and thought about it. The first thing that hit me was depression. I knew that you wouldn't want to be a part of my life anymore and I didn't want to do it alone. I need you, Donn!

"My counselor would come in and we would talk for a while. She thought that I should get rid of it. She said that I wasn't ready. She said that I would put the child in danger, and do you know what? She's right! I wasn't ready but then something happened to me that day in that room. Did you ever read the story of Bill Wilson, one of the founders of Alcoholics Anonymous?"

"Yes, I read his story."

"He had a spiritual awakening in the hospital room and that's where he changed. God touched him! He saw this beautiful white light and he was transformed and was never the same again. From that day on, he never touched another drop of alcohol! Ever!

I nodded in agreement.

"Donn, the same thing happened to me. While I lay there thinking about killing the seed that you had planted within me, God spoke to me. That white light that Bill Wilson saw and felt came to me too! My room was so bright that I could see nothing but light and with it peace came over me and changed me from the inside. I'm not the same! I realize that I am who I am. Crazy is as crazy does! I'm mentally ill but I don't have to be crazy. There's a difference, you know. I'll always be mentally ill, but I don't ever have to be crazy again! Donn, do you understand? Am I making sense to you?"

"Yes! Perfect sense!" I waited a long time to hear her talk that way. It was music to my ears!

"I'm keeping this child, your child! I'm going to be the best mother that I can be, and I want you to be the father that you know that you are. I love you, Donn! You love me! I love this child and even though you're upset now about it, you love it too! You and I need each other, don't you see that? We need to be together for our child!"

I wasn't ready to make a commitment like that. Any type of commitment would alter the course of my life in a way that I wasn't ready to accept, but I began to soften.

She was definitely pregnant, and it probably was my child. She swore that it was, but I still had my doubts.

We talked about it for a while, and I did commit to being there for her but not exactly in the way that she wanted. I was willing to accept her pregnancy and help her through it. I was willing to be her lover and friend but that was as far as I was willing to go. She reluctantly accepted that and promised that she would never stop taking her medication again without the doctor's approval. I promised to stick by her as long as she kept her promise. The issue of paternity was left unsettled in my mind, although in hers it was an open and shut case. Donn was the daddy!

We went to the Coronet for a late lunch. I opened the store that afternoon after finding notes from customers in my mail slot requesting service. She stayed with me and surprisingly enough I discovered that she was particularly good at convincing people that they needed a particular item that they hadn't given much thought to before. She had a knack for customer relations and a gift of salesmanship. Her personality was bubbling and brimming with joyfulness. She brought a feminine essence to the store that wasn't there before. It was a zest that attracted the female customers in a way that I never could.

By 4 PM, the store was full of people milling around. They were browsing and buying. Diana knew just what to say to put each person at ease about spending their hard-earned cash on frivolous knickknacks, or specially made one-of-a-kind items.

I remembered what she said about working at the restaurant and how much she loved it and how much people loved her. She was in her element providing a service to the public. It was something that she was incredibly good at, and it showed. By closing time, the cash register was full, and my order book was bulging with the names and orders of new customers. Diana had noticed the way that I did business without any trouble had added her zest to mine. I had to admit she was an asset not a liability when it came to salesmanship.

Mrs. Reynolds was the last customer to leave. She was an elderly woman that lived across the street and the senior citizens building. She was one of my first and best customers who lived in Allentown. She sometimes told me things that were shocking and surprisingly true. She seemed to know me even although I had never seen her before the first time that she came into my store. But I had a special feeling for her and whenever she asked for something I tried my best to take care of it for her. Once she told me something that saved my life, and I never forgot it.

Diana connected with Mrs. Reynolds in the same manner as I did. I watched them as they talked. I watched because I wasn't sure how Diana would react to Mrs. Reynolds now silvery blonde hair! Diana looked at it but quickly fought off her fear and embraced Mrs. Reynolds. As they headed for the door with Diana carrying her purchases, Mrs. Reynolds said.

"What's your name again dear?"

"It's Diana ma'am."

"You're such a sweetheart! You've been so nice!" She stopped and spoke to me.

"Donn?"

"Yes Mrs. Reynolds?"

"Where did you find this lovely child?"

"I didn't! She found me!"

"Well son, don't you ever lose her!" She shook her finger at me. "You hear?"

"Yes ma'am."

Diana looked at me as if to say, 'you'd better listen to her' then she smiled and winked.

"I'm going to walk Mrs. Reynolds to her door. Okay?"

"Fine." I said. "Have a nice day Mrs. Reynolds."

She waved over her shoulder as she exited.

Diana returned about 15 minutes later with a huge smile and a brand-new attitude. I was in the back behind the counter sorting checks, receipts and cash. After she locked the door, she came to me skipping and grinning.

"What the hell are you grinning about?" I was sitting on my stool when she came up behind me and put her arms around my shoulders and hands across my chest.

"I'm happy! I hope you don't mind, but Mrs. Reynolds and I talked about you."

"Well, it depends on what you said."

"Nothing bad. She thinks very highly of you. She said she thinks of you like a son."

"Really?" The thought of it brought a smile to my heart. "I didn't know that! We do have a strange connection. I don't know what it is, and I just can't put my finger on it, but it's almost like I've known her before."

"She said that you wouldn't charge her for cleaning her Windows."

"That's right. She's special. What did you two talk about?"

"Nothing much. Just that I'm in love with you and that we are…"

"No! You didn't tell her that, did you?"

"What?"

"About the baby?"

"No. Only that we're working on solving our problems so that we can be happy together. Like a family!"

"Not about the baby? I don't want people knowing my personal business, not even her!"

"I'd never do that, but she knows more about you than you think. I think she's psychic! When I took her things into her apartment and was ready to leave, she handed me a five-dollar bill and said, 'sweetheart, don't stop taking your medicine anymore. You need it! If you want to keep him, keep yourself right.' She patted my hand and told me to come to visit her sometimes. I said I would. Isn't that strange that she would say that to me? It's like she knew all about me!"

"Yes. She is psychic!"

"Really?"

"Really. Last year I cleaned her windows for the first time. She tried to pay me, but I wouldn't take the money. She took my hand and attempted to put the money in it but when she touched my hand an electric shock hit me. She froze and after a few seconds, very quietly she said. 'Son, don't go to Beltzhoover today. Your life depends on it!'"

"What did she mean by that?"

I was planning to go to Beltzhoover to play cards with a friend. His name was John Scrignoli. He had a sister named Betty, who was married to Freddie Carthage. Do you remember hearing that name? Betty Carthage?

"I remember. She was the lady that was killed by her husband last year." Diana was intrigued by what I was about to divulge.

"That's right. When her husband killed her, he also killed John and two other friends of mine that were there that day to play poker. I was supposed to be there too!"

"OH MY GOD!" She jumped up. "OH MY GOD!" She grabbed me and started kissing me all over my face. "OH MY GOD! If it weren't for Mrs. Reynolds, you'd be dead too! OH MY GOD!"

"If I hadn't listened to her, I'd be just as dead as Betty, John, Bruno and Lonnie! I don't know how Mrs. Reynolds knew that something was going to happen, but she knew, and she saved my life.

"I met John about a month before his death at an NA meeting and we hit off right away. We had a lot in common and we could talk about things that I couldn't talk about with other guys. John and Betty's parents were like mine. Black father, white mother! The only difference was that their mother didn't give up on them and put them up for adoption. They went through some of the same things that I went through. They felt the same things that I felt when people called them names and treated them like they didn't belong. We all felt like we didn't fit in the Black neighborhood, and we didn't fit in the white neighborhood either. When I met Betty, I really liked her I knew that she liked me, but she was still married to her husband although they were separated. I didn't want to interfere with that. She said that she was going to divorce him because he was violent whenever he got mad or drunk, he would beat her. I needed to stay out of it, but I didn't like the fact that he beat on her, but it still wasn't any of my business. I remained friendly with her but that was it.

"John was a big guy who spent a lot of time in the gym. He was one of those guys that had muscles on top of muscles. He told Betty's husband that if he ever put his hands on her again and he was going to tear him limb from limb. The day that they were supposed to play poker, Betty called John and told him that her husband came back to the house and tried to get in. She called the cops, and he left but not before he threatened to come back and kill her. John decided to move the poker game over to her house so that he could keep an eye on her and watch out for her husband. It turned out to be the last day on earth for all of them!"

I told the story while Diana cried. She hugged and kissed me over and over again. She was very moved and shaken by what I had said.

About seven o'clock that evening she said that she wanted to talk to Mrs. Reynolds and asked if I objected.

"Of course not! Why would I object? Go ahead. Tell her that I said hi and if she needs anything let me know right away!"

"Okay."

She jumped up, showered, and dressed and left in a big hurry. I was at the window before she made it down the steps and out of the door. When she appeared on the sidewalk, I called her.

"Diana!"

She looked up. I threw her my spare key.

"Here. You may need this to get back in. I might go to a meeting!"

She caught the falling key.

"Thanks baby. I love you!"

She blew me a kiss and dashed across the street. I wondered what was so important that was driving her to Ms. Reynolds. I waited until almost 8 o'clock before I decided to go to a meeting, and I almost didn't go because I knew that I was going to get there late. I didn't like being late but sometimes it happened. I walked into the room at 8:15.

My life was about to drastically change, and I wasn't sure if I could handle it. I wasn't sure if I wanted it. I really wasn't sure if I wanted to talk about it either. But most people there knew me and knew Diana. They knew about our relationship and the changes that I've gone through with her, and they knew the end of the story as I had told it, but now they were hearing a brand-new chapter unfolding and they were shocked. I was speaking to them as if I had relapsed and started using drugs again. That was how I felt.

I got advice, a lot of advice! Some of it was so ridiculous that it was laughable. Phil and Danny had similar thoughts and told me the same thing. They knew that Diana and I would get back together again. They said it a long time before it happened.

"You two belong together!" Phil said. "I saw that from the door!"

"Diana is a good woman," Danny smiled as he spoke, "she's a lot to handle but you're just a guy to handle her. I wish you well."

Darla was there. She told me that I really wasn't looking for advice but that I was searching for confirmation for what I had already decided to do.

"So, you don't agree with me?" I asked.

"It doesn't matter whether I agree or not, you're the one who has to live with your decision. Besides, I don't think you have any choice in the matter!" She was always honest, sometimes brutally honest.

"What do you mean?"

"Simple! You're addicted to the one thing that creates the strongest addiction known to man. There is no cure for it and there is no 12-step program for it either! It's called… LOVE! You just have to live with it! But Donn, Diana is a beautiful person when she is clean, sober, and taking her medication. If she really did have that spiritual awakening, then she will be fine and so will you. I'm your friend no matter what. I'm her friend too! Just do what you feel is right and do what your heart tells you to do."

My heart said give it one more try with Diana but proceed with caution. Be vigilant and never let Big Al call the shots again!

When I got home, Diana was there. There was an aroma coming down the steps from my kitchen. I could smell the aroma of expertly cooked beef. I could hear the hamburger sizzling on the stove, and I wasn't sure if I wanted to eat them. Diana wasn't a good cook at all, and I didn't want to alienate her again like I did before. The food smelled so delicious which made confusion in my mind. I had to face her, and I had to be firm but gentle. I took a deep breath and then climbed the stairs.

She greeted me at the kitchen door with a kiss. "Baby, before you get mad about my cooking again, let me tell you what I did. Okay?" She continued without stopping. "Please sit down."

Reluctantly I sat but I wasn't about to eat. I had to concede and acknowledge that the aroma was heavenly. I smelled onions, cumin, peppers, curry, and other spices. The combination was filling my brain with the desire to taste.

"This is why I went to see Mrs. Reynolds. I wanted to learn to cook for you!" She was extremely proud of herself. "She showed me that what I was doing wrong and how to do it right. She's a great woman. Do you know that she has grandchildren that live in Oakland and Shadyside, and they won't come to visit her?"

"No. I didn't know that!"

"That's a shame. Anyway, she's going to teach me how to cook everything that you like. Today hamburgers and French fries, tomorrow, who knows! Maybe pork chops, macaroni & cheese. I don't know. But I'm going to learn to cook for you. I'm going to take care of you! Now," she placed a plate in front of me. "tell me if you don't like it, but don't be cruel!"

I looked at it. I picked up the fork and cut a small piece off of the meat and tasted it with caution. It was delicious! Absolutely delicious!

"How do you like it?" She asked. She waited patiently, but I wasn't ready to answer. Not yet! Not until I had a big bite and tasted those crispy French fries.

"I'll tell you in a minute." I threw the hamburger on the bun and added some lettuce, tomatoes, pickles, and mustard, then I took a bite.

"Baby, do you like it? You look like you like it!" She was grinning and anxiously waiting for me to reply.

I chewed furiously. It was really delicious. The combination of spices and meat was perfect. I nodded my head in response to her question, but I didn't stop chewing. I took another bite, grabbed a few French fries, and stuffed them into my mouth and winked at her. She was pleased with my reaction. She sat down and watched me eat. In minutes all of it was gone and my plate begged for more. She fixed herself a plate and brought me a second helping.

That was the beginning of many meals that she prepared for me under the tutorial guidance of Mrs. Reynolds. From that day forward, she never cooked anything that I didn't like, except for liver! That's just because I hate liver with a passion. Always have, always will!

CHAPTER 12

Donnte

Weeks passed, then changed into months. She and I spent almost all of our free time together. Most of our time was spent in the store or at an NA meeting, or riding up and down the incline, but without sex! She was a great asset to the business and was able to keep the store running while I concentrated on expanding the window cleaning business. She was true to her word and did not stop taking her medication. She attended AA meetings along with the NA meetings that she attended with me. In addition, she found support with others that share her mental illness. When she felt herself slipping, she first told me and then contacted her sponsor and her support group.

She rarely spent time at her place for she was always at mine and I preferred it that way. She and Mrs. Reynolds became as close as mother and daughter.

The winter months came and went and with their passing, Diana grew more and more radiant and beautifully pregnant. It became impossible for my customers, or should I say, our customers, to stay out of our business. Our business became everyone's business as the child grew in her belly.

Most people wanted to know why we weren't married, or when we were getting married, or when the baby was due, or was it a boy or girl, etc. etc. Diana couldn't have been happier. Her pregnancy agreed with her and she loved the attention that she received from all of the ladies that came into the store. Every now and then I would watch her wrench and twinge at the sight of a blonde woman in the store, but she valiantly fought off the feeling and if by saying, 'the only way to fight it was to face it', she would smile and approached the lady and help her. There was no longer an army of blonde, white women trying to kill her! There wasn't even one! When they came around, she made them her friends.

The baby, a boy, was due the first of June. The ultrasound showed without a doubt that it was a boy. Of course I wanted a boy! What a man doesn't? To carry on the genes and name, a boy was needed. She said that she also wanted a boy, but I knew that deep inside it was really a girl that she wanted. She tried to hide her disappointment when we were shown the boy parts on the ultrasound. She was still happy about her pregnancy and happy because we were doing the family thing together.

For the majority of the time, I had accepted and operated on the premise that I was the father of her child. I accepted it because I had no reason to disbelieve her. I had questioned her several times in various ways about the child and the answers were always the same without variance and without hesitation. She was steadfast in her answers and convincing. But, there were those times when I doubted my parental validity. The thought nagged me even though she gave no reason for me to doubt her. I often thought about Bill and his involvement with her. She swore that he was nothing more than a friend.

He had been out of the picture for quite some time and he made no attempt to interfere in our relationship. Just before the big snowstorm in January, I told her to tell him exactly what was going on with us. I felt that she was leading him on and I didn't think that it was right. She did as I asked. Weeks passed and I heard nothing from him, then one day he showed up at my door looking for her. She was at Mrs. Reynolds' place when I noticed his Lexus pull up and park across the street. He got out and approached me as I stood on the steps of the store.

"Hi Donn!"

"Bill. What are you doing here?"

"I was concerned about Diana. I had been by her place a couple of times but her neighbors said that they hadn't seen her in weeks. I'm just concerned."

"There's no need to be concerned." I told him. "She's in good hands!"

He looked down his nose at me as if he felt that he was so much better than I was.

"Yes, I can see that." His words were drenched with sarcasm and contempt. I tried valiantly to be civil because I knew that I had what he wanted and that was the basis for his cutting remark. He also knew that even with all of his money, his fine car, his job and education, that he could not have what I had… Her!

"Look Bill, you have to accept the facts. Diana is with me. I believe that she told you from the start how she felt about me and how she felt about you. She doesn't like you in the same way that you like her and all of your money won't change that. It's nice that you're concerned about her, but you don't have to be. She's WELL taking care of,… You know what I mean?"

I paused and gave him a penetrating look. He looked away and I continued.

"Let me ask you something Bill. That Lexus that you drive is a very expensive and beautiful car. I can't afford anything like that but I'd love to have one someday. Now, I'm sure, just by looking at it, that you take really good care of it and you treat it well. You give it the best gas that you can get and when you drive it you take care so that you don't do any damage to it, right?"

He nodded and straightened his back with pride and produced an Ivy League smile.

"And you clean it or have it cleaned as soon as it gets a little bit of dirt on it, don't you?"

He beamed with pride and he nodded this time.

"And you probably even gave it a name!"

He was bubbling over with pride by this time. "Yes! Her name is Darla!"

"And if someone tries to temper with, Darla, or steal her, you'd be very upset and you would do anything and everything that you could to prevent that, wouldn't you?"

"Of course!" He replied. He was looking stern and strong and protective.

"Well Bill, the way you feel about Darla is the same way that I feel about Diana! I love her! I cherish her! I take very good care of her and I will protect her at all costs! I won't let anyone tamper with her, or try to steal her! Do you understand what I'm saying Bill?"

"Explicitly!" He said as he understood my meaning.

"Thanks Bill. I appreciate that!"

"You made your point crystal clear. I won't bother you again." He extended his hand in friendship and I extended my. "She's very special!" He added.

"Yes, I know."

"If I had gotten to her before you, Donn, things would be much different!"

"I know that too, but there's someone special out there for you. You seem like a good guy. You'll find her." I said.

There was a moment of silence.

"I know it's really none of my business, but is she really pregnant? She said she was. I wondered if she just said that to back me off." He waited for my response.

"Yes she's pregnant. Are you concerned about who the father is?" I asked.

"No, not really. I know it's you and not me. Actually she never allowed me to get that far. Congratulations!" The disappointment showed on his face but I believed that he was sincere.

"Thank you."

"Well, I'd better go."

He pulled a business card from his wallet and handed it to me. I took it but I didn't look at it.

"Just in case you need a good attorney!"

"Thanks Bill." He crossed the street and was just about to enter his car when he saw Diana come out of Mrs. Reynolds' building. When he saw her he froze. There was no doubt that he was falling for her. I felt sorry for him. To love someone and not have that love returned was torturous.

She didn't see him at first but she saw me standing on the steps. Her face lit up like a roman candle. I pointed to him. She looked and most of the brightness left her face. She didn't know what to do. I let her know that it was okay and then she walked over to him. I retreated back into the building unconcerned over what they may be talking about. My trust level in her had risen after he confirmed what she had been saying all along. They had never been sexually active and it left me feeling better about her and believing a little more that the child in her womb was put there by me.

I looked at the business cards as I went back into the store. I read it as I walked behind the counter, then I threw it in the trash.

June 1st: 4:35 AM.

I woke up as Diana shook me.

"What's wrong sweetheart?"

"It's time!" She gripped my hand. "The baby's is coming!" She squeezed it hard.

"Now?"

"NOW!"

Ten minutes later we were at the hospital. Her contractions were five minutes apart but it seemed closer to me. She didn't panic at all, she left that to me! I was afraid that something would happen to complicate the delivery.

In the delivery room the nurses fussed over her and did all that was necessary to prepare for the birth. The doctor came in a few minutes later to check her cervix.

"You're eight centimeters. You're almost there. We will check again in about a half an hour." The female doctor said.

I expected Diana to be nervous and afraid, but she was as cool as a cucumber. The only time she even flinched was when the contractions hit. Then she squeezed my hand so hard that I thought she had broken bones.

Throughout her pregnancy she was in discomfort but she had very little pain. She was so happy and excited to be pregnant that the few aches and pains that she experienced had no effect on her attitude or spirits. She loved it when I spent time rubbing cocoa butter oil on her stomach and when I put my head there to talk and sing to the baby. She said that he was listening. She could tell because when I spoke he would react.

As she lay, about to give birth, she handled the pain valiantly. She was offered an epidural but she refused. She wanted to feel the experience of the birth of her first child naturally!

She was in labor for about five and a half hours and delivered our gorgeous son at ten o'clock in the morning. I stood by her side holding her hand and watching for the first time the actual birth of a child. It was the most amazing thing that I had ever witnessed and it's something that I will never forget. I watched the crown of his head appear full of black curly hair like his mother. He was face up but the doctor turned him over once his head was out. Then one shoulder and then the other came out and the rest of him just slid out so easily. She cried a little from the pain but it was over before she knew it. I cut the umbilical cord cautiously, afraid that my son, (the first time I truly thought of him as my son) would feel the pain of it. The doctor assured me that he would not, but still apprehension gripped me. One swat on his behind after they cleared his airways and the decibels of his cries filled the room.

The nurses took him to the far side of the room and began to clean him. I looked down at the beautiful woman who had just delivered our gorgeous son and tears filled my eyes. She was sweating across her forehead, her hair was everywhere, she was tired and exhausted and in pain but I had never seen her more beautiful than at that moment.

She looked up at me as I mopped sweat from her face and tried to straighten her hair as best I could with my fingers. She smiled through the pain. She tried to talk but I stopped her with a kiss. She wanted her son. They brought him and placed him in her arms. She looked at his tiny beautiful face and began to cry.

"Thank you Donn!" She said. "He's beautiful! He looks just like you!"

I sat on the side of the bed and put my arm under her head and gently hugged them both.

We named him Donnte' Carver Diamond!

CHAPTER 13

The Beginning of Trouble

On August first, Donnte' turned two months old. For two months I had observed Diana and Donnte' together. I kept my mind vigilant to the possible danger that could strike at any moment due to her mental illness, combined with the possible onslaught of postpartum depression, but none of that happened. She proved to be the perfect mother doting over her newborn child. I hardly had a chance to be close to her after the initial six weeks because he usurped all of her attention. But it was all good. She never came close to being depressed. With Donnte', Ms. Reynolds, (who had become like a mother to her), and the store and all of the new customers, Diana was in Heaven on Earth!

But that was the beginning of the changes in our lives even though we didn't know it at the time.

Thursday morning business was slow, and I was in the store in the back when Darla came in. She greeted Diana and coo-chee-cooed Donnte', but looked at me with those eyes that said, 'we need to talk, now, in private'! Whatever she had to tell me wasn't for anyone's ears but mine, not even Diana's!

"Baby, I'm going across the street to get a pizza. Do you want something?" I asked.

Diana picked Donnte' up over her head to see him laugh, then she lowered him to her chest and gently hugged him. Finally, she recognized that I had asked her a question.

"Oh, oh. Yes baby. Get me a couple slices with pepperoni and anchovies, please?"

Her focus was still on him and not me.

"Yuck! Anchovies! How can you eat those nasty things? Are you sure you're not pregnant again?" Darla questioned.

"Not yet!" She winked.

Darla and I met up in the pizza shop. She didn't waste any time breaking the news to me.

"Carl relapsed!" When she spoke, it was almost as if she were telling me that someone that we loved had died. In essence, a relapse for most addicts was a death sentence.

"Oh no! I'm sorry to hear that. What happened?" I asked.

There obviously was a lot more to it than what she was saying. She could have called and told me that. She looked deep into my eyes searching and wondering because she didn't know if I knew what she knew about Carl.

"Donn, do you know who Carl is?" She asked.

"Sure! I know Carl!" I said somewhat ignorantly.

"I mean, did Diana tell you who he is? Did she tell you about their relationship? Did she tell you what happened?"

"Yes, she told me. If you're wondering, stop wondering. She told me everything!"

"Everything?"

"Everything!" To ease her mind, I added. "Even about what she did to Carl."

"Oh, I'm so happy about that. I didn't want to have to tell you that part if she didn't tell you yet, especially now that you two are so happy." She felt relieved. "Donn, you're in danger. Carl has been talking crazy ever since Donnte'" was born. It messed him up when he found out that Diana was pregnant, but now he's totally lost it! He spoke at a meeting last week about his hatred for you…"

"Why does he hate me? I've never been anything but a friend to him!"

"He's jealous. He's envious and he's pissed off because Diana had your baby and not his. He can't have kids and he blames her. He wants revenge. He wants to get even. He wants you dead!"

"He's just blowing off steam. He's upset but he's really got no reason to hate me!"

I tried to believe the words that I had said but I knew that hatred doesn't need a reason to hate. It just does! John, Betty, and friends died because her husband hated her, but he killed all of them just because they were there.

Carl must have hated Diana all along and what kept his loathing under control were his religion and his recovery, which he gave up. Darla was right, danger was lurking just outside of my comfortable and secure world, but I wasn't concerned for myself but for my newly created family and just like any man worth his salt, I was determined to protect my family at any and all costs.

August Second: 1:00 AM. I was awakened by Diana's hand. She shook me from my sleep and my dream world.

"Donn? What's going on?"

"What do you mean? What time is it?"

"It's about one o'clock in the morning. I just fed Donnte' but I can't go back to sleep. He's sleeping, you're sleeping and I'm awake! So, talk to me!"

"Well, I was asleep but I'm not anymore." I wiped my eyes.

"What did Darla tell you and why are you keeping it from me? It's about me, isn't it?"

I didn't want to tell her about Carl, but I had to. She needed to know. I had planned to tell her in the morning once I figured out how to say it but that wasn't the way it was going to be. She had become impatient with my silence and demanded to know what was going on.

"Carl relapsed!" I said softly as if the softness of my voice would soften the blow.

"Oh no!" She was visibly upset.

I told her what Darla had told me. She listened and absorbed but she was very afraid. She got up from the bed and picked Donnte' up. He stirred in her arms but didn't awaken. She said nothing about it, but I knew that she was worried about his future. Why she was worried, I didn't know! At least not yet.

"As long as Carl was in the church everything was fine, but when he left, I became worried. I always tried to be friendly with him, but I knew that one day it would come to this. I knew one day that he would relapse too! Now, I'm scared! Baby, I'm really scared!"

She told me of how Carl was when she met him. He was very nice and gentle to his friends but fierce to his opponents. Sometimes he became vicious and cruel when crossed. When he became angry or when he drank, his rage took control of him. She knew that he hadn't forgotten what she had done to him! How could he?

"Baby?"

"What?"

"He's going to try to hurt us!"

"Diana, I think you're exaggerating. Why would he want to hurt us? It just doesn't make sense to me." I was definitely puzzled.

"Before I cut his, I mean, before I did what I did to him, he and I were trying to get pregnant. He always talked about having a son. He wanted a son so badly and I promised him that I would give him one. Now he can't have any kids and I just had your child, a son! It bothered him so badly that he couldn't stand it and he relapsed." She knew that he hadn't forgotten her promise to give him a son. She knew that now that he had forsaken his God and his recovery that he was going to come after her.

She began to cry. Donnte' woke up and started crying too. Immediately she stopped and rocked him back to sleep. She put him in his crib and laid down with me.

"Make love to me baby. I need it... Please?"

She hadn't spoken that way in a long time. There was that sadness in her voice that signaled the coming of depression and the beginning of a downward spiral that usually landed her in the hospital. I didn't know what to do about it, so I held her while she continued to beg me for sex. I wanted her too. It had been a while and the times were too far apart. Before I could act or react, she rolled over onto me and took control.

My mind wasn't into what she was doing to Big Al. I always loved it when she went down there and it always left me feeling good, but exhausted. Why? Because she was an expert!

I couldn't help wondering what depths Carl was willing to go to extract what he considered revenge. I had a feeling that if he were to do anything against us, it would be directed towards Donnte' and not directly at Diana or me. That would create the most painful effect imaginable.

In the two months that Donnte' had been on this Earth with us, my way of thinking had drastically changed. Before him, my thoughts were mostly personal and selfish, but now they had become parental. I no longer thought of myself first. His welfare became more important than mine. I became a father in every sense of the word, and I went from wondering about him to loving him so much that I would kill or die for him. No one was going to harm him as long as I was alive! There was no way I would allow Carl, or anyone, to harm my son. If anyone tried, I would kill them first!

August Second: 5:30 PM.

I had just returned to the store when I noticed the sadness and terror on Diana's face as I walked in the door. I rushed to the counter thinking that something was wrong with Donnte' but he was right there in his stroller beside her smiling into my face when I looked down at him.

"What's wrong?" I asked her.

"It's Mrs. Reynolds. She had a heart attack!" Diana was distraught.

I moved close to comfort her. I was afraid to ask the obvious question. "Is she…?"

"No. They just took her to the hospital."

I closed the store immediately and drove my family to the hospital.

When we got there, she was alive and alert but hooked onto machines that monitored and controlled her condition. There were wires and tubes connected to her that looked so unnatural. She smiled when we entered the room. We weren't permitted to stay long because she needed her rest. She was glad to see us, and I was definitely relieved to know that she was going to be okay. When we left, she became sad. She tried to hide it, but I could see her sadness even through her smile.

The doctor said that she had suffered a severe heart attack but the life alert bracelet that she wore help to save her life. I was thankful for that. I had seen the commercials many times; 'I've fallen, but I can't get up!', but I never knew anyone who had been saved because of it, until then!

On the way home Diana was silent. She kept looking at Donnte' while he was strapped in his seat in the back, and I could tell that she had a lot on her mind. All of a sudden, she spoke.

"I don't want him to grow up to hate me!" She looked at him again.

"Why do you say that?" I didn't see the connection. I was puzzled.

"Some kids grow up to hate their parents for no reason even though they do everything that they could do to raise them right. Mrs. Reynolds' kids live in Philadelphia and two of her grandchildren live here but none of them give a damn about her. That's not right! They never come to see her, and you know that she's lived in that building for over 10 years and she said the only time her daughters came there was when they helped her to move in and about a year later when they came to try to get more money out of her.

"When her husband died, she gave them money that he had left in his will for them and sold the house and property that she and her husband owned. They wanted money from that too even though they weren't entitled to it! They were nice and helpful so that they could get their hands on her money but after she moved in and they realized that they had gotten all that they were going to get, they moved to Philadelphia. Her grandchildren are grown too! They're almost my age. They live right here in the city, but they don't call her or visit her, or anything! I've got their names and phone numbers and I'm going to call them and let them know what's happening. I already called her oldest daughter in Philadelphia just before you came home. Do you know what she said when I told her that her mother had just had a heart attack? She said, 'is she still alive?' The way she said it was like she was hoping that she wasn't. She wasn't even upset or worried. She didn't ask what hospital she was in her how she was doing or anything like that. She just said, 'call me if there's any change', and she hung up before I could say anything else!"

"Baby, I don't want to Donnte' to grow up feeling like that about me!" She looked back at him again and her face was still sad.

"Sweetheart, he's not going to feel like that towards you."

"How do you know? You can't predict that."

"No, but I don't believe it. I won't allow it!"

She was right, I couldn't predict but...

She spoke as she continued to stare at Donnte'. "I'll bet that something happened in their family to make those girls hate her. Maybe, well, I don't know!"

We got home, I put Donnte' to bed while she called Mrs. Reynolds' family.

August Thirteenth: 7: 40 PM. Saturday.

A crowd had already gathered outside of the church where my NA home group was held when I arrived. I saw many faces in the crowd that I knew. Some were smoking cigarettes and talking. Some were drinking sodas, some were laughing, but they all turned to notice my Van as I parked across the street from the main entrance.

"Hi Donn!" Eduardo said. He pumped my hand as I approached.

"Hi Eduardo. How's everything?"

"Good! Muy Bueno! I can't complain. Life is good these days."

"I know."

I moved past him to enter the building. Others greeted me as I made my way through the crowd.

"Hey Donn! You look good man! Family life must agree with you!"

"Thanks Floyd! Maybe you ought to try it, before you get caught up!"

"Not me man! I'm a confirmed bachelor!" He chuckled and smiled.

"Hey Donn!" Lisa said between puffs of her Newport. Lisa was a chain smoker. I told her that she had substituted one addiction for another, and she agreed.

"Hey Lisa! Girl, you look good! Recovery agrees with you, but you need to stop smoking those nasty cigarettes!"

"I know! I know! If I didn't, you'd remind me! You tell me that every time you see me!" She hugged me and as I hugged back. I could smell the stale cigarette odor in her clothes. "I know I need to quit Donn, and I will one day!" She smiled at me, took another puff then moved away from me to talk to her friend Gwenice who was just arriving.

I continued to walk by. Freddy was standing in the doorway as I walked up the steps.

"What's up Doc?"

"Nothing much Freddie. It's the same ol' same ol'!"

Freddie was 50 years old. He had been addicted to heroin for over 20 years and had been clean for ten. He was considered one of the leaders of NA. Some call him an NA Guru because of his knowledge and his desire to keep NA the same as it is always had been. He always wore something like a baseball cap, or T-shirt that promoted Narcotics Anonymous. This day he had on a T-shirt that had the same message as did his front license plate on his car. It simply said; NA-IOU1.

I stopped and chatted with Freddie for a few minutes and just before I entered the building, he said.

"Carl is in there!" He said nothing else, and he didn't have to. I understood his message.

"Thanks Freddie." We hugged and I stepped through the doors of the building.

My home group was one of the biggest in the city. It was held every Saturday evening at 8 PM in a large church on the North Side. People attended from all across the city, but I had rarely seen Carl there. That night he was there, and he was sitting alone and looking sad and dejected as if he had just come out of the street from a 'run'. When Freddie told me that he was there I wasn't upset but when I saw him sitting alone, I became angry.

(What was he doing here?) The thought came and passed quickly. Just like me, he needed to be there because he needed help. The entire purpose of our fifth tradition was based on helping those that are still suffering. I thought about what Diana had said about him and what Darla had told me of him voicing his hatred for me in a meeting and I didn't want to help him. I thought of how we were friends before Diana became pregnant and how that slowly changed when Donnte' was born. He cut off the friendship altogether. I wanted to walk right past him and get to my duties, but I stopped and sat beside him. His head was in his hands, and he didn't recognize me at first.

"Carl?"

He recognized my voice and immediately lifted his head.

"Are you okay? Do you need to talk?"

"Not to you!" He snapped at me and then lowered his head again.

"Man, what have I done to make you so upset with me?"

"Nothing man! Just stay the hell away from me! I don't need your damned help!"

The room was beginning to fill with people and most heard his outburst. Some were there when he spoke of his hatred towards me the previous week. They observed us from a distance thinking that something was about to happen.

Carl got up and stormed out of the door. I watched trying to decide whether or not to go after him. I decided against it. I walked through the leering crowd to the back room to set up for the discussion meeting that was to take place after the large group introduction meeting in the large hall.

Everything went smoothly in the large group and also for about 10 minutes into the discussion group. Then Carl came storming into the room and disrupted a woman speaking about her plight. All eyes turned his way.

People began to move away in a hurry and screams and shouts were heard that broke the calm and silence of the meeting.

"He's got a knife!" Someone shouted.

That caused the entire group to scurry from their seats knocking over chairs in an effort to get out of his way. I didn't see the knife at first because he was trying to hide it from me. I knew that he was coming after me and so I stood up. He was about twenty feet from me and there was nothing or no one between us. I looked around for a weapon of defense but the only thing that I could see was a small three-legged table with a lamp on it. He raised his knife and lunged me towards me. I snatched the table from under the lamp causing it to fall on the floor and break.

"You bastard!" He shouted. "I'm going to separate you from your dick and flush it down the toilet like she did mine! Then we'll see if she still wants you!"

The knife looked just like the one that Diana had that night. It was long, thick, and well made. It was a butcher knife. If he got close enough, it would slice me up like soft butter.

People were rushing out of the room, but no one tried to stop him or help me. No one! I was on my own! He swung the knife right to left, chest high. I jumped back and readied the table for the next blow. One chance would be all that I would get so I'd better make the most of it.

"Put the knife down Carl. You don't really want to do this. I'm your friend. Put the knife down!"

"No! I'll put it down when I'm finished. You're going to be a eunuch once I'm done with you!"

He wasn't thinking clearly. Most likely he was high, and I had to use that to my advantage. I had the advantage because my head was clear, but he had the knife! When he lunged the second time I backed against the far wall and almost tripped over a chair that was thrown on its side when someone hastily removed themselves from it. I couldn't be so clumsy when he lunged the third time, or I would be his victim.

"I got you now, you punk bitch! I'm gonna cut you up like a ripe tomato!"

He lunged again. This time he tried to stab me below the belt. I raised the table and caught the knife in it. He tried to pull it out and that's when I hit him in the jaw. He let go of the knife as staggered backwards but he didn't fall. I threw the table to the side. The knife was still lodged in as it fell to the floor.

Carl put his hands up and stood defiantly in the boxer stance.

"Carl, you really don't want to do this. Let's talk!"

I said it for the benefit of those still watching, but what I really wanted to do was to beat him senseless and that's what I intended to do. Big Al agreed!

"Okay! Let's talk about how I'm going to kick your ass! Let's talk about how you stole my life!"

"Carl, I didn't steal your life and you know as well as I do that you can't win without that knife!"

He looked around for the knife. I reached over and snatched it from the table. Fear overtook him and he began to back away thinking that I was going to use the knife on him. Everyone collectively gasped as they thought the same thing, but I had no desire to use it on him. I handed it to one of the members and told her to take it outside. She did.

Carl moved close again. I was finished talking. I put my hands up and my head down and waited.

(Counterpunch.) I thought to myself. (Wait for him to swing first and then knock his brains out!)

He swung and missed. I countered with a body shot to the ribs with my left hand and a right to the jaw that sent him staggering backwards onto the floor. He rolled backwards and struggled to get up. I stepped up and as soon as he got to his knees, I hit him again. He fell over sideways, and I waited for him to get up so that I could hit him again, but all of a sudden, I heard shouts coming from all around me urging me on.

"Get that mother f....!"

"Kick his natural ass!"

"He tried to kill you! Beat his ass!"

"Yeah, kick his ass!"

I looked around and saw that the room was packed, and everyone seemed to have lost their minds in the frenzy. I came back to mine. We were in the middle of an NA meeting and this type of thing shouldn't be happening. I stopped.

"This isn't right!" I said. I turned to Carl who was still on the floor. "Not here, not now! You name the time and place and I'll be there!"

He looked at me. I waited but he said nothing. Everyone quieted down and I walked right past Carl and out of the door.

As I walked up the steps in my building, Diana ran to me and started hugging me and crying. Someone had called her and told her all about it. She was hysterical. I became angry. Whoever called her did it maliciously. They couldn't wait to upset her with the news, but I calmed her down and sent her into the living room where Donnte' was crying. I went into the kitchen and poured us both a glass of pure orange juice. I thought of what I might have to do, and I wasn't happy with it.

Carl threatened my existence, my family, and my stability. I was trying to manage the situation rationally, but he wasn't rational, and my way wasn't going to work. I knew I would soon have to change my approach because Carl and I were going to bump heads like two stubborn rams, and I was determined to be the winner.

August Fourteenth: 2:15 PM. Sunday.

Diana and I returned from Nona's church with little Donnte' strapped to her chest. She loved carrying him that way because she said it was the closest thing to being pregnant again. She was already talking and thinking about having another baby and Donnte' was just two months old. She unhooked him and handed him to me.

"I'm going to check on Mom Reynolds." She announced. "I'll call you if I need to stay with her a while."

"Okay."

She hurried off to the building as I crossed the street to ours. Upstairs, the phone rang, and I assumed that it was her.

"Hello, Diana?"

"No! It's not Diana! Is your worst enemy and you're going to pay for what you've done!" It was Carl. "You embarrass me! I won't forget that!"

"Where are you man? I'm ready to pay right now. You're not going to harass me in my own home. I'll kill you first!"

"Don't worry about where I am. Worry about where I'll be!" He hung up.

He had crossed the line! Nobody threatens me that way. He had just turned me from the hunted to the hunter. I knew what he meant when he said, 'worry about where I'll be', and if he showed up, I'd let him come in and I'd kill him on the spot. That would be the end of it. I didn't want

Diana or Donnte' around at the time, so I called Mom Reynolds number. Diana answered.

"Reynolds residential. How may I help you?"

"Diana, it's me. How is Mrs. Reynolds?"

"She's tired but she's okay. Baby, I think I should stay with her a while. Do you mind?"

"No sweetheart. That's fine. Stay as long as you like. In fact, I'll be over a little later. I've got something I need to talk to you about."

"Is it really important? Do you want me to come home?"

"No. Stay there. It's important, but it can wait until I get there."

There was silence as she thought.

"Is it Carl?"

"Yes."

"Okay." Silence. "I'll see you when you get here. Be careful."

"I love you!" I hung up.

I picked up Donnte' from his crib and he smiled his innocent trusting smile knowing that his daddy would handle anything that would come his way. He trusted me completely and had no worries about anything. I kissed him on his tiny lips.

"Nobody's going to hurt you!" I promised. "Not as long as I'm alive! You can take that to the bank!"

Later when I went to Mrs. Reynolds, I told Diana about the phone call. She stood silently listening as I spoke. I began to see a side of her that never surfaced in my presence before. Her look was Stern, aloof, determined. She was thinking as a mother would think to protect her child. She didn't have to say the words because both of us had the same thought in mind. Donnte' would survive even if we didn't. Carl would die if he came calling.

She was no longer the scared, crying, girlish female that occupied my house in days past. She no longer trembled at the name of Carl Bladen, but she stood tall like a lioness watching over her cubs, ready to kill or be killed to protect them.

We were standing in Mrs. Reynolds living room and Mrs. Reynolds was in the kitchen, so Diana looked around to see if she was within earshot. Then she whispered.

"What do you want me to do?"

She knew that I had a plan, and she didn't ask what it was but was just content to play whatever part that I asked her to play.

"Baby, I don't want you involved because when I kill him, someone has to take care of our son."

"I love the way you said,... 'Our son'. You really believe he's yours now?"

"Diana, I don't have any doubts anymore. I know he's mine. I'm sorry that I ever doubted you. I'll never doubt you again!" I drew her into my arms and kissed her. Mrs. Reynolds came slowly to the doorway that separated her living room and kitchen.

"Hey! No hanky-panky in my house!" Her voice sounded strong and stern, but she was smiling after she said it.

"Hello Mrs. Reynolds. How are you feeling?" I smiled. It was a pleasure to see her up and about.

"I'm feeling fine, but obviously not quite as good as you are!"

Diana rushed over to help her to her chair. She sat and Diana fixed her TV tray and then sat at her food on it. She began to eat.

"Donn?" She said between bites.

"Yes ma'am?"

"When are you two getting married?" She looked straight into my eyes. "You know it's not right in the eyes of God to be living together and not be married. You've been shacking up long enough! You've got this baby boy to think of and Diana needs the security of your name!"

I didn't know what to say. She caught me completely off guard.

"Son, think about it. You don't have to answer me. Just think about it. If you love her, treat her right! Do the right thing!"

"Yes ma'am. I'll think about it."

I left Donnte' there with Diana and Mrs. Reynolds. I didn't want them at the house because I felt that Carl was coming by. When I got onto the elevator and journeyed down to the ground floor, Mrs. Reynolds' words reverberated in my head. She was right. If I loved Diana and she was doing the right thing, (and she was), then I should marry her. She had already given me a son and she never complained or nagged about marriage or anything else.

I exited the elevator and walked out onto the street. I didn't realize how late it had gotten. I had been upstairs longer than I anticipated, and darkness was beginning to set across the horizon. I went home and prepared myself for the assault that I was sure was coming from Carl. I made a strong pot of coffee, Diana style! I used no cream or sugar in my cup. I needed to be awake and alert. No TV! The radio was set low enough to hear but I also was able to hear any sound throughout the building that would let me know that Carl was there. I sat back and waited.

Diana had called me twice throughout the night to make sure that I hadn't fallen off to sleep. She remained calm and assured me that no matter what, she would always be there for me. The unspoken words were 'when you kill him and go to jail, I will always be there for you'. It was strange how we communicated now that we were parents protecting our child. Before we severed the phone line for the last time, she lovingly said.

"Donn, I love you! There will never be anyone in my life that would ever take your place!"

I felt like she thought I was going to die the first time that she said it, but the next time I knew that she had faith that when it was all over, Carl would be the stiff one and I would be going away.

"When this is all over," I said, "there's something that I have to say to you. I wish I could now, but I can't. It's just not the right time."

She hesitated. "Is it important?"

"Yes, very!"

"Really?" I could feel her smile. "Is it something that I'm going to enjoy hearing?"

"Yes. Immensely!"

"I'll be waiting."

"You'd better be."

"And if I'm not, are you going to spank me?" She was almost giddy.

"Yes, and make you like it!"

"You nasty boy!"

"You love it!"

"Yes, I do!" She blew me a kiss over the phone. "Be careful. I love you!"

"I love you too! Bye-bye!"

"Bye-bye!"

The night came and went but Carl never showed up. I was both angry and glad that he didn't. I wanted to get it over with, but I didn't want to have to go through the consequences of my actions. I didn't want to leave my woman and my son before we really had the opportunity to become a family.

CHAPTER 14

Bubbles & Sherman's

Monday, August 15th eight o'clock AM.

I opened the store. Diana was across the street at Mrs. Reynolds place. She wanted to stay with Mrs. Reynolds for a while. She would be back at the store around nine. That was fine with me because I didn't want her to know about certain things I was about to do, ... Not yet!

At 8:30 AM, I made a phone call to Diamonds Jewelers, downtown location. (No relation). I wanted a special ring for Diana. They gave me several ideas and about an hour later, sent me a photo of their design based on my preferences. It was exactly what I wanted. It wasn't something that was difficult to make so they promised to have it ready by 4 o'clock.

I then called Bubbles and Sherman's restaurant in Squirrel Hill. I spoke to a very nice and very personable woman who told me that she was the maître d'. I reserved a dinner table and spoke to her concerning the red velvet chair. Her level of excitement rose. I could feel it, even through the phone. Diana had told me about the chair, but I didn't know any more than what she had said, so I asked the maître d' to fill me in. Perfect!

A bottle of champagne came with the dinner. Because we were non-drinkers, non-alcoholic champagne would be substituted.

Next, to the flower shop across the street. As soon as Diana came in from Mrs. Reynolds', I dashed out of the door. She had a look of puzzlement across her face, but she didn't ask, and I didn't offer. I left the flower shop and immediately I went to see Mrs. Reynolds. When she opened the door, it was obvious that her sixth sense told her why I was there.

"Come inside!" She said smiling. "I've been expecting you!"

"You have?"

"Yes, I have. I saw your face last night. You've been thinking about what I've said."

I entered and closed the door.

"Sit down. Tell me all about it. I'm all ears!" My God! She seemed even happier than I was.

I started to sit but before I did, she spoke again.

"Son? Please get me a glass of water so that I can take these pills?"

"Yes Mrs. Reynolds."

"Wait a minute! Wait a minute!" Her hands were beckoning me to stop. "Now you've known me a while. Right?"

"Yes ma'am."

"And lately you have been over here every day since my heart attack, right?"

"Yes ma'am."

And you and I have always had a unique connection. Am I wrong or right?"

"You're right!"

"One question. When you think of me, what do you think? Do you think of me as a customer, or a friend?"

"I think of you more like family. Like a mother, a little."

"That's so nice to hear. I have always wanted to have a son. I have two girls and they don't give a good Owl's hoot about me."

"I know. If you don't mind me saying it, I think they're crazy!"

"I think you're right!" She started to chuckle.

I knew what she was getting at, and I was okay with it. I did have that special connection with her and I always wanted a mother figure in my life since the day that I lost mine. She wanted me to call her mom. Diana was already doing it and I noticed the happiness that emanated from her whenever Diana spoke to her. I went into the kitchen and returned with a glass of water. When I returned, I spoke these words.

"If you don't mind, I'd love to call you mom too!"

She took several of her pills, washed them down with the water and then she spoke to me.

"That would be wonderful! You are the son that I've always wanted!"

She reached out and we embraced. When she let go of me she sat back.

"Now, tell me all about your plans." She said.

The entire time that I talked, she never stopped smiling. She was genuinely a beautiful woman with a heart of gold. I just couldn't imagine anyone, especially her own kids, treating her badly or neglecting her, but I didn't know the whole story and it really wasn't any of my business.

I finished laying out my plans and she was so excited by it that she got up and started walking, almost skipping around the room.

"Son, I wish I could be there when you pop the question. She's probably going to cry like a baby. She's a big crybaby, you know?"

"So, mom, you think my plan is okay?"

"Okay? It will blow her mind!"

"Mom, where did you learn that?"

"Diana, who else!"

"Ha ha ha ha ha!"

We laughed and continued to talk and I told her all that I had planned in great detail. She listened and occasionally commented.

"Son, I knew that you would do the right thing. I'm tickled to death!"

"Mom. Why don't you come along with us?"

She reached out and patted my hand as she often does in her motherly way.

"No. That's something special between the two of you and I would probably have another heart attack with all of the excitement. No, you take her. I'll keep Donnte' but you promise me that you will come here as soon as you can. Okay?"

"Yes ma'am. I will."

"Now, give me a kiss!"

She extended her wrinkled cheek and I kissed it.

Back at the store, Diana was waiting on customers when I walked in. The bell at the top of the door tinkled when I opened it and immediately she looked my way with concern. Carl was obviously foremost on her mind. It showed on her face just for a second or two until she recognized me and a beaming, loving smile replaced it.

"Excuse me." She said to the lady that she was helping. She came from behind the counter and into my arms. She didn't care that there were customers all over the store and that they were watching. She wanted to hug and kissed me and that's what she did. When she finished, she said to everyone. "For those of you that don't know, this is my man! His name is

Donn! I love him more than anything in this world, except for our son. So if you see me acting strange, he's the reason why!"

Everyone understood. Some laughed and some just smiled as she left me and went back to work.

To ease her mind and relieve her worries about Carl, I stayed in the front of the store. I sat in a lounge chair and turned on all of the television sets to HBO and watched the movie in stereo while I relaxed.

At 3:30 PM the jewelry store called. Diana answered the phone and called me. She listened as I spoke and her level of curiosity was high as she tried to figure out what was going on.

"Yes... that's right... fine... fine... that's perfect... I'll be there shortly... thank you... goodbye!"

"What's that all about?" She asked.

"Oh nothing! Just a little thing I ordered."

"What little thing?" She looked into my eyes. "Baby, what are you up to? You're up to something, I can feel it. What is it?" Her inquisitive curiosity burned within her. She knew that I had some gift, or surprise for her but she had no idea what it was.

I couldn't keep the smile off my face. "It's nothing baby. Don't worry about it. I've got to go and I'll be back in about an hour." I hurried for the door.

"DONN! Don't you leave me like this!" She shouted over the counter at me but I was already at the door. "Tell me, what's going on?"

I opened the door and blew her a kiss. "Be patient. All in good time. Love you!" I closed the door before she could say anything else.

There was frustration on her face, but I knew she would be fine by the time I got back. I just had to figure out some way to keep from telling her before the appointed time.

At the jewelry store I looked at the ring. The diamond was a beautifully flawless stone, sitting in the midst of the gold and platinum ring. It was made exactly as I had wanted. Eight small diamonds surrounding the large stone. It was beautiful and expensive but she was worth it. I paid with my credit card and had the box wrapped. Then I remembered that I had to have something to divert her curiosity with, so I looked around and found a small heart-shaped diamond pendant on a gold herringbone chain. I bought it. It would look beautiful around her neck.

I left the ring in the van and took the pendant with me when I returned to the store. Several of the ladies that were there when I left were still there. I knew that they were about to gang up on me so I was thankful that I had thought clearly enough to buy the pendant. Without it, I would be ground meat. They all looked at me suspiciously when I came through the door. Diana put her hands on her hips and a scowl on her face as I approached.

"Hello ladies!" I said with a polite smile.

"Hummmm!" One mumbled.

"You'd better come clean!" Another said. "If you don't, you won't be getting any goodies tonight!"

"They laughed. Diana tried not to, but she couldn't help but join in.

I approached them and walked around the counter to where Diana was. I bent over and kissed my little smiling son and tickled his belly. "I think I'll be getting more goodies tonight than I've gotten in a while!"

"Oh really?" Diana said. Her hand was still on her hip. "We'll see about that!"

"Yes we will. Now, close your eyes!"

"What?"

"Just close your eyes woman! Don't be so stubborn and hardheaded!"

"What's in the bag?"

"Close your eyes and you'll find out!" She closed her eyes. "Don't peek!"

"I won't!"

I pulled the pendant out and when the women saw it, they gasped collectively.

"My God, it's beautiful!"

"It's gorgeous!"

"My man doesn't buy me stuff like that!"

"What?" Diana asked. She was bubbling with emotions and ready to open her eyes. "What is it?"

"Don't open yet." I said. I stood holding it up in front of her. "Now, open your eyes."

Her breath left her when she saw it.

"Oh my God! Baby! It's beautiful! Oh my God!"

She took it into her hands as if it were so fragile that the slightest movement would send it shattering into 1000 pieces. Delicately she held it and admired it.

"Let me put it on you." I said. She pulled her hair out of the way and I draped the chain around her neck from the back and clasped it together. I kissed her neck just above her right shoulder, one of her special places, and she shuddered.

" Now, what's this about the goodies?"

"Baby, you can have all the goodies you want!" She turned and kissed me.

"That's what I thought!" I said proudly. "But Diana, I've got other things planned first."

"What! Baby, what?" She jumped with excitement. It was good to see her happy again. The thing with Carl had her just about ready to go south again.

"Well, first I'm taking you out to dinner and then we're going to do whatever you want. Dancing, movies, club, whatever you want to do!"

"That sounds good." She reached for me and sensuously draped her arms around my neck. "Where are you taking me?"

"Bubbles and Sherman's!"

"Bubbles and Sherman's? No baby, that's too expensive. You don't have to do that."

"Girl!" One of her friends spoke up. "You'd better go. This man is up to something and I think I know what it is!"

"You don't know anything. What do you know?" I looked at her and it was obvious that she knew something. Her expression told it all.

"Oh, I know!" She waited until Diana was looking away from her and then she held up her left hand and wiggled her ring finger. She knew. I smiled.

"What's up baby? Tell me." Diana begged me.

"Not yet. Trust me, okay?"

She looked at her friends but thankfully, they didn't reveal my secret. They also didn't want to spoil it for her.

Diana had never been taken out to dinner at Bubbles and Sherman's. It was a very exclusive place for dinner meals. Dress attire was suit and tie with reservations required. The ambience was perfect for romance. She had worked there so she knew the place well, but only from the perspective of an employee. That night, my plan was that she would see it from a different perspective. She would be the one served, not the one serving.

By the time the limo arrived at 6:45 PM, she had appropriated a beautiful V-cut Champaign evening gown from the store and had it fitting every curve of her body as if she had been melted and poured into it. The pendant sparkled when she moved. It was almost as beautiful as she was. Her purse and shoes matched fabulously. And her hair, what can I say other than it was the crowning glory of the most beautiful woman that I had ever seen! She had it draped across her right shoulder and breast. She had lost all of her baby weight and regained her hourglass figure and she looked incredible. My breath left me when I saw her step out of the shadows of the doorway and into the night. She was beautiful beyond belief and I took her hand and walked her to the limo.

"You didn't tell me that you hired a limo."

"There's a lot that I didn't tell you!"

I helped her into the limo and then entered. There were people staring as if they had never seen a limo in the neighborhood before. I smiled as we passed them.

"Baby, this is costing you a fortune." She cozied up to me and I breathed in her aroma along with her White Diamonds perfume. I loved her fragrance as well as the fragrance of the White Diamonds on her. It complimented her so well. I told her that Elizabeth made it with her in mind!

"Don't worry about it. I can afford it and you're worth every penny!" I drew her close and kissed her.

At the restaurant we were shown to our booth which was close to the front window and away from the bar. Diana and I had just sat down when she heard a woman's voice.

"Hello Diana!"

Diana jumped up immediately and hugged the woman.

"Marva!" She shouted. "It's so good to see you!" They hugged and grinned at each other.

"You finally made it!" Marva said. I stood up.

"Marva, this is Donn, the love of my life! Donn, this is Marva. She's the one that took me home that day,… remember?"

"It's a pleasure to meet you Marva." I said with all sincerity.

"And you, Donn."

They turned to each other and began to chit-chat like two long lost friends. I felt strange standing there, but etiquette said I dare not sit down, so I stood listening in on their conversation. After a minute or two, I excused myself and went to the restroom.

Nervousness began to creep up on me as I gave thought to what I was about to do. I reached into my jacket pocket as I stood in front of the mirror and retrieved the ring. I gave thought to unwrapping the box, but then I decided against it. The wrapping was beautiful and the bow was perfectly tied, but the box itself was awesome and stunning in purple and black with a white diamond shape in the middle of the top. The jeweler's name was engraved in the center of the diamond.

I looked at myself in the mirror and checked my suit, tie, shoes, and hair. After telling myself that everything was in order, I took a deep breath and returned to the table.

Diana was seated and looking better than anyone and everyone there. There were several older couples dressed to the "T" and it was obvious to me that money just dripped from their fingers. They had the look of superiority, elegance and refinement that, just for a moment, had me feeling out of place. But that quickly passed when their smiles of approval warmed the atmosphere and dispelled my feelings of inferiority.

Most of the people there were white, many of them were blond. I wondered if it would have any effect on Diana's mood. There were two other black couples there. They seemed to be the ones that gave me the cold shoulder, but I smiled and gave them a nod of the head anyway. Nothing or no one was going to spoil this night for us!

"Sir!" Marva said. "Would you prefer your champagne now, or later?"

"Now please. Thank you."

Marvel was the one that I spoke to on the phone.

"Champaign?" Diana became irritated. "Baby, you know that I can't drink champagne!"

"It's non-alcoholic, sweetheart."

"What are you up to Donn? You're up to something. I can feel it. What is it?"

"Yes, I'm up to something. Just be patient and you'll find out in good time."

"How can I be patient? I'm so excited that I'm about to pee on myself! I've always wanted to come here and eat. I've dreamed about this night! Marva and I used to fantasize about it and talk about it all of the time. Now I'm here and I don't know how to act!" She began to fidget.

"You're doing fine. Just stop fidgeting. Look around you,… you're the most beautiful woman in here. All of the women wish that they were you, and all of the men wish that they were me because of you! Just look around! Look at their faces!"

She looked, and discovered that just as I had said, all eyes were on her. She quickly looked back to me.

"Now I'm really nervous. They are looking at me."

"Don't pee on yourself, not yet!"

Marva returned with one waiter carrying the Champaign buried to the neck in ice in a stainless steel ice bucket and two more waiters carrying the red velvet chair. They set the chair in the middle of the floor where it could be seen from every vantage point in the restaurant.

I was so nervous that my hands began to sweat and my heart was racing faster than Dale Earnhardt Junior! Diana was astonished.

Marva took her hand and said, "Come with me."

Meanwhile, the fake Champaign was poured into two chilled glasses.

"What's going on?" Diana asked.

"Shut up girl! Just go with the flow! Your dream is about to come true!" Marva took her by the arm.

"You mean? … No! … baby?"

She looked at me as Marva escorted her to the red velvet chair. She had witnessed the ritual many times. She had seen many women sit in the chair as their man proposed marriage to them. She had cried tears of joy for them and wished that one day it would happen to her just that way. Now, it was about to happen! She sat in the chair nervously waiting for me to say the words.

A red velvet pillow was placed at her feet and with one knee I knelt on it. The unwrapped box was still in my hand. Everyone in the place paid attention to what was going on in the middle of the room. Their expression paid homage to the ritual taking place. Even the uppity Negroes were looking on with admiration.

Diana was so nervous that she was shaking. Tears were already forming in the corners of her eyes and I had yet to speak one word. Her hands were wrenching together in her lap. I took my free hand and placed it over hers.

"Diana, you are the most incredible woman that I have ever known. You're the one who has stolen my heart and my thoughts. You have unlocked the door to my soul. You are that part of me that's been missing, the part that I need to make me whole. You have changed the course of my life. I had no real direction before you came and now because of you, I know exactly where I'm going and I'm pretty sure how to get there.

When I first saw you at the Onala club, I couldn't believe how beautiful you were and when you sat beside me in my van, I almost peed myself because I was so excited!"

She giggled.

"I love you, Diana! I believed I always have from that very first day. We have been through hell at times with each other. So many times, I wanted to, and tried to, give up on you, but you always found your way back inside of my head and my heart. I don't ever want to live in this life without you by my side."

I placed the box in her lap and released her hands. She tried to speak but nothing came out but a gasp.

"Open it!" I said and I waited while she fumbles with the wrapping paper until the box was visible.

I could hear the people murmuring and whispering to each other. Everyone that had been eating stopped and gave us their undivided attention. Marva was standing to the side dabbing at her eyes with a large table napkin. The waiter standing next to her holding onto two glasses of near Champaign, was smiling. I took the box from her trembling hands and opened it revealing the ring. Heads leaned forward from all across the dining room to get a better view.

Diana saw the ring and came close to fainting. She started fanning herself with her hands. Her feet and legs were jumping uncontrollably.

"Diana." I continued. "So far, my life with you has been an adventure that I wouldn't trade for all of the gold in Fort Knox and I look forward to spending the rest of my life with you. You are already the mother of my son, but now I want you to be my wife. Diana, will you marry me?"

There was silence of a second or two before she spoke, but to me it seemed much longer.

"Yes!" That was all that she said, and it was more than enough.

I placed the ring on her finger while she cried. Everyone broke the silence with cheers and the clapping of their hands. The waiter brought us two glasses and everyone in the place stood with us and with a salute, we drank together.

Diana couldn't stop crying. She kept looking at the ring in disbelief and then she cried some more. I didn't mind, she was happy and it was just her way of expressing it. After a while, and after all of the women in the place congratulated her and the men did the same to me, the place returned to normal. Diana became as close to normal as possible considering she had just become engaged to be married and the center of attention in the place where she once was an obscure employee.

"I love you, Donn!" She kept saying as we hugged.

"I love you too, Diana!"

"So, this is what you had planned?" The tears continued to well up her eyes.

"Yes! Aren't you glad?"

"Baby, you've made me the happiest woman alive. I can't tell you how much this means to me. I love you! (Kiss kiss) I love you! (Kiss kiss) I love you!"

"Diana?"

"Yes baby?"

"You can pee now!"

"I already did!"

We didn't go dancing, clubbing or anywhere after we ate our prime rib dinners. Instead, we went straight to mom's place. People noticed the limousine when we pulled up in the darkness but most of them didn't recognize us as we went dashing into the building.

Mom was so overcome with joy that she had to sit down and catch her breath.

Diana told her everything and gave her the blow-by-blow description of all that had happened. Mom sat smiling, and looked at me with approving eyes. I was sitting beside her on the sofa as Diana knelt before her talking a mile a minute while her diamond ring lit up as the room each time she moved her hand.

Mom continued to smile and occasionally she patted me on the knee. My mother used to do the same thing when she was proud of me.

"So, what are you two going to do for the rest of the evening?" She asked.

"We're going to take you for a ride in our limo!" Diana exclaimed. It was the exact thought going on in my head.

"It's been a while since I've been in a limousine. The last time, if I remember correctly, was at Albert's funeral. Albert was my husband. He was a good man, and everyone loved him but," She took a deep breath of sadness, "he died too young!"

"Well, tonight we're going to ride in a limousine, but no funerals!" I said.

"Well, what are we waiting for?" Mom struggled to get up from the sofa. "Let's go!"

Diana helped her get ready and I scooped up my bouncing baby boy and off we went.

Donnte' and I were really just along for the ride. Mom and Diana were chatting and planning and ignoring us, so I just sat back and enjoyed the ride while I play with my son.

August Twentieth: Saturday.

Everyone now knew about the impending wedding. Her friends from AA and our mutual friends from NA all knew. Some were shocked and others saw it coming. Friends from her support group at the hospital stopped by regularly. Those that didn't know me wanted to see who I was. I'm sure some thought that I was crazy, and others didn't know what to think. Once their curiosity was satisfied, some returned no more while others made the store their second home. They were Diana's new-found friends and they wanted to share in the joy and euphoria with her.

Around 6:30, the store was closed, and the door was locked but several of her friends stayed with her. They were laughing and talking and having fun. There was plenty of girl talk going on which made me feel unwanted, like an outsider. I decided to put down the work that I was doing and retire upstairs for a while. I unlocked the side door that led to the hallway and stepped through. When my foot hit the first step, I felt two hands grabbed both of my rear cheeks. Thinking that it was Diana, I turned with a huge grin to find out that it wasn't Diana at all, but it was one of her so-called friends, Carolyn! My grin faded immediately.

Carolyn was as fine as Japanese silk. She was small, petite and beautiful. She had hair almost down to her waist and possessed smooth silky skin the color of heavily creamed coffee. She was a mere 5 feet tall and she was known for having an insatiable sexual appetite that caused her to cross the line with several of her former friends. If I had met her before Diana, I would have been all over her like white on rice!

"I want to give you some pussy before you get tied down!" She said as she poked her breasts out in my direction.

"I'm already tied down! What the hell is wrong with you coming on to me like that? You don't have any respect for yourself, me and especially not for Diana! If she found out what you just said, she'd probably kill you! If you ever do that again, I'll tell her! Now get the hell away from me!" I spoke angrily and she knew that what I said, I'd do.

I left her standing with her mouth agape and I went upstairs. She never did anything like that again and I never said anything to Diana about it, but it placed an evil thought in my mind that I had to fight each time that I saw her.

Carl hadn't bothered us at all up to that time and he was all but forgotten. I kept my eye out for him at meetings, but I was careful to keep my thoughts about him to myself. I didn't want to spoil Diana's happiness. I didn't see him at any meetings I attended, and I hoped he wouldn't show up at my home group that evening. Diana decided to go with me because, she wanted to show off her ring.

At the meeting everything was fine. Those who hadn't heard that we were engaged, knew after the meeting was over. She made sure of it! But, there was no Carl, and no incident. No one had even seen Carl since the last time and everyone just assumed that he was still drinking and getting high.

CHAPTER 15

The Fight

It was about 4 AM and Diana and I were in bed asleep with Donnte' asleep in his crib beside us. The phone rang and woke me up. The first thing that I thought was that someone had died. I was apprehensive about answering it until it rang again. I looked over to Diana and she stirred but she didn't wake up. I answered the phone before the third ring.

"Hello?"

"Donn?"

"Yes?"

"It's mom!"

I jumped up, praying that she was okay.

"Are you all right? Is everything okay?"

"I'm okay, but I just couldn't sleep."

"Why? What's going on?"

"I don't know. I just felt the need to call you!"

"Do you want me to come over?"

"No. It's okay. How is Diana? Is she sleeping?"

"Yes ma'am. Like a rock!"

"Tee-hee, tee-hee! That's good. Well, I'll be fine. Just forget that I called. Kiss my grandson for me, okay?"

"I will."

"Goodnight!"

"Goodnight!"

I hung up but I couldn't get back to sleep. The call disturbed me, and I kept thinking that something was about to happen. I was worried about mom.

"What's wrong baby?" Diana was now awake.

"Nothing sweetheart. Go back to sleep."

"Something is bothering you. I can feel it. Sweetheart, tell me! What's wrong?"

"I'm worried about mom. She just called and she said everything is fine, but she said that she couldn't sleep."

Diana jumped up. Anguish covered her face.

"Let me call her. You've got me worried now."

"That's why I didn't want to say anything."

She picked up the phone.

"What's wrong?" I asked.

"There's no dial tone!" She clicked the receiver button, but nothing happened. "The phone's not working!"

I took it from her hand and tried it, but nothing was happening.

"That's strange. I just got off the phone with mom. I wonder if the connection is bad."

I checked the connection, and it was fine. There was no reason for the phone not to work.

"Where's your cell phone?" I asked her.

"I left it at mom's house."

"I left mine in the van. I'll go get it."

I dressed and headed for the steps. Halfway down, I heard a noise in the back of the store. I stopped and listened. I heard it again. I couldn't tell what it was from where I stood but it was not something that was normal at four in the morning. It reached my ears again. The sound was like the crackling of fire from a distance, but I couldn't be sure. Then I heard the crash of glass. It was muffled but it was definitely the sound of breaking glass. Someone was breaking in! The burglar alarm didn't go off which puzzled me.

"Diana!" I tried to keep as quiet as I possibly could. "Get up! Someone's breaking in!"

She didn't say anything, but I heard her moving around so I knew that she had heard me and was up and alert.

I proceeded down and into the store. I didn't turn the light on because I wanted to catch them in the act. I moved behind the counter and reached for my pistol. It wasn't there!

"Damn!" I whispered.

Diana had taken it upstairs the other night and had forgotten to bring it back. I grabbed a short length of pipe that I kept as a backup weapon and started for the rear of the store. When I got back there, I could see that back wall of the building was on fire. The fire was on the outside of the building, but the heat had broken the rear window and the flames were licking their way through. I ran to the light switch. Click! Nothing! Click! Again nothing! My lights along with my phone had been disabled. It had to be Carl! He had finally come! I ran back to the stairs and yelled out to Diana.

"DIANA! GET DONNTE' AND GET OUT! THE BUILDING IS ON FIRE!"

"Okay!" She yelled back.

I ran to the back again feeling that I had to find a way to put the fire out before it destroyed everything that I had worked so hard to establish, but I had to go outside to do it and there was no way that I was going to leave my son and future wife inside. To hell with the building! Everything was insured!

When I got to the front and made my way to the stairs, I noticed that the hallway door was open. I knew that Diana didn't go out because I didn't hear her come down the stairs. There were splinters on the floor just inside the door and it made me realize that the door had been broken in! Carl was inside! I panicked! I stopped thinking clearly and rushed to the stairs thinking that Carl was upstairs with Diana and Donnte'. I started up the stairs blindly and that's when he hit me in the back of the head. He had been hiding under the stairs waiting for me to come out.

I fell backwards down the stairs and hit my head again. I was dazed but still conscious. My eyes were out of focus and my head was spinning like a top.

"Now, I'm gonna kill you, you punk bitch! Then I'm gonna kill that little bastard baby of yours!"

He had a piece of wood in his hand that looked like the shank from a claw hammer. He dropped it and picked up the pipe that flew out of my hand when I tumbled down the steps. He came over to me and I attempted to get up. He reared back to swing and as he came down with the pipe, I rolled out of the way causing it to strike the wooden floorboards. I was able to recover before he had a chance to strike again, and I leaped to my feet.

My eyes were focusing and the spinning in my head was slowing, and even though I wasn't quite ready for a confrontation, I wanted him to believe that I was 100%.

"Carl, you should have left it alone! You're right about somebody dying tonight, but it's going to be you, not me!"

"You punk ass bitch! I got the pipe! You ain't got nothin', not even a prayer!" He was grinning when he said it.

"You're right. You've got the pipe, but you still ain't nothing but a scared punk! You had a knife the last time, remember?"

I grew tired of waiting. My building was on fire and my son and Diana were still upstairs. I didn't have time to play around with him. I rushed him and grabbed him around his neck. He was shocked at the speed in which I moved. He dropped the pipe as I pushed him against the wall and tightened my grip around his neck. His eyes were wide with fright and his mouth opened trying desperately to breathe but I refused to let go until I knew that he was dead! He struggled and tried to get free, but I was just too strong for him. His eyes bulged and he knew that he was about to die. He tried to pry my fingers from his neck, but it didn't work. I saw panic in his eyes and all across his face. He began to weaken, and I applied more pressure. His eyes were begging for me to let go. His strength was fading fast. I smiled as he struggled.

"You're about to die, Carl! How does it feel? Are you scared? Can you see the demons from hell coming to get you? Can you?" I taunted him and I took immense pleasure in it! He had crossed the line when he threatened my family.

Suddenly I felt a sharp pain in my chest. At first, I didn't know what was going on but after a few seconds, I realized that he had stabbed me! My strength began to fade as I found it extremely hard to breathe. My hands stayed around his neck, but I couldn't maintain the pressure to finish the job. Finally, my strength subsided, and I was forced to let go.

We dropped to the floor together. His knife was still in my chest, and I tried to reach for it, but I didn't have the strength to pull it out. The blood began to flow, and I became weaker and weaker. I saw him struggling to get up. He was coughing and his feet weren't holding him, but he still struggled. I reached for him to hold him down because I knew that once he got up, it would be all over for me. My arms would not do what I willed them to do. They barely moved at all. I thought about my family as I watched him struggle to his feet. I was about to die a failure. A failure because I wasn't able to save my family! They would be at his mercy.

Carl staggered to his feet and then he stood over me as I lay helpless on my back. I was unable to get up or even move! I was just barely breathing. He began to grin at me, but that grin faded quickly and in the next second there was blood squirting from his throat and sounds that made no sense came from his mouth. Shock and surprise covered his face as he attempted to stop the blood flow from his neck. I didn't know what had happened until he dropped to his knees and fell sideways to the floor just seconds from death.

Diana stood behind him holding Donnte' tightly under her left arm while in her right hand she held a bloody butcher knife! She had slit his throat!

She dropped the knife. It stuck into the floor. With Donnte' still under her arm, she reached down and grabbed hold of the knife in my chest.

"Baby, don't move! It's going to hurt but I I've got to take it out!"

I nodded. Before I could finish, she snatched it out! The pain was excruciating! It hurt like hell! My head was spinning, and my eyes went completely out of focus. I wanted to scream but I couldn't. I must've blacked out for second or two because the next thing I knew she was dragging me out of the burning building with one hand and clutching our son with the other.

Out on the sidewalk I laid face up bleeding from my chest. There was so much blood that you couldn't tell where the knife wound was. I knew only because of the pain. It was getting harder and harder for me to breathe so I assumed that he had punctured a lung. I felt fluid in my throat, and I fought the gag reflex.

Diana knelt over me and took one of Donnte's diapers and pressed it against my chest. I flinched. She jumped.

"Baby, I know it hurts but I've got to try to control the bleeding until the paramedics get here. Don't worry baby, the ambulance is on its way. I can hear it!"

I nodded and prayed that if I had to die that it would come quickly. I tried to sit up. I wanted to see Donnte'! I didn't believe that I was going to make it and I wanted to see his tiny face one more time. I struggled but I couldn't move. The pain increased in my chest as well as the fluid in my throat. I felt as if I were choking.

"Relax. You've got to relax and save your strength until the paramedics get here. If you keep struggling, you're going to die, and you can't die on me. You promised to marry me, didn't you?"

I nodded slightly.

"Did you mean it?"

I nodded again.

"You still mean it?"

Again, I nodded.

"You love me?"

I nodded twice.

"Look at this face!" She held Donnte' up to where I could see him. "He needs you. I need you, so relax!"

Donnte' was wide awake and looking at me with great big, soft brown baby eyes. He seemed to be agreeing with what his mother was saying. He smiled at me.

I heard the people who had gathered around me and the police who were trying to move them back. I heard the ambulance as it pulled up, but I only saw the faces of two people that I loved most in the world, and then everything went dark.

CHAPTER 16

She's Got My Back!

"He's coming around!" It was a male voice that I didn't recognize.

"Baby, you can you hear me?" That was definitely Diana.

"Don't try to talk! Just blink your eyes!" Another unrecognizable voice. Female this time.

"Dr., he's going to be all right, isn't he?" Diana again.

I heard voices that seem to be off in the distance but at the same time seemed to be just in my head. I opened my eyes to see what was going on. I had no idea where I was or what was happening around me.

I felt something in my throat. It made me want to gag. I tried to raise my right arm to remove whatever it was that was putting pressure on my arm and preventing me from lifting it.

"Dr., can he hear us?"

"Is he conscious?"

"Please. Everybody give the doctor a chance."

My mind began to function properly again, and I realized that I must be in the hospital. I remembered the knife that Diana had removed from my chest. I remembered the pain, but the pain was no longer there. My eyes focused and I saw the doctor standing over me and the I-V bottles on metal stands with their cords flowing like tentacles towards my body. Then I saw her! Her eyes were swollen and red. She had been crying a lot and her hair looked like it hadn't been combed in days, but she still was the most beautiful sight imaginable!

A smile broke across her face and a tear rolled down her cheek and she blew me a kiss. I was alive and I realized why. She had come to my rescue and killed Carl without hesitation. If not for her, I would most certainly be dead! The best that I could do was wink. It was enough. She began to cry but they were tears of thanksgiving and joy.

I stayed in the hospital for a week before I was released. The knife had punctured my left lung, but it completely missed my heart. It also had cut a blood vessel but Diana's quick thinking and calm behavior along with the expertise of the paramedics and skill of the surgeon kept me alive. Each day Diana, Dante, Mom, Darla and of all people Bill, came to see me. The first time I saw Bill coming into my room I became upset, but he quickly reassured me by explaining his intentions.

The first day of consciousness was spent learning what had happened while I was out cold. I had lost an entire day. The doctors kept me sedated after the operation and it was Tuesday night when I entered the hospital and Thursday morning when I awakened.

Diana held little Donnte' up so that I could see him.

"He told me to tell you that he loves you." She said. "And that you have to teach him how to fish and play basketball, baseball, football and all kind of guy stuff so you better hurry up and get well!

I lay unable to speak, barely able to move my head, watching those that really cared about me fuss over me and try their best to make me comfortable. Mom was there. Even in her poor state of health she had come and before she left, she put her hand on me and prayed.

"God has got his hand on you, son. You're special. Don't you ever forget that!" She said. "Everything will work out fine, but you have to take it easy and get well, okay?"

I smiled. She patted my hand and left. Diana stayed about a half hour after everyone else departed. She needed privacy to tell me what she had to say. She sat beside the bed and began to speak.

"Donn, what I've got to tell you may be difficult for you to handle right now, but I have to say it now because I may not be here later."

My eyes grew big with concerned and she understood why.

"Please Donn, just listen and try not to get upset because Mom said that it will all work out and I believe her. She's always right! Just listen, okay? If you understand me just blink your eyes."

I blinked.

"Once for yes, twice for no!"

I blinked once.

"Okay. First, do you remember what happened?"

One blink.

"Good. Now let me fill you in. You know that I killed Carl. He died right here in the hallway. I couldn't let him kill you. I was upstairs when I heard you two fighting. I had just grabbed Donnte' and a few things and I started for the steps. I saw him pull out the knife and stab you. I thought he had stabbed you in the heart and I really got scared. I had only come down about three steps, so I went back up and took a butcher knife out of the kitchen drawer and eased down the steps again. I thought that he would see me, but he had fallen to the floor right along with you. I was determined to end it right then and there. I thought about the time I cut him up and I should've killed him then, but I didn't! I wasn't going to make the same mistake twice. He got up and never saw me standing there and I just slit his throat!"

She paused for a minute but not to cry. There was no remorse in her. She just needed to collect her thoughts.

"I was arrested right after they took you to the hospital. They thought that you had killed Carl, but I told them that I did."

I wanted to ask her why? It would have been so much simpler if they had thought that I had killed him. But I still couldn't speak so I just listened.

"At first they thought that you and I were the ones that broke into the house and that Carl was you, so they sent the cops in the hospital to guard you but somehow they got it straightened out. They charged me with criminal homicide and second-degree murder. Bill said, oh, by the way, he's my lawyer. He said that I'll be exonerated once we get to court because I was defending my home and Carl had broken in. The District Attorney is trying to say that it was your house and not mine, so I had no right to defend it with lethal force unless he came after me."

She tried to be brave, but I could tell that she was worried about it, and she really needed my arms around her. She needed physical comfort from me, but I was unable to give it, so she summoned up her own strength.

"The DA doesn't want me out. He said I'm a menace to society because of my mental condition and that I had a history of violence. He called me a psychopath! Imagine that! The only person I ever cut was Carl, but he calls that history of violence. Anyway, Bill is a really good lawyer and because of him I am out on bail now when they were talking about no bail at all.

I have a hearing scheduled next Wednesday. The Dr. said that if you continue to recover as well is you have been then he will release you on Monday or Tuesday. I really hope so because I really need you to be there with me.

"Carl set fire to the back of the building and it's burned up pretty bad on the outside. There's damage to the stock room and the downstairs bathroom was completely destroyed. There is smoke and water damage all over downstairs and upstairs too. It's a mess! Donnte' and I are staying at mom's but only until you get out. We can't stay in our place."

As she talked, I thought about the insurance. It would cover everything, and it also would pay for a place to stay until repairs were complete. I didn't worry about that, but my concern was on the day in court that she faced. Lawyers always said that there was nothing to worry about, that was their job. That's just the way they operate. Who wants an attorney who says that there is nothing that they can do?

After she left, I laid thinking of all that had happened. I mentally kicked myself because I hadn't been thinking clearly that night and the result was that I lay in a hospital bed just barely alive, and she had to step up and handle the business that I should have taken care of. Because of that, she now faced a possible long-term prison sentence. I was so intent on killing Carl that I didn't think that he possibly could have had a weapon hidden on himself. If it had been a gun or if he had the strength to pull the knife out of my chest, I would be dead. Then what would become of Diana and Donnte'? It wasn't a good feeling that came over me. It wasn't life that I wanted, not anymore, not at that time!

Later, a nurse came in to check on me and found me staring off into the blue.

"Are you all right, sir?"

I looked at her and felt ashamed.

"Are you in pain?" She adjusted the flow of the drip bag that hung just to my left shoulder. She looked at the machines behind me and made notations on my chart. Her questions were not for me to answer, for she knew that I couldn't with the tube down my throat.

"The doctors will be in shortly. They will be removing the tube from your throat. You're doing much better than anyone had imagined. Did you know that people have been praying for you? Do you believe in God? It's because of him that you are still alive, you know. I've seen people come in with injuries like yours and most die on the operating table, but you? Well, let me just say that you're a special case!"

She fumbled with another piece of equipment.

"Are you right-handed, or left-handed?"

I turned my head slightly to the right.

"Right-handed! Okay. I'm going to release your right hand."

She unstrapped my right wrist. My arm seemed to rise all by itself from the bed. I flexed my fingers, and I was happy to see that they all worked. She put a round object into my hand and referred to the drip bag to which it was connected.

"This is a solution of morphine. I caution you to use it only when you cannot stand the pain. It's on a timer so you can't get more than your prescribed dosage." She took my thumb and placed it on the button. "Press this once and it will work, if you try to press it more than that, it will not. Do you understand? Blink your eyes if you do."

I blinked.

"Good. Try not to think about your dilemma. There are people all around you that care. Doctors, nurses,..." She curtsied. "Friends and family. You're in good hands. Kind of like Allstate, you know? So just relax, take it easy on the button and thank God that you're still alive!"

She smiled a warm and friendly and then she left, leaving me alone with my thoughts. My thoughts turned to the button in my hand. Although I had begun to feel the pain long before she entered her room, when she mentioned the word morphine, the pain seemed to intensify. It was just psychological. The fact that I had been addicted to narcotics and my body still remembered what wonderful things they did, set off the unconscious thought that I could retrieve that feeling with the morphine. Addiction was still alive and well within me although I had not used drugs in many years. My thumb tensed on the button, but I fought against it. I didn't really need the morphine because it was just psychological. Not physical, so I dropped the ball and endured the pain.

On Saturday before Diana came with Donnte' and mom, Bill and Darla came to see me. It was a surprise to see them together, but I had learned earlier through Diana that they had started dating. They hit it off immediately. But I was also curious to know why they had come without Diana.

The Dr. had removed the tubes and most of the monitoring devices from me, so I was able to sit, talk and occasionally walk around. The morphine had been replaced with pills that were just enough to take the edge off of the pain without removing it completely. He said I was recovering far better than he had thought and far ahead of schedule. Faster than anyone he had ever seen.

"Hey Donn!" Bill said as he held the door for Darla.

A real gentleman I thought, but what are they doing here so early?

"Hey baby!" Darla rushed to me as I struggled to sit up. "Let me help you!"

"I'm not an invalid!" I said.

"Oh, so you can talk now! I'm still going to help you, if you don't like it, sue me!"

I gave in with a smile. She finished fluffing my pillow behind my back and then she sat down. Bill stood the entire time that she fussed over me and only sat after she did.

"I guess you're wondering why we're here." Bill offered. "Well, it's simple. Diana is in a lot of trouble. I will do all that I can to get her out of it, but it doesn't look good."

He paused and I wished I had that morphine back so I could press the damn button and drift away from what I was hearing.

"The DA wants to pursue second-degree murder. Personally, I have every confidence that we will overcome that, but it's the other charges that concerns me. We're pressing for a dismissal of all charges and that is where our problem lies.

"Donn, I need to hear from you exactly what happened that night. Diana has told me her version, but I'm sure that when this goes to court that the DA will subpoena you to testify. I need to know what I'm up against. Do you remember anything that happened?"

"Yes, I remember it all!"

How could I forget? I had failed in my duties as a man. I would never forget it!

"Well, tell me from the beginning. Tell me everything that you remember. Details are important, very important! If you remember something later, no matter how small or insignificant it seems, tell me. Okay?"

I nodded. He placed a small tape recorder on the serving table and swung a close to me.

"Ready?"

I nodded again. He turned it on, and gave some preliminary information, i: e., date, time, my name, etc., and then I began.

When it ended, he asked me several questions to clarify things that I had said. He was very meticulous and very business minded. His focus was totally on the information that I gave. He seemed very competent and sure, just as he did the day we had our last conversation. I answered his questions as straightforward and as honest as I could. I could see that he had become even more concerned, and I knew why. What I had seen, wasn't much, but it was enough to sway the jurors away from a not guilty verdict to a verdict of manslaughter. He and I both knew that I would be subpoenaed to testify against Diana. It would be disastrous for her.

Bill and Darla left about 45 minutes after they came, and both of their faces were drawn with concern. They were not the happy jovial ones that they wore coming through the door.

I thought the situation over. If I left town and ducked the subpoena, then I would look like a coward. The trial might be postponed for months, maybe years. I couldn't stay away that long. If I received the subpoena and refused to show up or refuse to testify, then I would be held in contempt of court and jailed. I could have my business license revoked and then where would I be? There had to be another way out. There must be another option. Even if I chose one of those, Diana still could be convicted without my testimony. That wasn't good enough.

About an hour after they left, Diana came in carrying Donnte' with mom at her side. Their faces lightened the room as it brightened my mood. I looked into Diana's face and saw what I hadn't seen there before. It was strength, courage, determination, and purpose. They were qualities that she possessed but they didn't come together the way that I saw her that day. Strength and determination I saw the day that she tore Darren's face apart in a fit of anger. Singleness of purpose was there when she chopped off Carl's manhood, but that was in anger. There was no anger in her now, just happiness and love for our son and her man and her new mother. She had become a complete woman. No longer struggling with alcoholism, drug addiction, and the downside of mental illness. She walked through the door proud of whom she had become and not ashamed of what she had gone through to get there. She was ready to face life on life's terms without cowering and trembling like a scared child. She was all woman, holding her family together in a time of crisis. When I was down, she stood up. When I was weak, she became strong. I always wanted a woman who had my back and there was no doubt that she was that woman. She proved it in the hallway, and she was proving it now.

Seeing her, I realize what I had to do to get her off of the judicial hook. It was like a light had come on in my head and I saw clearly what has eluded me.

I left the hospital on Monday around 9 AM. Mom wasn't feeling well so she didn't come. She wanted to come, Diana said, but she already had more excitement than she needed. Bill didn't show up either. He was busy working on Diana's case. Darla and Diana came along with the cutest little face imaginable, Donnte'! Although I could walk, and my strength was slowly coming back they made me sit in a wheelchair to be discharged. Donnte' sat in my lap along with my paperwork and prescriptions.

We went straight to mom's house from the hospital. We passed by my store and my heart sank deep into my gut as I looked at the window that's used to stay lit with colorful signs and used to be adorned with furniture, clothing, and assorted items, but now the windows were boarded up. There were police barricades and yellow crime scene tape across the entire front of the building. I looked away.

Diana hugged me and said, "It will all work out. Just have faith."

I looked at her curiously. She normally didn't talk like that. I'm sure that mom was influencing her. Her confidence and positiveness and courage had grown tremendously since being in mom's presence.

"Faith, huh? I'll work on it." I said dryly. I knew that it took faith to do anything that was difficult but at that moment I just wanted my store back. I just wanted things to be the way that they were before Carl came to die.

"Baby, don't get depressed. It only makes things worse. Believe me, I know!" She spoke from experience. I had to accept what she said.

Of course, she was right.

"Yeah, you're right. Besides the insurance will handle everything." I leaned over and kissed her. "You're 'all that'!" I said.

"I know!" She kissed back. "I'm all that you will ever need."

Up in mom's place, after all the hugging and kissing and mom telling me how good I looked, we sat down to some serious talk about the future.

"What about the store?" Darla asked. "Are you planning to reopen?"

"I don't know. Maybe, if I can get someone else to run it."

"What does that mean?" Diana cut in.

"What it means is that you're going to be with me. We're not going to be around here. You're not going to jail and nobody's taking you away from me! I've got a foolproof plan that will put an end to all of our courtroom troubles. Everybody listen up because I'm going to need a little help from everyone."

We leaned close to each other as if there were spies around and we had to whisper so not to be heard.

"Darla, what you're about to hear, you have to keep to yourself. You can't tell Bill..."

"Why? Why can't I tell him? He's your lawyer!" She questioned.

"It's because he is our attorney that he can't know anything about this until the proper time."

"This isn't anything illegal, is it?"

"No. Nothing like that, but it might be considered unethical if he knew beforehand. Believe me, it's okay and you will understand why when you hear what I have planned."

I told them the plan. Everyone's eyes lit up and smiles appeared across their faces. All agreed that it wasn't illegal, and they agreed that Bill should not know until afterwards and that it would most definitely work! Darla was eager to do what I had asked of her.

"Donn, are you sure they'll give me all of this?" She asked.

"I'm sure. All I have to do is call them. It's a short notice but even if you don't get it all, it will be fine. Don't worry." I assured her.

"What about me?" Mom asked. "What do I get to do?"

"You're coming with us. There has to be a witness!"

"Me? I haven't flown on a jet in a long, long time."

"Well, it's about time you did."

I made all of the necessary phone calls while mom and Diana packed. Darla wrote down all of the information for the things that she needed to handle and before long we were in the van headed towards the airport with Darla at the wheel. Two hours later the four of us, mom, Diana, Donnte' and myself were on the jumbo jet heading West.

Wednesday morning, I had a file folder full of papers that I had compiled. Diana, mom, Donnte' and I left mom's house headed to Bill's office downtown. It was time to give him the information that he needed to effectively manage Diana's case. All of the information that I asked Darla to get while we were away, was there in the folder along with several other papers that I had possession of.

We arrived at Bill's office at 9 o'clock as he requested. The hearing was scheduled for 10 o'clock. We entered his private office and sat across the desk from him. He shuffled papers that were in front of him and then he pushed them to the side.

"It's good to see you, Bill." I said.

"And you, Donn. Hello Mrs. Reynolds! How are you feeling today?"

"Just fine and dandy. I am ready for you to work your magic and get this mess over with so that my daughter can stop worrying her pretty little head off!"

He turned to Diana. "How are you feeling Diana?"

"I'm feeling great. This is going to be a beautiful day!" She said it so cheerfully that you wouldn't have thought that she was going in front of the judge in an hour and her whole livelihood was on the line.

Bill wasn't so cheerful.

"I've got to be honest with you; this is going to be a difficult appearance today. I spoke to the DA, and he is dead set against dropping any of the charges, especially the second-degree murder charge. He's really pushing for that, and it looks like he might get it. If he does, he'll likely ask that you be held without bond and that you be remanded back into custody and placed in the county jail until trial. The judge might agree, but I'll fight it all the way." It was obviously he had been racking his brain trying to produce something that he could use to fight with.

"Don't worry Bill. They're not going to get it. In fact, I'm going to walk out of here free, today! It's never going to get to trial!" Diana's confidence was overflowing. Bill looked my way with curiosity.

"Bill," I said. "Stop worrying." I handed him the file. "Just read this."

He took the file, opened it, and began flipping through the pages. With each page, his depression and downtrodden look began to ease and slowly but surely it turned into a smile. Then it turned into a grin that erupted into a hail of laughter!

"Ha ha ha ha! So, this is what you have been up to!"

All three of us nodded at the same time.

"When Darla came home yesterday with all of these papers that she tried to hide from me I knew something was up. Then she refused to talk about it, and she talks about everything. Everything! I asked where you two were and she said, 'I can't tell you!' She was really acting strange. Now I understand why. Ha ha ha ha!"

"We couldn't tell you beforehand, you understand." I was grinning from ear to ear.

"Perfectly! Congratulations! This is the best news I've heard all year!

CHAPTER 17

Courtroom #7

The sign on the wall outside of the highly polished hardwood doors read,

ALEXANDER K. FIAT – COURTROOM # 7.

It was just a hearing and I assumed that it would be held in a local magistrate's office, or at the office of the District Justice, but because of the request of the district attorney, it was being held in courtroom number seven in the Allegheny County Courthouse. I didn't know why but I knew that the DA had introduced a legal maneuver to get Diana before Judge Fiat.

We entered together. Diana, Darla, myself, mom, Bill, and Donnte. Diana took her seat at the defense table while Bill and the rest of us sat directly behind them, behind the railing.

I looked around the courtroom. It was almost filled with people while people were still coming through the door in a constant flow until there was no more seating available. I saw several familiar faces sitting throughout the courtroom. Some were friendly and others were hostile. Bimini, Diana's cousin, was sitting in the first row across from us on the prosecution's side. Sitting beside her was Darren, Mr. broken nose! They looked at me and then Darren smiled a sinister, scowling smile before he looked away. Bimini winked and blew me a kiss. I didn't like the fact that they were sitting opposite us and obviously were there to give testimony against Diana. I had to admit that Bimini did look a lot better than she did the last time that I saw her. Somewhere along the line, she had stopped using drugs. She was able to come out of that slump and I wished her well.

Marva, Carolyn, and one of the waiters from Bubbles and Sherman's were there and sitting behind us. They waved and smiled. I was surprised to see Carolyn and I wasn't sure why she was there but she was sitting on our side so it couldn't be all bad.

Most of the people that were there, I didn't know. Some of the faces I recognized as reporters from the various local news programs. Diana had made the front page of the local newspapers and had her picture flashed across the TV screens. Mom and Darla tried to shield me from it when they came to visit me in the hospital. But Diana told me all about it. She brought me a copy of the Pittsburgh Press. Her picture was plastered across the front page. The caption read:

EX-MAYVIEW MENTAL PATIENT
CASTRATES AND KILLS EX-LOVER.

It angered me when I read it because it painted a grim picture of her.

In the courtroom there were curious onlookers, courtroom groupies, law students and friends and family of those involved. I saw many faces from NA, and AA and a few other women in Diana's mental support group that came to support her.

I turned to face forward again and looked into Diana's radiantly beautiful smiling face. She looked as if she hadn't a care in the world. She blew me a kiss and mouthed the words "I love you!" I returned it before she turned back to face the judge.

"Hear ye! Hear ye! This court will now come to order!" The bailiff shouted. "All rise!"

Silence prevailed and everyone stood as the judge entered the courtroom.

"The court of common pleas in the County of Allegheny, in the Commonwealth of Pennsylvania is now in session. The Hon. Judge Alexander K. Fiat presiding!"

The judge straightened his robe and sat.

"You may be seated!"

Everyone sat quietly. The district attorney approached the bench.

"Your Honor, the case before you on this docket is case number..." He read off a string of numbers. "The Commonwealth of Pennsylvania in the County of Allegheny versus Diana Carver. The charges are listed as follows: murder in the second degree, criminal homicide, voluntary manslaughter, assault with intent to kill, assault with intent to do bodily harm, and the unlawful use of excessive force!"

He then walked straight over to me and dropped a folded court document in my lap. "Mr. Diamond, here is your subpoena. Please don't leave the courtroom. I will be calling you as a witness for the prosecution."

I wasn't surprised. I anticipated the subpoena and was fully prepared for it. I didn't look at it at all. "Thank you." I said.

With a puzzled look, he walked away and proceeded with the hearing that looked more to me like a trial.

They went through the preliminaries with very few objections from either side and then the prosecutor began.

"The prosecution will establish a prima fascia case against Ms. Diana Carver and will show that she did intentionally, willfully and with malice of forethought, murder Mr. Carl Bladen on the night of August 30th. The defense will claim that she acted in self-defense, therefore rendering Miss Carver immune from prosecution, but we will prove that the defendant killed Mr. Bladen with pre-meditation.

"Ms. Carver knew the deceased for several years and had been lovers at one point. In a fit of blind rage, Ms. Carver sliced off Mr. Bladen's penis when she found him in bed with another woman. She attempted to take his life then, but he managed to escape. Ms. Carver made statements at that time vowing to one day 'finish the job'. On the night of August 30th, she followed through with her plan to kill Mr. Bladen. In cold blood, she finished what she had started several years ago! She killed Mr. Bladen! She is guilty of cold-blooded murder!

"This was not a case of self-defense! True, Mr. Bladen had broken into the home where Ms. Carver had been staying the night. That mitigating factor is why the prosecution has not issued a warrant in the first degree! Mr. Bladen had attacked and stabbed Mr. Diamond, who is sitting there." He pointed to me. "And had not turned on Miss Carver, but Ms. Carver seized the opportunity to 'finish the job' and snuck up behind Mr. Bladen slashing his throat with this butcher knife!" He held the knife up so that everyone could see it. The courtroom gasped at the sight of it. "Ms. Carver felt that she could get away with murder!

"We will establish through the truthful testimony of several witnesses, that; A: Ms. Carver is an extremely violent perpetrator; B.: she previously attacked Mr. Bladen with a similar weapon as this;" he showed the knife again. "C; she threatened to kill him; and D: she boldly and brazenly carried out her threat in cold blood!" He sat down.

A hush swept across the room as the words of the Dist. Atty. Found roost in the ears and minds of everyone who heard them.

Bill sat the entire time with his head held low. His eyes were reading something in front of him, but the page never turned. Diana sat beside him and heard all that was said about her. She turned to look at me and I let her know by my expression that everything would be all right. Slowly Bill rose from his seat. He walked to the middle of the room and stood silent for a moment before he spoke. His words were short and to the point.

"Your honor, the law clearly states that in the event of a home invasion when the residents fear for their lives, when an intruder, or intruders, are armed with weapons of violence, that they are well within their rights to use whatever force necessary to repel, subdue, and or stop the intruder. That force includes the use of deadly force. Mr. Bladen invaded the home where Ms. Carver lived with her infant son and Mr. Diamond. This was her residence, her legal residence!

"Ms. Carver feared for her life, the lives of her infant son and the life of the father of her child. It's true that she took the life of Mr. Bladen but there was no malice, no conspiratorial plan, or cold-bloodedness afoot. It was simply an act to save what she held dear. Her home and family!

"Mr. Bladen had already set fire to her home while she and her family slept, and then proceeded to stab Mr. Diamond. There was no doubt in her mind that he would have come after her and her infant son if she hadn't taken action. She was well within her rights as a legal resident of the dwelling to act as she did.

"Your Honor, the defense will show that these charges brought against the defendant, Ms. Carver, are in violation of her rights as a citizen of this country and this great Commonwealth. They are preposterous and they should be vacated immediately. Thank you."

The judge shuffled papers and peered over the top of his horn rim glasses. He then began to speak. "Gentlemen, remember that this is just a hearing to establish a prima fascia case! This is not a trial! Let us act accordingly! Let's not get into theatrics here, just present the facts and let me decide the outcome. Is that clear?"

"Yes, Your Honor!" Bill replied.

"Yes, Your Honor!" Was the D: A.'s response.

"Good! Is the prosecution ready?"

"Yes, Your Honor!"

"Is the defense ready?"

"Yes, we are, Your Honor!"

"Thank you. Then let's proceed. Mr. Prosecutor, please begin."

"Thank you, Your Honor. The prosecution calls Ms. Bimini Carver!" Bimini took the stand and was sworn in. The prosecutor asked her name, address, and age. She replied with the information. With that out of the way, he proceeded.

DA: Mr. Carver, what is your relationship to the defendant, Ms. Diana Carver?"

Bimini: We're cousins. First cousins. Our fathers are brothers.

DA: How long have you known the defendant?

Bimini: All of my life.

DA: Would you say that your relationship with her is good?

Bimini: Well, it used to be, but not anymore.

DA: What happened to change it?

Bimini: She caught me in bed with her man.

DA: Who was that? What is his name?

Bimini: Carl Bladen.

DA: The same Carl Bladen who was murdered...

Defense: Objection! It hasn't been established that a murder has taken place!

Judge: Sustained.

DA: I'll rephrase. Was this the same Carl Bladen who was killed by the defendant?

Bimini: Yes Sir.

DA: Please tell the court what happened that night.

Defense: Objection! We're here to establish whether the defendant had probable cause to act as she did on the night of August 30th, not to dredge up an incident that happened several years ago! I see no relevance in the prosecutor's line of questioning.

DA: Your Honor, if you'll allow me to continue, I will show relevance. The connection between the defendant and the deceased goes back several years. Ms. Carver is a witness to that bad blood between them and will testify to that effect.

Judge: Overruled! I'll allow it, but Mr. Prosecutor, be very careful.

DA: Thank you, your honor. Now, Ms. Carver, please tell the court what happened that night.

Bimini: Well, Diana was at work. She worked out in Squirrel Hill at a restaurant, and she wasn't supposed to be home until around eight or 8:30 in the evening. Carl called me over to the house to take a few hits with him…

DA: What do you mean by… 'Hits'?

Bimini: We smoked cocaine.

DA: Are you still using cocaine now?

Bimini: No Sir. I've been clean and sober for over seven months now.

DA: Good for you!

Bimini: Thank you.

DA: When you went over to Ms. Carver and Mr. Bladen's house to smoke cocaine, is that all that you did?

Bimini: No Sir.

DA: What else did you do? Was there sex involved?

Bimini: Yes Sir. I knew when he called me that he wanted to have sex with me.

DA: And you were okay with that?

Bimini: Not really, but when you're strung out, you'll do just about anything to get it. I wasn't proud of what I did, but he had the drugs that I wanted. I had what he wanted.

DA: Was Mr. Bladen strung out too?

Bimini: No. He snorted it and he smoked it now and then, but he wasn't strung out. He just used it to get the women that he wanted.

DA: Was your cousin, the defendant, strung out?

Defense: Objection! Hearsay! Irrelevant!

DA: The mindset of the defendant at the time that she perpetrated an act of violence against the deceased is relevant!

Judge: Counselor?

Defense:[He thought for a moment.] I withdraw my objection.

Judge: Proceed. The witness may answer the question.

Bimini: No Sir. She hadn't had any coke in months. She had been going to NA and AA meetings almost every day.

DA: So when you say, NA and AA, you're referring to what?

Bimini: Narcotics Anonymous, and Alcoholics Anonymous.

DA: So, you would say that she was pretty clearheaded?

Defense: Objection! The prosecution is calling for a conclusion from the witness as to the state of mind of the defendant. The witness clearly is not a psychologist or psychiatrist or professional in the field of mental health.

DA: Your Honor, I'm just trying to establish the fact that the defendant was or was not on drugs.

Defense: That was already established in the witness' previous answer.

Judge: Hummm. So it was. Objection sustained. Move On. And Mr. Prosecutor? Proceed with caution. You're walking a thin line here!

DA: Yes, Your Honor. Ms. Carver, please tell the court what happened when the defendant came home. You were in her home, correct?

Bimini: Yes Sir, I was. We didn't hear her when she came in because by that time we were in bed,…ah,…you know,.. doing it. But I felt funny. I felt like someone was watching me, so I opened my eyes and I saw her standing over us with a butcher knife in her hand. I screamed and Carl jumped up. When he did, she chopped off his di,… I mean, his penis! She tried to cut me, but I managed to get out of her way, and I ran out of there!

DA: What happened next?

Bimini: I was outside, and Carl came running out all cut up and bleeding all over. Diana leaned out of the window and shouted that she would kill us if it was the last thing that she did.

DA: Thank you. No more questions. Wait! There is just one more thing. Did you know that your cousin, the defendant, has been in a mental hospital several times?

Defense: Objection! [He thought for a moment, and then changed his mind.] Sorry Your Honor, I withdraw that objection.

Judge: So be it. The witness will answer the question.

Bimini: Yes Sir, I knew.

DA: Did you also know that after she sliced up Mr. Bladen that night and removed his penis, that she didn't go to jail?

Bimini: Yes Sir. I knew. She went to the state hospital again.

DA: Thank you Ms. Carver. No more questions. Your witness counselor.

He sat down owning a huge smile believing that his job had been completed.

Bill got up with papers in his hand. He looked at his legal pad and flipped a few pages and then he approached the witness stand.

Defense: Good morning Ms. Carver. I won't keep you long. I just have a few questions. Before you began using drugs, were you and the defendant friendly?

Bimini: Yes.

Defense: And did you spend a lot of time at her house and in her company?

Bimini: Yes.

Defense: After that incident with the deceased, Carl Bladen, why didn't you try to patch things up with her?

Bimini: Because she threatened to kill me. I was afraid of her. She's crazy!

Defense: What do you mean when you say she's crazy?

Bimini: I mean she's crazy! She's mental! She's been in and out of Mayview most of her life!

Defense: But you knew that before you slept with her boyfriend, in her bed, didn't you?

Bimini: Yes, but…

Defense: You also knew that if you were caught that your life would be in danger, didn't you?

Bimini: Yes, but…

Defense: So, you knew that what you were doing was dangerous and that your life was on the line, and you believed that she was crazy and would kill you if she caught you, but you did it anyway. Ms. Carver, don't you think that's crazy also?

DA: I object!

Defense: I withdraw the question. Now Ms. Carver, you say that on the night that the defendant chased you out of the apartment, you stood outside and watched her lean out her window and threatened to kill you and Mr. Bladen. Is that correct?

Bimini: Yes Sir. That's correct.

Defense: What exactly did she say? Do you remember exactly?

Bimini: Not word for word, but I remember she said that she would kill us if it was the last thing that she did.

Defense: Okay. Where was Mr. Bladen standing when she yelled at you?

Bimini: He was standing beside me.

Defense: The two of you were standing outside of her building looking up at her. Is that correct?

Bimini: Yes Sir.

Defense: Were you standing on the sidewalk or in the grass?

Bimini: I'm not sure. I think we were on the grass,… Yes,… We were on the grass.

Defense: Now Ms. Carver, when you ran out of the apartment, you were fearful for your life, correct? You thought the defendant was going to kill you?

Bimini: Yes Sir.

Defense: Did you stop at all before you reached the outside?

Bimini: No Sir. I just ran as fast as I could.

Defense: Did you pick up anything on the way out?

Bimini: No Sir. I didn't have time. My life was at stake and all I could think of was getting the hell out of there!

Defense: Now Ms. Carver, let's go back to the bedroom. When you were in bed with Mr. Bladen, doing it, as you said, were you completely naked or did you still have your clothes on?

Bimini: Naked! Nobody does it with their clothes on!

Defense: So, you were naked?

Bimini: Yes Sir.

Defense: Completely naked?

Bimini: I already said I was naked!

Defense: And Mr. Bladen, was he also naked? Completely naked?

Bimini: Yes, he was naked too! [She was becoming agitated.]

Defense: Ms. Carver, I believe that you're lying about the threats that you say the defendant made against you! I believe she never threatened you! I believe you ran so fast and so far, that you didn't stop until you got home. I believe that you are a liar!

Bimini: I'm not lying! She did threaten us! [She tried to force tears.]

Defense: If that is true, then answer this question. Why would you run outside, butt naked, then stop and stand in the grass and listen to someone threatening you? You weren't embarrassed to be standing outside naked?

Bimini: Naked?... I wasn't naked! I… Well… I… ah… um…

Defense: You weren't naked? Are you now telling the court that you stopped and put on your clothes before you ran for your life?

Bimini: No!… Yes!..: I…

Defense: You stood outside naked with everyone looking at you while you listened to a crazy woman shout out of her window?

Bimini: Well,… I… I….

Defense: And you want us to believe that Mr. Bladen, after being carved up like a Christmas Turkey, and castrated, ran outside butt naked, fleeing for his life, bleeding like a pig but stopped and stood beside you in the grass to listen with you?

Bimini: No! Yes! You're confusing me!

Defense: No, Miss Carver! I'm not confusing you. You're confused because what you have said isn't the truth! You're confused because you have been perpetrating a lie on this court and now you have been exposed. No more questions. I'm finished with this witness!

Bill turned his back on her and walked away leaving her sitting in the witness chair feeling and looking stupid. He had destroyed her testimony and her credibility. He had won the battle and it showed on his face. He looked at me and smiled.

The district attorney hung his head and licked his wounds. It was just getting started for him, but he didn't know it yet!

DA: Your Honor, I have several questions on re-direct.

Judge: The witness will remain. Proceed.

DA: Thank you, Your Honor. Now Miss Carver, is it true that you have witnessed the violent nature of the defendant on other occasions?

Bimini: Yes sir. That's true. [She dabbed at the tears in her eyes.]

DA: A particular incident happened In Monroeville last year. Can you tell the court about that?

Bimini: Yes sir. I was out there with a,…ah,…friend to see a movie. Diana came in…

DA: Are you referring to the Defendant?

Bimini: Yes Sir. She came in with Donn and sat behind us.

DA: Donn? Is that Mr. Diamond? Is that the gentleman seated behind the defendant?

Bimini: Yes Sir. [She looked at me] That's him. They were only there for a few minutes before she said something to my… ah… friend and then she walked out. After they left, he wanted to go too, so we left. Outside they got into an argument.

DA: Let me clarify something here. The defendant and your friend got into the argument, correct?

Bimini: Yes Sir.

DA: What were they arguing about?

Bimini: About something that happened the night before, but it was over so quickly that I really don't know what it was about.

DA: What did she do next?

Bimini: She raked his face with her fingernails and tore it all up.

DA: Was there any reason for that?

Defense: Objection! Speculation!

DA: I'll rephrase. Was there any reason that you could see for her to do what she did to him?

Defense: Objection. Still speculation.

DA: Your Honor. She was a physical witness to the confrontation. What she saw and thought is relevant.

Judge: Objection overruled. You may continue, Mr. Prosecutor.

DA:(He turned his attention back to the witness.) Please answer the question.

Bimini: Not as far as I could see. She just went off on him.

DA: After she 'went-off' on him, did she do anything else?

Bimini: Yes. She slapped me for no reason and knocked me to the ground.

DA: Did you say anything to her you provoke this behavior?

Bimini: No! I didn't say anything!

DA: Thank you. No more questions.

Judge: Does the defense have any further questions?

Defense: Yes, Your Honor. We do. [Bill approached the witness.] Ms. Carver, this 'friend' of yours, does he have a name?

Bimini: Yes Sir. Darren.

Defense: Does he have a last name, or do your friends have first names only?

Bimini: Scott. His name is Darren Scott.

Defense: Is Mr. Scott present in court?

Bimini: Yes Sir. Right there. [She pointed and all heads turned in his direction].

Defense: That is the gentleman that you came in with, correct?

Bimini: Yes.

Defense: Are you two romantically involved?

DA: Objection! The witness's personal affairs have no direct bearing on this case.

Defense: But they do Your Honor. The witness has already shown to the court that she has not been completely truthful, so her credibility is questionable and therefore does have a direct bearing on this case and moreover, the future of the defendant.

DA: But what she is doing now is irrelevant. What is relevant is what she witnessed the defendant do, not what her love life may be or not be today.

Defense: She claims that she is a different woman today than what she was at the time of these incidents. Drugs made her do it, she says. She has been clean from drugs for seven months, but her behavior remains the same. Deception for her is a way of life. If she deceives other than why wouldn't she attempt to deceive the court?

Judge: Objection overruled. Proceed counselor. The witness is instructed to answer the question.

Bimini: What was the question? I don't remember.

Stenographer: Are you two romantically involved?

Bimini: Yes.

Defense: How long have you been romantically involved with Mr. Scott?

Bimini: I don't know,... I... ah...

Defense: Just take a wild guess. Has it been a year? Two years? Five years?

Bimini: Not that long. Maybe a year and a half.

Defense: A year and a half? Maybe? Okay. So, what about this incident in Monroeville? How long ago was that? A year?

Bimini: Yes, maybe a little longer.

Defense: And you say that the defendant slapped you for no apparent reason, is that what you want us to believe?

Bimini: Yes. It's true. I didn't say anything to her. I didn't do nothing!

Defense: You call sleeping with her man nothing? And I'm not talking about Carl Bladen. I'm talking about your 'friend' Darren Scott. You knew when you began your affair with Mr. Scott that your cousin, your blood relative, the defendant, was involved with him! Didn't you?

Bimini.(She remained silent.)

Defense: Your Honor, please instruct the witness to answer the question.

Judge: The witness will answer the question.

Bimini: Yes... But...

Defense: So, this is the second time that you went behind your cousin's back and slept with her man. First Mr. Bladen and then Mr. Scott! Isn't that the truth, Ms. Carver?

Bimini: Yes, it's true but I was strung out on cocaine then. I was...

Defense: But you're not strung out now, are you?

Bimini: No, I'm not!

Defense: But you continued a relationship that started with deception and drugs even after you stop using drugs. Isn't that correct?

Bimini: But he's the one...

Defense: Just answer the question.

Bimini: Yes.

Defense: So, you really haven't changed much at all. Drugs or no drugs you'll still do the same things that you've always done! You're still the same! You can't be trusted! No further questions.

Judge: The witness may step down.

Bimini was furious.

The DA wished that he hadn't put her on the stand at all. He then began to decide what to do about Darren. He was having second thoughts about putting him on the stand because his case was falling apart, but he still had his ace in the hole! Me! He hesitated as the room filled with sounds of talking, whispering and discussions of what they had witnessed. The DA looked at Darren and then turned away.

CHAPTER 18

Magnificent

Bill was a first-rate attorney and would eat him alive. All the DA really needed to do was to establish a prima facie case against Diana and then worry about it once he got to trial. He was confident of that so he abruptly stood up and addressed the court.

DA: Your Honor, I'd like to make a statement before I call my next witness if I may.

Judge: Does the defense have any objections?

Defense: No objections Your Honor.

Judge: You may proceed.

DA: Thank you Your Honor. And you, counselor.

(Bill nodded as the DA spoke to him.)

DA: In the interest of time as well as fairness, I offer this statement to the court. There is no doubt that the deceased, Carl Bladen, was killed on the night of August 30 by the hands of the defendant, Ms. Diana Carver. The defendant herself admits to killing him and the defense acknowledges that fact. It is also a fact that on the night of August 30, Mr. Bladen set fire to the rear of the home of Mr. Donn Diamond and then broke into that same with the intent of doing bodily harm to Mr. Diamond. What is not clear is whether or not Mr. Bladen knew that Ms. Carver was present at that time.

I offer this. Mr. Bladen did not know the defendant was there and therefore had no intentions of harming her or her infant child. Mr. Bladen's fight was with Mr. Diamond and him alone. I believe that Mr. Diamond and Mr. Bladen fought in the hallway, Ms. Carver saw the opportunity to complete the vendetta that she carried for years. She vowed to kill Mr. Bladen and so she did. It was an act of vengeance, an act of cold-blooded murder! Now she wants to try to hide behind the law claiming that it was self-defense and that Mr. Diamond's home was also her home, but Ms. Carver has had an apartment on Burrows Street for the past five years. The same apartment where she remove Mr. Bladen's penis and tried to kill him and her cousin several years ago. She still holds that apartment to this day. No, your honor. 714 E. Warrington Ave. is not her address according to records which I hold in my hand.

(He held up the papers that were in his hand and waved them.)

Phone bills, rental contract, section 8 papers, personal correspondence, etc. They all list her address on Burrows Street, not Warrington Avenue.

(He placed the papers on the judge's bench. The Judge began to look at them.) Your Honor, I submit that a prima facie case has been established for all charges in this indictment except for the charge of second-degree murder. The testimony of my next witness will set the foundation for the charge of second-degree murder to be bound over for court also. I call my final witness, Mr. Donn Diamond.

The entire courtroom rumbled with sounds as he spoke my name. All eyes were on me as I approached the witness stand and stood to be sworn in. Then I took my seat.

DA: Good morning Sir. Please state your name for the record.

Donn: Donn Diamond.

DA: Is your true name Donn, or Donald?

Donn: It's Donn.

DA: Please give us your correct address.

Donn.714 E. Warrington Ave.

DA: Are you here to testify of your own free will?

Donn: No.

DA: Let the record show that Mr. Diamond is here by subpoena and he is a witness for the prosecution. He is considered to be a hostile witness because of his relationship with the defendant.

Judge: Do you have any objections Counselor?

Defense:: No Your Honor.

Judge: So be it. You may proceed.

DA: Mr. Diamond, under penalty of law, you are required to answer all questions asked of you honestly and truthfully regardless of your affiliation with the defendant or the defense, is that clear?

Donn: Yes, but...

DA: But what Sir?

Donn. By law, I am not required to answer any questions in this case other than those that give you my personal information.

DA: Sir, you are terribly mistaken! (He was visibly upset.)

Donn: No Sir! I am not!

DA: TabSir. This is a court of law. You are required to answer the questions that I ask you and answer them all truthfully! If you don't, you will be held in contempt of court and you may find yourself in the County jail! Do you understand that, sir?

Donn. If that happens, then this Court will be in violation of my constitutional rights!

DA: Your Honor, will you please instruct the witness to answer my questions?

Judge: Sir, is it that you don't understand what the Dist. Atty. is saying to you?

Donn: No Your Honor. I understand perfectly what he's saying. It's just that he is wrong. May speak your honor?

Judge: You may.

Donn: Thank you Your Honor. Under the Constitution of the United States of America, we all are afforded certain rights. When it comes to criminal law and criminal proceedings a defendant cannot be forced to testify against himself or incriminate himself and It also goes on to state that...

DA: But your honor! (The DA interrupted.) Mr. Diamond is not on trial here! These proceedings are not about him, but are centered on the defendant, his girlfriend, Ms. Carver!

Donn: May I finish Your Honor?

Judge: Proceed.

Donn: Thank you Your Honor. As I was saying, a person cannot be forced to incriminate themselves and, a husband cannot be forced to testify against his wife!

With my last statement, the courtroom went wild with chatter and laughter. It became so loud that nothing could be heard. The judge beat his gavel on the block and demanded order. After a minute or two it began to quiet down.

Judge: I'LL HAVE ORDER, OR I WILL CLEAR THIS COURTROOM! IS THAT CLEAR?

(The courtroom quieted immediately. The judge turned to me.)

Judge: Mr. Diamond, are you saying that the defendant, Miss Diana Carver, is your wife?

Donn: Yes sir. She is my wife!

Diana lifted her left hand and flashed her diamond ring and wedding band. The courtroom erupted again, but became quiet when the judge raised his gavel. This time he didn't have to bring it crashing down on the woodblock.

DA: What is this? Is this some kind of trick?

Donn: It's no trick. The defendant is my wife! We are legally married!

Defense: Your Honor, may I approach? (Bill rose from his seat)

Judge: You may.

Defense: I have here in my hand several documents that will substantiate Mr. Diamond's statement.

(He placed the marriage license and several other papers on the judge's bench. He waited until the judge inspected them all before he spoke again.)

Your Honor, until this morning, I was not aware of this union. Mr. Diamond presented me with their marriage license as well as several other documents that I have placed on the bench. They all seem to be valid and in order.

DA: Your Honor, I object! This is some kind of trick! Mr. Diamond knew that he would receive a subpoena to appear and testify. He also knew that his testimony would seal the fate of the defendant, so he concocted this scheme to avoid testifying. He should be held in contempt of court!

Defense: Your Honor, Mr. Diamond's desire to wed the defendant was, and is, genuine. Mr. Diamond proposed to the defendant long before he received his subpoena, which I might add, was only served a few moments ago. His desire to wed the defendant came about long before this unfortunate incident that took the life of the deceased, Mr. Bladen. How could he possibly conceive of a plot before the inception of the circumstances that brought us all here today? The prosecution should be held in contempt for making such an outlandish and slanderous statement!

Judge: Gentlemen! Gentlemen! Mr. Prosecutor, please approach the bench.

(The DA approached and looked over the paperwork.)

Judge: They are all valid and legal documents. This marriage license is legal in all fifty states. The Commonwealth of Pennsylvania recognizes the validity of Las Vegas marriages. The witness is correct! You cannot force him to testify against the defendant, his wife!

(He turned to me.)

You may step down sir.

Donn: Thank you, Your Honor.

Judge: Do you have any more questions for the witnesses?

DA: No Your Honor. The prosecution rests.

(He returned to his table and sat down heavily and slumped in his chair.)

Judge: Is the defense ready to proceed?

Defense: Yes we are, Your Honor.

Judge: Call your first witness.

Defense: The defense calls Ms. Darla Nicholson.

Darla took the stand and was sworn in.

Defense: Ms. Nicholson, on the eve of July 28 did you hear the deceased, Carl Bladen make threats on the life of Mr. Donn?

Darla: Yes I did.

Defense: Do you recall what he said?

Darla: Yes I do. He was very upset that Donn and Diana had had a baby and that they were living together. He said that he was going to put an end to it. He said that Diana was supposed to have his baby and not someone else's. He threatened to kill all three of them! Especially the baby!

Defense: He stated that they were living together?

Darla: Yes Sir.

Defense: Do you know the defendant?

Darla: Yes Sir, I do.

Defense: How long have you known the defendant?

Darla: About five years.

Defense: Do you know where she lives?

Darla: Yes. She lives with Donn, Mr. Diamond, at 714 E. Warrington Ave. overtop of his store.

Defense: Do you know how long she has been living there?

Darla: She has been living there for about a year or so.

Defense. Did she have any other place of residence?

Darla: Yes Sir. She also has an apartment on Burrows Street but she doesn't stay there at all.

Defense: Now Miss Nicholson, do you remember being in the presence of the late Mr. Carl Bladen on the night of July 28th?

Darla: Yes sir.

Defense: Do you recall the circumstances surrounding that encounter?

Darla: Yes sir, I do.

Defense: Would you please tell the court of what you witnessed?

Darla: Yes sir. Well, we were at an N: A. meeting on the North Side. Carl was upset about something and you could tell that something was really bothering him, but no one knew what it was until he began to speak. At first he was just talking about how he was saddened by the fact that Diana and Donn had just had a baby. He talked about how he still loved her and he wished he hadn't cheated on her. Then he started talking about them as if he hated them. He and Donn, Mr. Diamond, had been good friends for the past few years, but now he spoke of him as if he were his worst enemy.

Defense: Did he at anytime threaten to kill Mr. Diamond, the defendant, Miss Carver and their child?

Darla: Yes sir. He said that she wasn't supposed to have anybody's kids but his. He said he was going to kill all three of them.

Defense: When he made this threat, did you think that he was sincere, or just blowing off steam?

Darla: Well, at first I didn't believe him, but when he kept saying it over and over, …

Defense: What was it that he kept saying over and over?

Darla: He said; 'I'm gonna kill them! I'm gonna kill that lil' bastard baby!'

Defense: One last question. Was Miss Carolyn Hicks present at this time? Did she witness the entire incident?

Darla: Yes sir. She was there and she saw it all. She was sitting right next to me.

Defense: Thank you. No further questions.

Judge: Does the prosecution have any questions for this witness?

DA: No Your Honor.

Judge: The witness is excused.

(Darla left the witness stand and as she walked past Bill, she winked at him.)

Defense: The defense calls Miss Carolyn Hicks.

(Carolyn took the stand and was sworn in.)

Defense: Good morning Miss Hicks. Would you please state your full name for the record?

Carolyn: Carolyn Juanita Hicks.

Defense: Miss Hicks, on the evening of July 28th, were you in the presence of Mr. Carl Bladen?

Carolyn: Yes sir, I was.

Defense: Will you please tell the court what you heard Mr. Bladen say in reference to the defendant, Miss Carver and her family?

Carolyn: Well, he was upset about Diana,... ah,... the defendant, having a baby with Donn,... ah... Mr. Diamond, because he and Diana were once a couple and they were supposed to have a baby together. He threatened to kill all three of them.

Defense: All three of them? Including the defendant?

Carolyn: Yes sir. All three of them!

Defense: Were there any other witnesses that heard his threats?

Carolyn: Yes sir. There were at least twenty people there that heard him.

Defense: Was Miss Darla Nicholson present?

Carolyn: Yes sir.

Defense: And do you agree with the testimony that she has given concerning the incident?

Carolyn: Yes sir.

Defense: Was there any other time that you heard Mr. Bladen threaten the defendant, her husband and her child?

Carolyn: Yes sir. Twice! The first time he came into our meeting with a knife and tried to cut Mr. Diamond, but Mr. Diamond took the knife away from him.

Defense: What did Mr. Diamond do?

Carolyn: He gave the knife to a friend to take out of the building. He tried to talk to Carl, Mr. Bladen, but Mr. Bladen attacked him and he and Mr. Bladen got into a fight for a minute but then Mr. Diamond stopped fighting and left.

Defense: What did Mr. Bladen do?

Carolyn: He started slamming furniture around and then he threatened to kill Mr. Diamond, the defendant and their baby! He said he would kill them if it was the last thing ever did. He would kill them or die trying!

Defense: Please tell the court about the second incident.

Carolyn: It was the day after Mr. Diamond proposed to the defendant. It was August 16th. We were all in the store with her admiring her diamond ring and congratulating her on her engagement. The phone rang and the defendant answered it. It was Carl, Mr. Bladen. I didn't hear what he said but Diana, … The defendant was very upset when she hung up the phone. She said that he threatened her and her family.

DA: OBJECTION! Hearsay!

Judge: Sustained.

Defense: Did you at any time that day hear Mr. Bladen threaten the defendant?

Carolyn: Yes sir. About a minute or two later, he called back. She put the call on the speaker and started recording it. I heard him say that he was going to kill her.

(Bill retrieved the tape from his table and approached the bench.)

Defense: Your Honor, I hold in my hand the actual tape that recorded the threats made by the deceased, Mr. Carl Bladen. On it you will hear him in his own words threaten to kill the defendant, Mr. Diamond and their infant child. This tape was certified by Jackson Phillips Detective Agency to be authentic and unedited. As you well know, Jackson Phillips Detective agency is most highly respected in their field. I would like to play the portion of the tape that recorded the threat by Mr. Bladen.

Judge: Mr. Prosecutor, would you care to inspect the tape or the certification?

DA: No Your Honor. We concede to the reputation of Jackson Phillips.

Defense: I would like to enter this tape into evidence.

Judge: Any objections Mr. Prosecutor?

DA: No Your Honor.

Judge: Proceed counselor.

Defense: Thank you Your Honor. I would like to play the portion of the tape that contains the threat made by the deceased.

(The tape begins play. The room was extremely quiet and everyone leaned forward as if that would cause them to hear better.)

"Hello? Diamond enterprises. Diana speaking. How may I help you?"

"You bitch! You think hangin up on me is gonna stop me?"

"Carl, you need to stop calling me. We've got nothing to talk about!"

"You're right for once, you lying bitch! But listen to this! It won't be long now! I'm comin for you! First I'm gonna get that backstabbin asshole you call your man, and then I'm coming after you! But before I kill you, I'm gonna slice up that little bastard baby of yours just like you sliced me! I'm gonna cut off his little Dick and you're gonna watch it all! I'm gonna kill you last, cause I want you to suffer like I'm sufferin! I know where you are and I'm comin for you! You dirty bitch!"

(He hung up the phone and the entire courtroom remained silent after the tape ended. Carolyn was still on the witness stand and Bill turned his attention back to her.)

Defense: Ms. Hicks, is that the same conversation that you heard on August 16 in Mr. Diamond's store?

Carolyn: Yes Sir.

Defense: What did the defendant do after hearing this threat?

Carolyn: She didn't say anything at first. She was really shaken up. She sat down and picked Donnte' up. Donnte' is her son! She hugged him, you know, real close? Then she said to him, 'nobody is going to hurt you, not as long as I'm alive!', Then she kissed him and put him back in his stroller. She reached under the counter and pulled out Mr. Diamond's gun. She checked it to make sure it was loaded and then she put it back.

Defense: Thank you Ms. Hicks. I have no further questions.

Judge: Does the prosecutor wish to cross examine?

DA: Yes Your Honor. We do!

Judge: Proceed.

DA: Thank you Your Honor.

Ms. Hicks, in your testimony you said that Mr. Bladen came into your meeting caring a knife to kill Mr. Diamond. With me are you referring to?

Carolyn: Narcotics Anonymous.

DA: Are you a member of that organization?

Carolyn: Yes sir.

DA: And how long have you been a member of Narcotics Anonymous?

Carolyn. Four years.

DA: Have you ever had a relationship with the deceased, Carl Bladen?

Carolyn: Yes Sir.

DA. Was it romantic?

Carolyn: Yes.

DA: How did that relationship end?

Carolyn: Carl stopped using drugs and I didn't. He couldn't continue to be around me and stay clean so he ended the relationship. He moved on.

DA. When he moved on, who did he move on with? Who was his new love?

Carolyn: Diana.

DA: Diana? The defendant? Diana Carver?

Carolyn: Yes.

DA: Didn't you feel slighted when Mr. Bladen left you for the defendant?

Carolyn. He didn't leave me for her. It just happened that they both were clean at the time and I wasn't. He didn't start seeing her until after he left me.

DA: Are you sure about that?

Defense: Objection! I don't see where this line of questioning is leading. The past history of this witness has no bearing on this case whatsoever.

Judge: Mr. Prosecutor, can you tie this up quickly? Remember, this is just a hearing, not a trial!

DA: No further questions. (He returned to his seat sulking and dejected.)

Judge: Anything on redirect, counselor?

Defense: No Your Honor.

Judge: The witness may step down. Call you next witness counselor.

Defense: The defense calls Mrs. Sally Reynolds!

Mom handed Donnte' to me. He was sound asleep. She got up and made her way to the witness stand with Bill's help. She was sworn in and she sat down. She turned and faced the judge, smiled warmly and spoke.

"Alex, how is your mother doing these days?" There was a familiarity in her tone.

"She's fine Mrs. Reynolds. She had a touch of the gout for a while but she's doing much better now." His smile was genuine and warm as he leaned over the bench and spoke to mom.

"Tell her that I finally got up enough nerve to go up in a jet! It was delightful! Not at all as terrible as I thought it would be!"

"I'll tell her." He then realized that the entire courtroom was paying attention to his conversation with mom.

Judge: Ah,… You may proceed counselor.

Defense: Thank you Your Honor. (Bill smiled at the judge.)

Good morning Mrs. Reynolds.

Mom: Good morning son. Isn't it just a beautiful day?

Defense: Yes ma'am, it is! Mrs. Reynolds, how long have you known the defendant, Miss. Diana Carver, correction, Mrs. Diana Carver Diamond?

Mom: It's been about a year now.

Defense: Do you know where she lives?

Mom: Of course! She lives just across the street from me with her husband, son and that wonderful young man sitting there. (She looked in my direction. She smiled at me.) She and her husband have been helping me, especially since my heart attack. They're wonderful people!

Defense: Where do you live, Mrs. Reynolds?

Mom: On Warrington Avenue, in the senior citizens high-rise!

Defense: Did Mrs. Carver Diamond ever tell you of another place of residence?

Mom: Oh yes! Burrows Street! That's where she lived before she moved in with Donn. It's over on the Hill somewhere. I've never been there so I don't know exactly, but she lives right across the street from me now. She's been there for as long as I've known her.

Defense. Thank you Mrs. Reynolds. Your Honor, I have no more questions for this witness.

Judge: Mr. Prosecutor?

DA: No questions Your Honor.

Judge: Mrs. Reynolds, it's always a pleasure to see you. You may step down now.

Mom: Thank you Your Honor. Don't forget to tell your mother what I said.

Judge: I won't.

Mom: I flew to Las Vegas! I didn't win any money in the casinos but I did get to see these two get married. You take care of yourself Alex. You look tired! Get some rest!

Judge: I will.

(Mom returned to her seat beside me.)

Judge: Is there anything else from the defense?

Defense: Yes, your honor. The defense has no more witnesses but we would like to present several documents into evidence.

Judge: You may proceed.

Defense: Thank you Your Honor.

"The crux of this case lies in whether or not the defendant had the right under the circumstances and under the law to exert lethal force, whether or not she had legal residence at the address where the death occurred and whether or not she believed lethal force was necessary to prevent the perpetrator from inflicting serious bodily harm or death upon her and her family. I believe that it has been demonstrated in this courtroom today that all three of these points of law have been met and exceeded by testimony and legal documents.

First, there is the issue of intrusion. Was there an illegal and unlawful attempt to gain entrance to the dwelling place of Mr. and Mrs. Diamond by the perpetrator, Carl Bladen, and was that attempt carried out to fruition? The answer to that question is a resounding yes! Mr. Bladen did not have permission to enter the building by any of the residents thereof, but the evidence clearly shows that, A; Mr. Bladen threatened to enter against the objection of the owner and resident Mr. Diamond, B; Mr. Bladen maliciously set fire to the building with the intent of entrapping the residence within, C; Mr. Bladen broke into the building by the use of several burglary tools which were found in the hallway containing his fingerprints, and D; Mr. Bladen's body was found 20 feet inside of the hallway of the building and according to the police report, there was no evidence that the body had been removed or tampered with. Mr. Bladen had died in the exact spot where his body was found.

Then we have issued the threat of bodily harm or death. We have heard testimony from witnesses who themselves heard Mr. Bladen threaten to mutilate and kill the defendant, her infant son and her new husband. But the most damaging and incriminating piece of evidence is the tape that the defendant made recording the deceased in his own voice threatening to mutilate and kill all three members of the defendant's family, including her.

Now comes the crucial part of it all, the issue of residents. Did the defendant actually live at 714 E. Warrington Ave. or was she just an overnight guest as the prosecution suggests? Well, let's look at the facts.

First we have testimony from several witnesses who for the past year have visited the defendant at the Warrington Avenue address. We have the testimony of a longtime resident of the neighborhood, a former city Councilwoman, former First Lady, and widow of former Mayor Albert Reynolds, Mrs. Sallie Reynolds, stating that she has known the defendant almost a year and knew of both addresses that the defendant holds."

"Mom," I whispered. "I didn't know you were famous!"

"Yeah!" She smiled as she rocked Donnte'. "Just like Jesse James!"

(Bill continued to speak.)

Your Honor, I have documents that I would like to present into evidence. First is a cell phone bill that is in the name of, Diana Carver. This phone was purchased for the defendant by Mr. Diamond as a Christmas present on December 18. If you would notice the address, it is 714 E. Warrington Ave. not Burrows Street. Also notice that every one of these bills were sent to the Warrington Avenue address and were paid by the defendant, and paid on time. My second piece of evidence is the birth certificate of one, Donnte' Carver Diamond who is the infant son of the defendant and Mr. Donn Diamond. The defendant is listed as the mother and Mr. Diamond is listed as the father. It was mailed to 714 E. Warrington Ave., and not Burrows Street! The date on Donnte's birth certificate is June 1. Ms. Carver could have given her address as Burrows Street, but she did not. Why? Because although she still maintained an apartment, she chose to live with Mr. Diamond and their son as a family.

(He placed the two documents on the bench in front of the judge.)

Also, you will find hospital and doctor bills that were acquired during her pregnancy and delivery. Each one has the address of 714 E. Warrington Ave., not Burrows Street! As further evidence, I have notarized statements from several witnesses. I submit, Your Honor that the defendant has met and exceeded all criterion required by law to exempt her from prosecution. We respectfully request that the court rule in favor of the defense and dismissed all charges against my client, Mrs. Diana Carver Diamond! Thank you!

CHAPTER 19

The Decision

The room went into pandemonium again. This time with hand clapping, whistling, and cheering. Bill had presented his case brilliantly and from the reaction of the crowd and the look on the face of the Dist. Atty., the case had been won. But one thing I had previously learned was that in a court room, the cheering of the crowd may sway of a lay-jury, but it had no affect whatsoever on a fair and impartial judge.

Judge: Order! Order! Order in this courtroom! (He banged his gavel three times and then the sounds subsided) Mr. Prosecutor, please approach and inspect these documents! (After the DA looked over the documents, the judge asked him.) Do you have any objections to these documents being accepted as evidence?

DA: No, Your Honor. (He was a beaten man, and it showed.)

Judge: Very well. The court will stand in recess while I review the evidence. (He banged his gavel once and stood up with all the papers in his hand.)

Bailiff: ALL RISE!

(Everyone stood until the judge disappeared through the 10 foot polished mahogany door behind the bench.)

The level of noise began to rise again as everyone began to speak their opinion on the case. Donnte' was lying across the lap of the former first lady of the city with his eyes looking around wondering where he was and what was going on. He saw me and a big warm smile appeared on his face.

"The boy looks exactly like you. You know that don't you?" Mom spoke. "You shouldn't have any questions about him. He is definitely your son!"

"I don't. Not anymore!" I replied.

"Good! You've got a good wife and a good spirited son. When this is all over take them out of Pittsburgh. Go somewhere where it doesn't snow and start over. People here aren't going to forget. They aren't going to let you to live in peace. Now that the neighborhood knows that Diana has mental issues, the same people that she calls friends will turn on her. I've seen it happen so many times. Your business, it isn't going to be the same."

"But mom, I think we can get through this. Everything will be all right!"

"No son. You're wrong! Think about where you are and who you are. Let's face it. You're Black living and operating a business in a white neighborhood. Do you remember how you were treated when you first opened up? Nobody wanted to buy from you. Not because of your prices or your stock, but just because you're Black. You're still the only black businessmen up in Allentown and although you've got steady customers, there are a lot of people who still won't cater to you. Why? Because of the color of your skin! Now son, add this in, your wife killed someone in the building. They published the fact that she is a former mental patient of Mayview State Hospital and Western Psych and that she castrated a man years ago before she killed him. It doesn't matter that she's going to be exonerated by the court; she'll never be exonerated by the people in Allentown, or the city. She'll always be, 'Crazy Diana'! I love you son. I don't want to see you go because you and Diana have been better to me than my own daughters have been, but you have to go for her sake and for the sake of this beautiful little boy here." (She rocked him gently)

"You're probably right."

"I know I'm right."

"What about you? Don't you want to leave? Remember Vegas? You had fun out there even though we only stayed a day. Why not leave too! Wherever you want to go, I'll get you there. We'll be…"

"Stop! I'm an old woman." She smiled. "Let me tell you a little secret but you must promise not to tell Diana!"

"What?"

"Promise me first!"

"Okay, I promise."

I looked up at Diana and at the same time she turned to look at me. I immediately and automatically felt guilty. I blew her a kiss, pickup Donnte' from mom's lap and held him up. She probably thought it was for her benefit but actually it was the cover-up my guilty face. She returned the kiss and turned back to await the judge.

"Okay mom. What's up? I feel guilty already and I don't even know what the secret is!"

"Son, I'm dying!" She said it quickly as if waiting would not allow her to speak.

"No mom! You can't be!"

I felt a stab of pain in my chest that transferred and became a sickening knot in my stomach. I didn't want to believe it or accept it, but I knew that if she said it, it must be true.

"Yes, it's true. My heart is getting weaker by the minute. Old age is catching up to me real fast. It's just a part of life!" And ingenuous smile came across her lips but did not make its way to her eyes.

"Isn't there something that they can do?" I asked but I already knew the answer.

"No. Nothing!"

"What about a new heart?"

"A new heart? What would I want a new heart for? I'm an old woman! I wouldn't let them waste a good heart on this old body. I've lived my life and it was a good one. It's time for me to go on home. I'm tired and it's time to rest."

She seemed to be okay with it but I wasn't. I didn't want to lose her. I wanted Donnte' to get to know her as I had. I wanted to spend many years with her.

"Mom. I'm so sorry!" I said it very weakly.

"Don't be, son. I'm going home to be with the Lord. My only regret is that I have to leave you, Diana, and this little angel!" She raised Donnte' to kiss him. "But I'll be up there watching over you."

"Why don't we take a trip out to California? Let's go out and see the ocean!" I was in total shock, and I didn't know what else to say.

"Oh no! I don't need to fly anymore. Thanks to you I've done it once. That's enough! The next time I fly it will be with my own set of wings!" She chuckled. "Besides I've already been to California, a few times!"

"Really? But you didn't fly? How did you get there?"

"Once by bus and I swore I'd never do that again! Then by train twice. Now those were some beautiful trips. You ought to try it. Flying is good if you need to get there quickly but you don't see anything. The train takes you through the land. I've seen the beauty of the land from the train."

I reminisced, thinking about the perfect train trip that I took to Chicago when I was very young. But that was as far as I went. Taking the train to California was something to think about.

"Mom, you have to release me from this promise. How can I keep this from Diana?"

"No son. You keep your promise. I will tell her. Let me do it, okay?"

"I, I will, but please do it quickly because she's going to know that I'm holding something in."

"What's this? You can't stand up to your wife? Are you whipped already? Ha ha ha ha!"

"Mom… I was whipped a long time ago!"

The judge was ready to return.

Bailiff: ALL RISE!

Everyone stood until the judge sat. He shuffled a few papers until he found what he needed and then he began to speak. The courtroom was hush-hush. The tension was thick in the air. Everyone quieted to listen to the Judge's decision.

I looked at Diana, but she had her back to me and didn't turn around. Bill was whispering to her and she listened intently. I could tell that mom was getting nervous. It didn't show on her face but her leg began to jump nervously sending Donnte' bouncing around.

Judge: After reviewing all the evidence, I have arrived at a decision that is prudent, just and in accordance with the laws of this state.

The prosecution alleges this to be a crime maliciously and viciously perpetrated by the defendant with the sole purpose of taking revenge and ending the life of the deceased therefore rendering her subject to prosecution by the law. The defense concedes that the defendant did take the life of the deceased but alleges that it was not with malice or prejudice, or aforethought, but strictly in the line of self-defense, therefore exempting her from prosecution. I have weighed both sides and have reviewed the evidence and I see my duty which is abundantly clear in this case.

Seeing this is only a hearing and not a trial, the prosecution has only to tip the scales in his favor by the preponderance of evidence. However the defense can only prevail if all of the evidence tips the scale in his direction. In this case the evidence is clearly one-sided.

I find that the defendant, Ms. Diana Carver, had legal residence at the premises located at 714 East Warrington Ave on the night of Mr. Bladen's death. I find that threats were made against her and her family by the deceased, Mr. Carl Bladen, and that he had every intention of conducting those threats of death and dismemberment. I find that the deceased, by setting fire to and breaking into the residence where the defendant and her family lived with the sole purpose of causing bodily harm and death, did intrude and attempt to carry out his plan. I further find that the defendant was well within her rights to repel, subdue, and stop the intruder by the use of force, which includes the use of deadly force, to protect herself as well as her family and home. Therefore, the charges against the defendant, Ms. Diana Carver, cannot stand and are therefore dismissed. My ruling is that the taking of the life of the deceased, Mr. Carl Bladen, was justified! His death is ruled, justifiable homicide. All charges against the defendant, Ms. Diana Carver, are dismissed. Case dismissed!

His gavel came down hard and struck the woodblock producing a sound that reverberated around the court room. It caused the courtroom to break out into pandemonium. People were shouting and celebrating. They were screaming, whistling, laughing, and jumping around.

The judge immediately stood up and headed for the mahogany door. Bailiff. ALL RISE!

Everyone stood and quieted down just long enough for him to disappear behind the door. Then the pandemonium began again.

Diana jumped in the air and shouted. "Thank you, Jesus!" She first hugged Bill and then she ran through the crowd that was starting to form around her and she came straight to me. She hugged me and kissed me.

"I love you! I love you! I love you!" She said over and over and over again. Then she hugged mom and picked up Donnte'. His little face lit up when he saw her. She kissed his face over and over again as tears streamed from her eyes.

Several people came by and patted me on the back. They wished us well and some reached over me in an attempt to touch Diana. Bill and Darla came by, and I reached out and took his hand.

"Thanks Bill!" I held fast to his hand. It wasn't so weak and mushy this time. "You're a good friend and a fantastic lawyer!"

He puffed his chest out, laughed and in a very silly tone he said, "Well, what can I say?"

I hugged him and laughed right along with him.

We left the courtroom and walked into a mass of reporters, photographers, and curious onlookers. Bill fended off the reporters by giving a statement and then we got into a taxi and left.

CHAPTER 20

Goodbye Burg

In the next few days I gave a lot of thought to what mom had said to me in the courtroom. She was always right when she gave me advice. She had a connection to God that kept her constantly and perpetually in good standings. At times she knew things before they happened and she always had my best interests at heart. Now that there were three of us, she looked out for us all. She had lived in the senior citizens building for over 11 years and she knew the people a lot better than I did. She was a lot wiser than me and had a sixth sense about things.

I hadn't been into my building since the struggle with Carl and now it was time to face the destruction. The police tape was gone except for one piece across the door and the barricade was no longer there. I stood on the opposite side of the street and looked with great sadness at the place that I once called home. I saw the boarded up windows of my once thriving business and the building itself looked sad without the lights and signs in the windows. Without the unique feminine touches that Diana had added, it looks completely dead. I couldn't see inside and I could only imagine what it looked like but I had to see it for myself. The keys were in my hand and I was apprehensive about going in. I didn't want to see all that I had worked so hard for and all that I owned in ruins but I had to do what I had to do!

Just before I crossed the street I heard the trolley rounding the corner and I waited. It past me and stopped at the corner in front of Mom's building. Several people got off. I knew all of their faces and they knew mine. I waved and shouted a greeting but only one returned it. The others looked at me as if I carried some horrible disease. One couple in their forties, who had been in my store many times, walked right past me. I spoke but they didn't. I felt the coldness that Mom had warned me of. It had started already. At once I made the decision to get my family out of there and move on!

I crossed the street and pulled the lone piece of yellow police tape from across the doorway of the store. When I inserted my keys the door opened freely and the familiar sound of the bell atop the door was like music to me as I stepped through. I left the door wide open so that I could see. I reached for the light switch and clicked it but there was no bright flood of light that usually overtook the darkness within. The electric company had disconnected the power after the fire.

My cell phone began to ring. It was Diana.

"Where are you, baby?" She said with the sweetness of voice that I loved so much.

I replied. "I'm in the store!"

"You should have told me you were going. I would have come with you. You know what the doctor said about taking it easy."

"Yeah, I know. I will, but this is something that I have to do. I didn't say anything to you because I have to do this alone."

"I understand. Just call me if you need me, okay?" She was so very understanding. Vastly different from when she refused to take her medication.

"I will."

I went behind the counter and picked up a flashlight. I clicked it on and began to survey the damage. It was a real mess! There was minimal fire damage but the water from the fire hoses soaked everything. Part of the original ceiling had fallen from the weight and the softening power of the water had totally destroyed the drop ceiling that I had put up. Parts were still attached to the ceiling towards the front of the building, but it had all fallen down in the back where the fire was.

I went out into the hallway were Carl and I had fought. There was a white chock drawing outlining the way that his body was laying. The blood that flowed from his neck was still there and dried on the floor. Also there was a trail of blood leading to the front door. It was mine! The knife that he had used on me was gone. The butcher knife that Diana had used on him was also gone. I stepped over the chock and went upstairs.

I reached the kitchen at the top of the stairs. Light shone through the broken glass in the charred window frame to reveal the total destruction of the kitchen. By the time the firemen arrived the entire rear of the building had been involved in flames. I walked out of the kitchen feeling anguish. I walked through the living room, through the computer room and into the bedroom. It was disheartening to see everything in the way that it had become. I had seen enough and I didn't want to go to the third floor. I went back downstairs and out of the building locking the door behind me. I slowly crossed the street, heading for my van.

Diana was no longer at mom's place, but she was sitting in the van and she was crying. She had just come out of mom's apartment so I knew why the tears were flowing. She moved to the rear seat and held out her arms to me.

"Baby,... Hold me!"

"What's wrong?" I asked, even though I already knew the answer.

"Mom! She said she's dying! She told me she's...(Sniff, sniff)... Dying!"

"I know. She told me too." I held her close as she cried.

"You knew? And you didn't tell me?" She was slightly upset but her grief was overpowering.

"She wanted to tell you herself." I told her.

"What am I going to do? She can't die on me now! Not now!"

"Baby, it's the best thing for her. She's old and tired and she's ready to go."

"I know but I just don't want her to die! She's the only mother I've really known. My own mother never helped me and treated me like she does." She sniffled and hugged me tighter.

"I know. I know."

She cried steadily for at least 10 minutes before she started to get herself together. The front of my shirt was soaked with her tears. When she finished, she wiped the tears away and prepared herself to go back up to mom's apartment.

"Look what I've done! I've got you all wet!" She had red swollen eyes, but she was still gorgeous and sexy. Big Al started to wake up.

"Now it's my turn to get you all wet!" I grinned and winked.

"You're so nasty!" She began to smile. "But you know what the doctor said, no sex before your check-up!"

"Yeah, yeah, yeah! He can say that because his wife is probably all fat and dumpy and wears bloomers! If he had a wife like mine, he would never say that! Look at you! You're stunningly beautiful, curves like a mountain road, skin soft as a baby's ass!" (She giggled) "Lips so sweet that I'm now diabetic! And you make love so good it makes me want to cry! And,... You don't wear bloomers!"

She couldn't contain herself any longer. She fell on me laughing.

"Would you like to see me in bloomers?" Her sadness disappeared temporarily and her smile reappeared.

"Yeah, the old-fashioned silky kind that the movie stars wore! The ones that were skintight! You'd be sexy as hell!"

"Ooooo! I love you! I'm ready to give you some now!"

"You're wet, huh?"

"Uh-huh!" She giggled again.

"Maybe later. Business first, remember?"

"Party pooper!"

We talked about the store and what we should do about it. We both wanted to reopen but we realized that it would be best for all concerned if we didn't. Mom had told her the same thing that she had told me about the people in Allentown. I told Diana how I had been treated just before I went into the building, and she became upset.

"Mom's right," she said, "she's always right!"

"So, what do you think?" I asked.

"It's your store. It's your decision!"

"No baby girl! You're my wife now so it's our store. I want to know what you think."

"Okay but do me just one favor before we talk about that, please?" The charming syrupy sweetness came through with the last word.

"What?"

"Say it."

"Mrs. Diamond!"

"Ooooooo! Those words… they really make me wet!" She kissed her rings. "Donn, do you realize what you've done? You've put up with a crazy woman and transformed her into a wife and mother. I love you and I promise you I'll never cheat on you. I will always be faithful to you! These legs will never open for anyone but you! Ever! Except… my gynecologist!" She giggled.

"You're insane!" I said playfully.

"I know. You like it."

"Love it, but Diana we have to get serious about what we are going to do. The place is a mess, upstairs and down. The only place that isn't really messed up is our bedroom and the computer room."

"I know. I snuck in there while you are in the hospital. It was really sad to see everything ruined because of some asshole and his jealousy. I don't want to live there again even if we open the business back up. I don't think I could deal with it every day, you know, crossing the spot where I,... he died. If you want my opinion, let's get rid of it. Maybe sell the business or at least move it somewhere else."

"I agree. I don't want to live there either. I really think we ought to do just as mom says and leave Pittsburgh altogether."

"That's fine with me but I don't want to leave before mom,... you know what I mean." She didn't want to say when mom dies.

"We won't. She's not going to be alone when it happens. We'll be right there." I promised.

"See, that's why I love you so much. You're so compassionate and caring."

"Maybe I am, maybe I'm not, but I'll never forget that she saved my life, and she has always been a friend. Actually, she's been more like a mother to me and I just want to give back to her a little of what she has given me."

We agreed first to recover whatever was salvageable and let the insurance company handle the rest. We weren't going to reopen. We decided not to leave town until all of our business was complete, including taking care of mom through her final days.

We told mom of our plans. At first, she tried to discourage us from staying with her until the end but we were rock solid about it and we knew that she really wanted us to stay. It was just her stubborn pride rising up. In the end, she gave in.

"You know that those no good children of mine are going to take everything that I have once I'm gone." She said.

"Well, they can have it all!" Diana replied. "But they can't have you! They're missing out now, and they'll be sorry later!"

Mom held Diana and kissed her cheek then she turned her attention to me.

"Son, when is your doctor's appointment?" Mom asked. Her face suddenly became serious.

"Why?"

"Never you mind!" She waved me off and turned to face Diana again. "Diana, when you drop him off at the doctor's office, I want you to take me somewhere."

"Where?" Diana asked.

"Why? Where? You two are awfully nosy! All in my Kool-Aid and don't even though the flavor! Can't a lady have any privacy?"

"Well, excuuuusssseee me!" Diana and I both said at the same time with the same long drawn-out tone.

The subject centering on what mom was going to do was abruptly ended.

On Monday Diana and I met with the insurance adjuster. He was a very nice guy, but I knew his niceness was just his way of suckering us in. He spent about an hour surveying the damage, taking pictures and notes, then about another half hour interview us and going over the paperwork. As soon as he was finished he said we would learn from the company in a few days what their decision was going to be and then he left. Diana and I went straight to Bill's office. I knew instantly that I was going to have trouble getting my just do from the insurance company. I need help. I needed a good lawyer. I needed Bill!

On Tuesday I went to my doctor's appointment. Diana was driving the van with Donnte' strapped in his seat behind mom. Mom sat in the passenger seat, and I sat behind Diana and next to my son.

Mom wouldn't tell me what she was up to but she kept this odd grin on her face the whole time. She has a thick manila envelope with her.

The doctor said he was pleased with my progress but that I still needed to take it easy for while.

"Doc, what about sex? Don't tell me that I can't have sex?" I waited and prayed that he would answer in the way that I wanted him to.

He was at his late forty's. A good-looking man and in very good shape. He had no overhanging belly or flabby arms. It was obvious to me that he was very health conscious with himself and not just with his patients.

"My suggestion to you is this. You had a very close brush with death. You are strong and virile and you're healing incredibly fast, but if you want to make a full and complete recovery, sex should not be in your plans for at least another week. I've seen your wife and she is an incredibly beautiful woman and I know that it's hard for you to keep your hands, and other body parts, to yourself, but let's see how you fare in the next week first. Okay?"

I was extremely disappointed, but I heeded his advice. After all, he was the doctor. He knew the body infinitely better than I did.

"Okay Doc, but if my wife comes storming in here after I tell her what you've said, you'd better have your running game in order!"

He smiled and then said. "I'll tell you what. If it gets critical go ahead and have sex, but you let her be on top. That's the only way! Let her do all the work and you just enjoy. Deal?"

"That's a deal! Because it's already critical!"

Diana called and said she was on her way. I was sitting in the lobby reading an article about prostate cancer in Men's Health magazine when I saw the van pull up. Before the article, I didn't even know what a prostate was, but that changed to knowing how critical it could be to life and death in men.

Mom was sitting up front, so I got in the back next to my son. He was making sounds trying his best to talk but only he could understand what he was saying. He was such a good child. He hardly ever cried but kept a smile on his face whenever I was around. His little arms were reaching for something in the air above him, something that I couldn't see.

"Hey baby. How did it go?" Diana asked. The van started moving again.

"Great! He said I'm doing fantastic!"

"What about... ah... You know?" She looked at mom hoping that she didn't know what she meant, but of course she did!

"You can say the word. Its sex! I've heard it before, you know!" Mom said. She turned to Donnte'. "Boy, you're not going to be an only child for long! You'd better enjoy it while you can!"

"Mom!" Diana was embarrassed.

"What? Go ahead and answer her, son! Go ahead!" Mom demanded.

"He said only if I take it easy and allow you to do all the work. You have to be on top!"

Diana turned and looked at me with a satisfied grin. "That's not a problem. Not at all!"

I changed the subject.

"Mom, where did you go today?" I asked.

"There you go. Getting into my business again! But if you must know, I went to see Attorney Nelson."

"Bill? For what?"

She gave me that motherly evil eye that says, 'you'd better watch it'.

"Okay, okay, I'll back off."

"Good!" She turned back to face the front, then very quickly turned back to me. "Because I don't want to have to turn you across my knee!" She winked.

I left it at that and sat back to admire my son and his airplay.

"You'll find out in good time, but not before!" Mom said without looking back. Again, the subject was closed.

The next two weeks were mainly uneventful other than a few things. The insurance company offered a settlement far below the true value. That was expected. Bill battled with them, and I stayed out of it. They raised the offer but still didn't come close to what I wanted.

My checkups stayed very positive and the doctor gave me the okay to do normal activities again, but with moderation. The store stayed closed despite several requests from customers to reopen.

I sold the window cleaning service to my crew leader, for a very reasonable price. Actually, he was the one that did most of the work and he ran everything for me. It was more his business than mine. I was just the one whose name was on the paperwork, but he was the one that the customers came to know.

Diana and I moved into an apartment just up the street and across the corner on Arlington Avenue. It was only a block and a half away and it wasn't an apartment that I normally would have taken but it was readily available, and it was close to mom. We didn't stay there much because most of our time was spent with mom at her apartment.

The changes in mom's health came quickly and by the beginning of that second week it was clear that she would not be around long. On Wednesday, she went into the hospital again. The doctor said her body was shutting down. They wanted her to stay, but she refused. She didn't want to die in a hospital. She wanted to die at home, so along with a full-time nurse and a lot of equipment, we took her home.

It was a very trying time for all of us watching her get so weak that she could no longer sit up without help. Seeing the machines monitor in her every breath and heart beat and seeing the numbers slowly dropping was heart wrenching. It wasn't her that was sad, it was Diana and me. She was excited over what was about to happen. She told me that she felt the same as she did when she was about to step onto the jet to go to Las Vegas.

"Don't worry son. I'm going to enjoy this ride even more!" She weakly whispered in my ear and raised her hand to touch my face. "Thank you for everything, Donn. I couldn't have asked for a better son than you. Son, I love you very much!"

"I love you too, mom!" I was almost in tears.

"It's okay for you to cry. Real men do cry sometimes. The Bible says that even Jesus wept when his friend Lazarus died. So, if Jesus can cry, so can you." She rubbed my face gently with her hand and looked lovingly into my eyes. "I've always wanted a son. God promised to give me one! He gave me you! He answered my prayers, and he was faithful to his word. Son, always trust in The Lord. Even when it looks like it's impossible, God can still do it! He is the master of the impossible!" She started to tire from all of the talking. "Take your wife and son out to dinner somewhere. Get her away from here for a while. She needs to relax. She's to tense worrying about me."

"But,…" I didn't get a chance to say it.

"Don't worry. He's not going to take me until I'm ready. I'll be here when you get back! I promise." She touched my cheek. "Give me a kiss and get out of here."

I did as I was told.

Friday morning, Diana and I were up in our apartment and getting ready to go over to moms when the phone call came. It was her nurse. My heart sank because I didn't want to hear what she was about to tell me, but I listened. Diana stood behind me with her hands wrenching together praying that the news wasn't what she was dreading.

"Mr. Diamond? Mrs. Reynolds asked that I call. She wants her family around her now. It's just about that time!"

"We'll be right there." I hung up relieved that she hadn't passed on yet.

"It's time Diana." I said.

She didn't respond but she just nodded her head. There was complete silence between us until we walked into mom's place.

Mom was laying flat on her back with her head held up by pillows, waiting, and smiled when she saw us. I stood on one side of her bed and

Diana stood on the other with tears in our eyes. She had become a part of our family and we had become her children. Nothing mattered, not color, age, ethnic background, race, money, nothing! Nothing, but love!

I leaned over with Donnte' so that she could see him. I put him close. She touched his face as she did mine and closed her eyes. She was praying for him.

She called Diana close. Diana bent over and kissed her on the cheek. Mom did the same with her as she did with Donnte'.

"I love you, mom. I'll always love you and I'll never forget you. Thank you for everything you taught me and thank you for being my mom!" Tears fell from her eyes as she spoke.

"I love you too, my child. I'll be waiting in Heaven for you." Mom smiled.

Then it was my turn. I leaned down and kissed her forehead and then both of her cheeks. "Mom, my life is so much better because of you. I'll remember all that you've told me and all that you've taught me and I will never forget you. I love you! I'll never forget you!"

"And I love you too, son! I want to see you in Heaven so read chapters 18 and 21 of Genesis and you'll understand God's promise to me about you. Bill has paperwork for you. Take good care of my grandson,… and my granddaughter,… she's on the way!" She winked. "Goodbye son!" I leaned closer and she kissed my cheek then she laid back. An angelic smile covered her face. Her face began to glow. I held her hand and Diana held the other. Slowly her breathing became shallow until it faded away as her spirit left her body!

The funeral was an event in the city. It was held in Mom's church on Grandview Avenue in Mount Washington. Mom was the city's former first lady and after the death of her husband, she had been forgotten, but now with her death she was remembered again. There were representatives from the Governor's Office in Harrisburg, the current Mayor and former Mayor attended. Members of the Heinz family, the DuPont family, the Mellon family, and the Carnegie family were there along with other prominent, but less known families in the city.

Mom's daughters took their seats in the front row in the family section with their children. Other family members and friends filled the next ten rows. They were all draped in black. Diana, Bill, Darla, Donnte' and I sat on the opposite side. We were not family, so we were not permitted to sit in the family section.

Everyone spoke highly of mom. They spoke as if they had spent the vast majority of their time with her. There were those that remembered her when they knew her as the city's first lady and there were those that remembered her as a much younger woman. They spoke of the good times that they had together and the entire room laughed at the quips and anecdotes and jokes that they told. I learned a lot about mom as I listened. And there were those that talked about her as if they were close personal friends and had been there when she died. It was clear to me that they didn't really know her at all but just wanted to be in the limelight. When her eldest daughter spoke, it sickened me to hear her speak and shed tears. Her other two daughters followed suit and tried their best to squeeze tears out. It was all for show. They cared nothing about their mother, but only for the money that she had bequeathed to them.

I was glad when it was all over because it was a spectacle where most people wanted to be seen and heard. Her family performed as if they cared, as if they had been there in her last days when in fact not one of them came. All three of her daughter's reaction to the news of their mother's death was, 'who was her attorney?', 'What was his phone number?' Their interests lay in her material possessions only.

In the days that followed we watched the daughters and other family members converge on the apartment and strip it of all that they had thought to be of value. We were banned and barred from the apartment by the family. In particular, it was mom's oldest daughter from Philadelphia. Once she was finished and her vehicle was packed with everything of value, she said to Diana,

"Dearie, please be a sweetheart and see that the place is cleaned up!"

Diana snapped. "You worthless bitch! I ought to kick your ass!"

"Now now, Dearie!" She said as I grabbed Diana and held on. "We don't want to end up back in the mental ward again, do we?"

I started to let go of Diana and see if this woman's fight game was as good as her talk game. But I held on. I had seen Diana in action and this prissy bitch was no match for her!

We walked through mom's apartment. Everything was torn up. All of her dresser drawers were pulled out and dumped. They left all of her clothes scattered across the floor. The mattress and box springs were cut open. The cushions and backs of the sofa and lounge chair were also cut.

They obviously thought that mom had been hiding money and valuables there. Everything was just thrown around with no respect or concern. As we stood looking around, Donnte', for the first time that I can remember, began to cry in mom's apartment. Diana began to cry too. I put my arm around her and guided her out of the door and we never went back.

The following Monday we were invited to the reading of the will. The family was there decked out in an array of brightly colored expensive clothes. The will was read by Judge Fiat. It was true, as her family had suspected, she had money stashed away but it wasn't in the mattresses or sofa cushions, but in the bank. She also had stocks and bonds worth several million dollars. When that information was revealed, the family's eyes lit with excitement and anticipation of receiving their share.

The bulk of her wealth was divided up among the family as expected, so no one was upset when Diana received $50,000 and I received mom's family Bible. In the end, everyone was satisfied and went away happy, except Diana! She didn't care about the money, she just wanted to tear a piece of mom's insolent daughter's face off!

The Bible that mom left me was old and leather bound. It was the same one that she had read from in my presence many times. She had marked her favorite passages in several assorted colors and had homemade bookmarks sticking out. There were a lot of papers stuck in various places with notes she had written to herself and references to things she intended to do. The Bible had a faded purple case that she had made herself when her first child was still a baby. It was a privilege to receive it but I wasn't sure why she wanted me to have it and not one of her children. I thought that there might be at least one person in her family that would want it, but I was wrong. They just wanted the money and the wealth.

When we left, we went to see Bill. He told me of the meeting that he had with mom and what was discussed. He produced a locked metal box with a Yale padlock but no key.

He spoke. "She told me to give this to you! I don't know what's in it but I do know that she signed over a beach house in Malibu California to you!" He placed papers on his desk and handed me a pen. "Sign here, here, here, and here! And I need your initials here, here, and here. Then sign there and date it!"

"A beach house in Malibu?"

"Yes! And it's all yours free and clear just as soon as you sign!" He pointed toward the paper in an effort to make me see the urgency of it.

I began to sign the documents and put my signature where he directed.

"Also," he handed me a sealed manila envelope, "she asked me to give you this. She asked that you don't open it until you're on the train! She said that you would understand."

"Yes, yes, I do. Okay."

"Also, the insurance company and I have come to a settlement. It's only final upon your approval and signature. Here's the figure we've agreed upon."

I looked at it. It was less than what I wanted, but not that much less. It was close enough, so I agreed.

"I'm interested in buying the building from you in its present condition." He wrote some figures on a piece of paper. "You keep the check from the insurance company, I'll give you this amount." He touched his pen to the figure. "And whatever stock I can salvage, I'll give you half of the value. What do you think?"

I didn't hesitate. I spoke. "It's a deal! So, what are you going to do with the place?"

"Upstairs, will be a photography studio for Darla. It's going to be her wedding present. Downstairs, is where I'll move my office. I'm tired of paying those white crooks for this place!"

"Getting married, huh? When?"

"Well, I haven't asked her yet." He smiled.

"Don't worry, she'll be as happy as a sissy in Boys Town when you do. You two belong together." I gave him a handshake and a manly hug. "Let me know. We will definitely come!"

"You'd better! I want you to be my best man. Diana, I'm sure that she will want you to be the maid of honor, but please don't say anything until I ask her. Okay?"

"Now why would I do a thing like that!?" Diana asked.

"Because you're a woman with a big mouth just like her!" He and I started laughing.

"I ought to kick you for that!" Diana said as she smiled at Bill.

We said our goodbyes and left with the locked box and the manila envelope. On the envelope the words were written; "MY SON, DONN".

I also had the check from the insurance company. The only thing we had left to do was to pack. The building sale to Bill would happen later.

Back at the apartment I gave thought to picking the lock on the box but I knew that there was a key somewhere. I probably had it in the manila envelope. Diana and I didn't have much to say to each other. We were both lost in the thoughts of mom. It started to become depressing.

"When do you want to leave?" I asked.

"As soon as we can. I don't want to be here anymore." She was almost in tears again.

"How about Wednesday?" I walked up behind her and put my arms around her.

"That's fine!" She turned to face me. "Let's make love baby. I need you inside of me! Make me feel good. Make love to me!"

I did. For the moment we were lost in ecstasy and had forgotten about our sorrows but when it ended and we lay in each other's arms, spent and breathless, it all came flooding back. Wednesday wasn't soon enough.

"I'm going to call the station and see what's leaving late tomorrow evening. We'll pack the things we're taking and leave the rest in storage. Bill and Darla can send it out later. Thinking of Bill and Darla, I've got an idea."

"What is it?" Life suddenly came back to her.

"Let's take them out tomorrow before we leave. Let's go to bubbles and Sherman's!"

"Baby, are you thinking what I think you're thinking?" She was on her knees on the bed looking at me and smiling.

"Yep. I sure am!"

She jumped up. "I'll start packing. You call Bill."

Diana couldn't stop crying when she saw the red velvet chair set up in the middle of the room. Darla didn't know what it meant, not yet, but she moved towards it and sat down as instructed! When Bill got down on one knee and presented the ring, Diana cried more than Darla did. But... all and all, it was a beautiful occasion.

Bill and I sat watching the two of them act like giddy schoolgirls while Darla proudly showed off her ring. Bubbles and Sherman's was alive that night with cheerfulness and laughter. Seeing Darla so happy lifted my spirits and I felt so much better because of it.

"Donn," Darla began, "you're a great friend and I love you. Thank you!"

"I love you too. I'm happy for you. Let us know when the wedding will be, and we will definitely be there."

The four of us sat back in the back of the limo and talked about our future. Bill and Darla said that they would come to Malibu for a few days while on their honeymoon. It was something that Diana and I looked forward to.

We said our goodbyes at the train station and Diana, Donnte' and I boarded the westbound Amtrak train. As the train pulled out, I watched Darla and Bill standing and waving with one hand and the other snuggly wrapped around their fiancés waist.

We found our sleeper berth and settle down. Donnte' was given a crib made especially for train travel. He laid in it as we lay on the bed and silently thought about mom. I pulled the mysterious manila envelope out and opened it. Inside was a letter and some very old certificates.

"What does the letter say?" Diana asked.

I began to read:

> "Dear son, I pray that you have followed my instructions and waited until you were comfortable on the train to read this. There is a method to my madness. What is contained in this envelope will make you a very rich man. I know that if my family found out about the stocks and bonds that they would fight you for them and they would probably win. But by now they have gorged themselves on my belongings and have gone home to spend my money. You have seen their greed and selfishness and disregard for anything sacred. The Bible was a test. Of course, none of them wanted it! It's the most valuable possession that I have but they could never see that through their greed and selfishness. It holds the secret to life and the ticket to Heaven!"
>
> "Once you get to Malibu, you will find an account in your name in the Central Municipal Bank of Malibu. It contains all of the dividends received over the years

from the stocks that you hold. There's also an account in Diana's name as well as a trust fund for my grandson and granddaughter."

Diana interrupted. "What granddaughter?"
"Oh! Mom said you're pregnant and you're having a girl!"
"Really? How does she?... never mind."
I continue to read:

> "Son, take loving care of yourself and your family. Remember that money is meant to be governed by you, don't let the money control you! Read that Bible son! Read it aloud to your family. I want to see all of you in Heaven one day. Remember to read Genesis chapter 18 and 21 about Abraham, Sarah, and their son Isaac. Thank you for your love and a good sendoff. Love eternally, mom".

It became Very quiet. The only sound to be heard was the click-a-de-clack of the wheels of the train.

I looked at the certificates. Most of them were old but there were a few fairly recent ones. I thumbed through them and saw the names like AT&T, Mellon Bank, Wells Fargo Bank, H: J. Heinz Company, General Motors Corporation, City Bank of New York, and others. But the ones that caught my eye were some of the newer ones, like Microsoft, Wachovia Bank, and Google!

I looked at the bonds and realized that most weren't ordinary bonds but were bearer bonds. The denominations were high in the five figures and two of them were six figures. I showed them to Diana. She smiled but that was it. We were rich beyond our wildest dreams, but the joy was not as I had hoped it would be. Mom was the reason for it all but she was gone. I would have given it all up just to have her back. I stuffed everything back into the envelope and put it away. Diana cuddled up beside me.

"Aren't you going to look for the key and open the box?" She asked.
"No! Maybe later!"
"Thinking about mom, huh?"
"Yeah."

"Well, you know that she gave all of this to us so that we could enjoy it. If she were here with us on this train you would be happy and smiling and acting stupid, right?"

"Yes, I would." I said.

"So, let's start enjoying the things she gave us. She wouldn't want us moping around." She kissed me. "I know what will perk you up." She grabbed Big Al. He responded just as always. It brought a smile to my face. "Mmmm, He likes me!" She purred.

"He always has! How's Jennifer?"

"Ready and willing and waiting for Big Al to come out and play."

I unbuttoned her pants and peeled them off. She finished undressing and laid back.

"Did mom say I was pregnant or that I'm going to be pregnant?"

"I think she said that you are pregnant!"

"Well, come here,…. Let's make sure!"

CHAPTER 21

On the Train

The train was approaching Cincinnati when I awoke. The moon was high in the sky and it was surrounded by hundreds of stars that reminded me of children gathering around their father. I laid in the dark beside my lovely wife and gave thought to all that had transpired in the last month. I gazed over at Diana and watched her sleep. I thought of how much God had blessed me and I silently said a prayer of thanks.

Mom always told me that God had a special blessing for me. She often spoke of God, Jesus Christ, and the Holy Spirit. Those concepts were somewhat vague to me, but I knew that I was blessed. Just having mom in my life was a blessing in itself.

Diana was now my wife, my lovely wife! I had vowed after my disastrous marriage and divorce that I would never marry again. No woman would ever take me through that horror and pain again. I meant every word but that fateful day in spring at the Onala club changed all of that. She was a far cry from what I had known her to be back then. She was still the most beautiful woman that I had ever known, she was the free spirit that I loved to be around, she was still the sex partner that had surpassed all others. She was the mentally ill woman that took me through changes, but she was no longer the crazy woman that I feared. She was no longer the practicing alcoholic and addict that would call me in the middle of the night for help or sex, or both. She was no longer the loose cannon freely moving at will on the deck of my emotional ship. And above all, she was the mother of my first and only son! She was, the stabilizing force in my life! She was my rock!

I remembered that first day when we met. I thought of the first time I went to her house and the crazy changes that she put me through. I thought of the first time we kissed, first time that we made love, the first argument we had, the first time I took her horseback riding, her first ride on the incline, and the first time that I really missed her! I thought about the time I sat waiting for her to call wondered what she was doing and where she was. I don't remember exactly when I fell in love with her because I was so infatuated with her beauty and so in lust with her body, but somewhere along the line, the infatuation changed, and the lust transformed and the desire to possess her for lust's sake ease and allowed real love to enter my heart.

I remember my life before Diana, and it was not the fulfilling life that I had believed it to be. In reality, it wasn't at all what I wanted it to be. I was running from being the man that I was intended to be. I ran for fear of being hurt again by the treachery of an evil woman. Donna!

I vowed not to become a husband again. Not to be committed to any woman in that way again, but here I was, married with a child and according to mom, another one on the way! Everything had changed. My whole life and thinking had changed. I did a detour from the path that I had chosen and now was headed in an entirely different direction, but as I pondered the old and the new, the new was definitely better.

"Hi baby! Are you okay?" She stretched and yawned as she opened her eyes.

"Hi sweetheart! Yeah, I'm okay. Just sitting here thinking." I leaned over and kissed her. I loved the softness and sweetness of her lips. I kissed her again. This time I wrapped my arms around her and held her for a moment.

"What was that all about? Are you sure you're okay?" She looked me in the eye with loving concern.

"Yeah. I'm sure."

"So, what are you thinking about?"

"Just stuff."

"What kind of stuff? Stuff like, the expansion of the universe, stuff? Or stuff like, mom leaving us all of this money, stuff? Or stuff like, what we've been going through, stuff? Or stuff like, MY STUFF?"

"What?"

"MY STUFF! You know, this good stuff that you love so much!" She began to smile.

"No. I wasn't thinking about YOUR STUFF,... But now I am!"

"You want some?" She asked.

"I just had some."

She snuggled up next to me.

"That was hours ago! Do you want some more? You know you can get it anytime that you want, and you don't even have to ask!"

"Oh, really? I remember a time when you snapped at me for touching your ass!"

"That was then, this is now. I'm different now! I'm your wife! Mrs. Diana Diamond to be exact. Mrs. Diana Diamond! I love the way that sounds. It has a certain ring to it. Mrs. Diana Diamond! Yes! I love that!"

"So, I can take it whenever I want to?"

"Sure. You do already."

"Uh-huh! And that's the way it should be! The way it always will be!" I said in my best manly voice.

"Until were dead and buried. I'll never deny you!"

"I've heard that before." I said with thoughts of Donna in my head. I didn't realize that I was projecting scenes from my past onto the screen of my present life.

Diana asked. "Are you comparing me to someone from your past?"

I didn't want to answer the question, at least I didn't want to answer it truthfully, but I had to. Lying was something that we promised each other that we would not do.

"Yes, I guess I was." I said.

I expected her to get angry, but she didn't show any signs.

"Your ex-wife?" She asked calmly.

"Yes."

"You know baby, you have never told me about her. You never talk about your life with her or what happened. Baby please, tell me about her. Are you still in love with her?"

"No. That's been over a long time ago. But I still sometimes think about what she did, and it causes me not to trust." I kissed her shoulder. "Before you came along, I vowed that I'd never let a woman get under my skin again. I vowed that I'd never get married again, ever! But here I am, married to you, and I loving it!"

"So, I'm special?" She began to grin.

"VERY special!"

"Tell me about her. I want to know. I need to know how she hurt you, so I'll know never to do it. You need to talk about it and let it go. That's what they tell us in recovery, right?"

"That's what they say." I tried to change the subject. "I thought you wanted to know what stuff I was thinking about." It didn't work.

"I do, and right after you tell me, then tell me about your ex-wife. What was her name?"

"Donna."

"You like the 'D's, don't you? Donna, Diana." She giggled a little bit. "Okay. What's the stuff?"

"The stuff is all that we have been through in the last month or so. The store, mom, Carl, the courts, Darla and Bill, mom's family, and all of that! There's just been so much that has happened so quickly. My life took 180° turn and all that I own is gone…"

"Not everything!"

"Yes, it is!"

"No! Not me! Not Donnte!"

"I don't own you, or him!"

"Yes, you do! We're yours for life. His birth certificate says so and so does my marriage license." She hugged me. "Just kidding."

"No, you're not!" I hugged her back. "Besides, I'm talking about material possessions. I loved that store, and I was really getting comfortable in the neighborhood. It was becoming a home to me. Now it's gone. All of it is… Gone! I guess I will get over it in time, but it just plays on my mind. That's what I was thinking about."

"Well baby, we can start all over again. When we get to California, you can start anything you want to. We've got the money to do whatever we want to do." She said.

"Yeah, thanks to mom. But it's just not the same. I worked hard to get where I was, and I took pride in knowing that I had something that I worked for and achieved, and it was good. It may have been small, but it was a start and it was growing. It's different when you work hard for something than when someone just hands you everything. Do you know what I mean?"

"Yes, I understand. But don't get down on yourself. I see it coming again. You can't let yourself sink into depression; you've got to fight it! Remember, I know a lot about depression…and how to get out of it!"

She got up on her knees and placed the palms of her hands on my cheeks.

"Baby, I know how you feel. I've lost a lot in my life too but look what I've found. Look at what I've got now. If I hadn't lost those things that I wanted to hold on to back then, then I wouldn't have the two best men in the whole wide world now. You and Donnte! Sometimes you must let go of what you think you want so that you can grasp on to what you really need. I know that if Carl hadn't cheated on me, I'd probably still be there with him, and I would have missed you. Donnte wouldn't exist and our little girl would not be on the way! This is what I really want. This is what I really need. You're in transition right now and it hurts but believe me it's going to get better. I promise!" She kissed me gently on the lips.

"I love you, Mrs. Diamond! No doubt… you're the woman for me!"

"Ooooooo! You know what that does to me?"

"Mrs. Diamond!"

"Oooooooo! You're going to make me all wet again!"

"Mrs. Diamond! Mrs. Diamond! Mrs. Diamond!"

I grabbed her around her waist and squeezed her. Her breath was labored, and her pulse was rising. I was ready for some of her stuff, and I was about to have it.

"Mr. Diamond?"

"Yes, Mrs. Diamond?"

"Our son is watching us." She said it almost in a whisper.

"Damn!"

"Watch your mouth!"

"Darn!"

"Were just going to have to wait."

"Darn! Darn! Darn!"

She pulled away from me and picked him up. I sat back again and told Big Al to go back to sleep.

We sat on the bed and played with Donnte for the next few minutes before she asked again. "Tell me about Donna!" Her tone was soft and sweet and almost begging, so how could I resist?

"What do you want to know?"

"Everything! I want to know how you met, where you lived, what you liked about her, did she had big breasts, why did you break up, what she did to you, everything!"

"Baby that will take too much time. Were just about in Cincinnati. Don't you want to see the city? I can tell you about her later. We'll be on the train for quite some time."

"No Donn! You're stalling! You're not getting out of this. And yes, I do want to see Cincinnati, but it's at least a half hour before we pull into the station, so start talking!"

She pulled out one of her breasts and attached Donnte to it. He began to suck as he looked at his daddy. He smiled at me as he sucked. I envied him. He knew it!

I stood my ground. It wasn't that I didn't want to talk and tell her about it, but I didn't want to get started and get into it and then have to stop in the middle while we explored the city and then start all over again. What I had to say was just too emotional.

"No Diana. I'm going to tell you, but not now. Is going to take some time, longer than a half an hour. I'll wait until after we get back on the train, and then I'll tell you all that you want to know."

She reluctantly agreed.

When she finished feeding our son, I took him and placed him over my shoulder and patted his back until he burped. I laid back and laid him on my chest. Diana lay down beside me. There was silence for a few moments. It was the silence of a loving family that didn't need to talk all the time to show love. It was love in silence that communicates more than words at times.

"Diana?"

"Yes Donn?"

I could tell that she was just a little bit upset with me because she didn't get her way. I knew it because she called me Donn, and not, 'baby'.

"Do you remember when you told me about why you had such a fear of blonde, white women?"

"Yes, I remember."

"What if I had forced you to tell me before you were ready? You wouldn't you have felt comfortable and you wouldn't have said all that you did. Am I right?" I asked.

"Probably not." She began to see my point. "Okay, I see where you're coming from, but as soon as we get back to the train, you're going to tell me. Okay?"

"Sure sweetheart. I promise."

We didn't get a chance to see much of the city because our layover was only a half an hour and the next train didn't come for 24 hours, so we spent the half hour layover sightseeing from the inside of a taxicab.

"Baby?" Diana began. "Who do you love the most? Donna, or me?"

"That's a silly question. You, of course!" I said it without any hesitation whatsoever.

"No! It's not a silly question. She was your wife, now I am. Which one of us is number one?"

"Diana, how can you ask me something like that? There's just no comparison. You win hands down!" I told her. "I know what you're getting at but listen to me. I married her when I was still a teenager and I didn't really know what love was all about. I thought love was just a good feeling that I got when I was between her legs. That's a piece of it, but that's not love at all! When things went wrong, love wasn't there to hold everything together. When I look back on it now that I'm more mature and I've got more knowledge of what life and love is all about, I realize that what she and I had was infatuation, plus an addiction for sex with each other. Maybe there was an element of love there, but it was nothing like what I feel for you. Of course, I lust after you, but how can I not? As fine as you are?"

She showed her appreciation with a gigantic smile.

"But if all that I felt for you was lust, then I never would have married you. I was thinking about how much I love you and I was trying to determine when I fell in love with you. When did the lust change and when did the love began? I don't know. I do know that somewhere along the line I went from lusting after you to loving you so much that I was willing to risk life and limb to have you!"

She cut in.

"Baby, that's so sweet!" She kissed me on the cheek. "I don't know when all that changed either, but I know that you were already in love with me when I told you about Carl and what I had done to him." She paused. "I expected you to leave me when I told you that I had cut him up and cut his dick off, but you didn't. You already knew! You already knew, and you still stayed with me. Either you were crazier than I was, or you were madly in love with me. I didn't understand but because of it, I started to look at you differently. You were more than just my 'boy toy', you were a real man, and I began to see that."

"Your boy toy?"

"Yeah, my boy toy! When I wanted sex, I called you! I could have called anyone I wanted to, but I called you. My boy toy!"

"Hummm, boy toy, huh? So, what were you to me? My girl toy? No, that doesn't sound right."

"I was your sex slave!"

"My sex slave? I like that!"

"Yeah, I thought you would." She smiled at me.

"When did you first realize that you were in love with me?" I asked her.

"I'm still working on that." She laughed from her gut. "Ha ha ha! Just kidding. It was the night I called you and you drove all the way to Homewood to get me. I was in trouble and you were mad at me, but you still got up in the middle of the night to come and get me. No man ever did anything like that for me before. I didn't really want to call you because I knew you were mad at me and I didn't think that you would come, but you didn't hesitate! You got up and drove all the way across town for me! When I was in the hospital months later and I had my spiritual awakening, I thought about you. I thought how much you meant to me and I refused to let you go because my stupidity got in the way."

She stopped talking. She was in deep thought and it appeared that she was about to cry.

"I love you, Mrs. Diamond!" I said softly.

"I love you too, Mr. Diamond. [Sniff sniff]!"

"Let me tell you something. Okay?"

"Okay!" She dabbed at her eyes.

I don't know what's in that box with the lock on it, but whatever it is, it's important. I don't know where the key is because she didn't tell me, but it's somewhere where we can find it. Maybe it's in the house in Malibu."

"What do you suppose is in it?" She asked.

"If I had to guess, from the weight of it, I'd say something like her cookbooks. When I shake it, it sounds like books. But you don't really need cookbooks anymore. When it comes to cooking, mom made you the heavyweight champion!"

Her smile was infectious, and it affected me.

"Thank you, baby. I have come a long way, haven't I? But I'd still like to have her cookbooks because there are so many things that she knew that she wanted to teach me but couldn't because she was,…. dying." She had trouble saying that word.

"I thought about picking the lock, but I decided against it. There's a key somewhere. Even if I can't find it, I won't tamper with the lock, I'll take it to a locksmith first. That box meant a lot to mom, and I don't want to destroy it.

"Respect?" She asked, still overcome with emotion.

"Yes!" It was time to change the subject back to Donna. "So, you want to know everything about Donna, huh?"

"Yes, everything."

"Okay."

She had been waiting a while to hear about 'the other woman' and she became excited.

Donnte' was lying in his crib with his angelic look on his face. He wasn't looking at anything in particular, but just looking up as if there were something, or someone above him. He was content and satisfied.

I laid back on the bed after removing my pants and shirt and beckoned her to come cuddle with me. She stripped down to her panties and bra and lay beside me in my arms, with her head on my chest.

CHAPTER 22

The Other Woman

We had already crossed the Ohio River and pass through Covington Kentucky. The countryside was passing us by while the streams of light from the warm sun came in and brightened the dark corners of the room. I was comfortable and at ease and ready to speak.

"Donna and I met when I was 15 years old."

"How old was she?"

"She was 14 years old."

"Where did you meet her?" She asked even before I finished answering the last question.

"Diana, slow down! Give me a chance to answer one question, before you ask the next. Be patient okay?"

"Okay baby. I'm sorry." She hugged me and tried to relax.

"I met her when I went up to Northview Heights with my cousin Ramon. His half-sister Rosetta lived up there. I had never been to the project before because my mother didn't want me to go there because she was afraid I'd get hurt. I had heard stories about how rough it was, but I grew up in Manchester and it was pretty rough there too! I always thought that I was pretty tough, so it didn't really bother me. But, to appease my mother I basically stayed away but this day I decided to go. After we left her house, we went over to the basketball court beyond the high-rise and got into a game."

She interrupted again.

"You can play basketball?"

"DIANA!!! You are interrupting again!"

"I'm sorry, but I didn't know that you could play ball!"

"Yeah, and I'm good at it too!"

"Hummm. We'll see about that once we get to Malibu. Maybe you don't know it but I'm very good!" She smiled. "Very, very good!"

"Get out of here!" I said. "Really?"

She nodded and smiled the entire time.

She had previously told me that she played volleyball and softball and was on the cheerleading squad, but she never said anything about basketball, until then. But, neither had I. Most of what we talked about centered on recovery and our sex lives. There were numerous things that we didn't know about each other.

"You never told me that you could play the game." I'm sure surprise was written across my face because it was evident in my tone.

"Sure, I can play. In high school, I was the star point guard for the girls' team." She beamed with pride.

"So was I! Well, not for the girls' team."

"That's it! I'm going to show you a thing or two." She boasted.

"Baby, we don't have to wait until Malibu. We can get it on in St. Louis! We're going to be there for a day or two." I said it with an abundance of confidence. "You'll be sorry when it's all over."

"No baby, you'll be sorry, not me!"

Donnte' was looking up at us as we spoke. I wondered what he was thinking. What was going through his mind as he watched his mom and dad act like children?

"You want to place a bet?" I asked.

"What kind of bet?"

"Anything you want. Make it easier on yourself because you're going to lose." I said.

"Not in a million years!" She turned to face me. "How about this? If you win, then I'll do whatever you say all day and if I win, you do whatever I say. Is that a deal?"

"It's a deal! Now can I get back to what I was talking about, CHERYL?"

"CHERYL? Who the hell is CHERYL?" There was a hint of anger in her voice when she asked that question. She thought I was calling her by someone else's name.

"Sheryl Miller! Because that's who you'd better be if you think you can beat me! Ha ha ha!"

"Oh." She softened and giggled. "Then you'd better be Reggie! As a matter-of-fact, I think Sheryl used to beat Reggie all the time when they were young, and she still probably can now!"

She was now laying, full-bodied, on me and talking directly into my face. She was smiling and grinning and looking as beautiful.

"Baby, we're going to have so much fun together. Do you know that?" She squirmed over me pressing her body flat against mine. "How many babies do you want?" She asked me.

"What does that have to do with what we're talking about?"

"It doesn't, but I just thought about it and decided to ask."

"I haven't given it much thought."

"Well, it doesn't really matter because whatever you want, I'll give them to you. 15, it doesn't matter. Whatever you want, that's how many we'll have."

She was beginning to transform into her super jovial state. It was the upside of her manic-depressive disorder. I started to say something about it, but I held my peace. It was the good side, not the bad side. I knew that both sides were signs of instability, but I allowed her to enjoy.

"Diana, if you want to hear about Donna, then you'd better let me talk, okay?"

"All right, but its' just so good being with you. I just feel GREAT! I want you to feel the same way that I do. Super excited!"

"I am excited, but you know how I am. I just don't show it as much if you do on the outside." I paused. "You'd really have 15 babies for me if I wanted them?"

"Sure!"

"No, you're just saying that now because you're all crazy in love, but after about three or four you'll change your mind."

"No, I won't! Do you want 15?"

"No. Not really."

"How many do you want?"

"I don't know. Maybe five or six."

"Okay. Six, and then we'll go from there!"

"No! We'll have these two and then we'll enjoy them for a few years before we have any more, Okay?"

"It's a deal." She rubbed her body against mine. She did it very sexually and deliberately to arouse Big Al, and she wasn't disappointed. "Now let's get back to Donna, Reggie!"

"Okay, Cheryl!"

We laughed at the sound of our new nicknames. She rolled off of me and against the wall and I reached down and retrieved Donnte' from the crib and placed him in the bed between us. He started making his baby sounds and she mocked him which made him laugh uncontrollably each time that she did. I joined in and Donnte' became hysterical with laughter each time he heard us, 'coo-che-coo-che-coo' him. He was having the time of his young life and so were we.

Mom was right about many things. She was definitely right about the train. What we were doing could never be done on an airplane. Having the privacy and the comfort wasn't happening on a plane, not at that level. The stress level was so much lower, and the comfort level was so much higher.

So far, we didn't get to see much of the countryside because we were not paying attention to what was going on outside of the window, or to what was happening outside of our door. All of our intentions and fun was right in the room with us. We were a family starting out on our new adventure and loving the time that we were spending together. The train crossed the bluegrass country of Kentucky, but we saw very little of it.

We were still playing with Donnte' when the announcement was made that we were approaching Louisville Kentucky. Donnte' was lying across my chest and Diana tickled both his feet and watched him squirm and laugh. I made funny faces in between the tickling and he cracked up each time.

We hadn't planned to get off at the Louisville stop at all. The train would only stop long enough to pick up and discharge passengers. At the last minute I decided to get off just long enough to pick up some souvenirs from the station's gift shop. I had been thinking about Bill and Darla and I had thought about getting them something from various stops along the way. Diana and I went together and picked out several things for them. One was a 12-inch likeness of Mohammed Ali that had an inscription across the baseplate that said, "The greatest comes from Louisville Kentucky!"

Back on the train, I called Bill. It was just after 7 PM. They were home getting ready to leave for an NA meeting. Darla and Diana talked and giggled like young schoolgirls out on their first double date. While speaking to Bill, the thought hit me that I should just give him the building. No charge! After all, he went out of his way for Diana and put his house up to have her released on bond while I was in the hospital. He deserved much more than just the money that he received for defending her. I didn't say anything to him about it because I wanted to talk to Diana first.

The four of us had never spent much time together as a group. We only had the time spent in court and that last night at bubbles and Sherman's, but there was the closeness that we had that may have been a result of the difficult times that we spent during Diana's trial and my hospitalization, but whatever the reason, it caused us to miss each other's company now that we were apart.

Darla had been my friend for quite some time. I had known her even longer than Diana. She was like my little sister.

I realized that I had misjudged Bill when I first met him. I perceived him to be a bourgeois, stuck up, uppity Negro that had no idea or understanding of how the average Black man lived. Although he was a little bourgeois, and occasionally stuck up, he also was a down to earth, laid back kind of guy. In essence, Bill was all right and I liked him.

"Diana?" I began. "I want to give Bill and Darla that building. What do you think about it?"

"I think it's a great idea! What made you decide to do that?" She asked.

"Well, I haven't decided. It's a thought and I wanted to talk to you first."

"Baby, I think that would be great. Financially, we don't need that building, and it would help them out a lot!"

"Okay, it's settled!"

I called him back and gave him the news. I wasn't sure but I thought that I heard Darla and the background crying.

I turned my attention back to Diana and began to talk again about Donna and how we met.

"Donna was sitting on the short wall behind the building. Her friend, Monica, was sitting next to her. They began to watch us play ball. Now, you must understand that I have always been a showoff and once I saw Donna watching me, I started to show off big time! I was coming down the center of the court with the ball and this guy who thought he was good tried to guard me. He checked me just before the foul line and I dribbled to the right, spun to the left and blew right past him straight to the bucket and two points. As I went back down the court with my team on defense, I winked at her. She smiled and gave me a little finger wave. All through the game I showed off. I was the best player out there and I knew it. After a while, they all knew it to! No one could stop me! No one! Ramon fed me the ball whenever he could and once the other players on my team realized that I couldn't be stopped, they fed me the ball too. We won the game by 22 points.

"After the game, I walked over to Donna and said, "Did you like that? It was all for you!" She said, "But, you don't even know me." I smiled and asked her name. "Donna." She said. "My name is Donn, and this is my cousin Ramon."

She introduced her friend Monica and I concentrated all my interests on Donna. Immediately I had Donna on the brain, and I was determined to get to know her and make her my girlfriend, and I did.

"After that, I went to Northview Heights regularly, and every time I did, I made it my business to find her. Sometimes we would sneak off into the woods and kiss and feel each other up, but she would not let me do it to her. She kept saying that she was going to be a virgin when she got married. Well, that's the way it went for over a year. I'd go up there and do everything with her except, 'the nasty'. That's what we called it back then.

"Her birthday was on May 16 and I bought her this great big birthday card that had a big heart on the front with two people in the middle kissing. Under it I wrote in my best calligraphy, 'Je' Teime'!"

"What does that mean?" Diana interrupted again.

"In French, it means, I love you!"

"You've never said that to me!" She began to pout.

"Yes, I have! I said it to you many times when we were making love!"

"OH! Is THAT what you were saying? I thought you were speaking in tongues because my stuff was so good! Ha ha ha ha!" She rolled on the bed forgetting that Donnte' was lying with us. "Sorry baby boy!" She apologized for her indiscretion. But he didn't mind. He just continued to smile and look at her with love.

"Diana, you're conceited! You think you're 'all that'!"

"Baby, I know I'm 'all that' and more! And so, do you!"

"Yeah, you're conceited. No doubt."

"Say that again." She asked.

"You're conceited?"

"No! That, I love you, thing."

"Je' Teime'!"

"I like the way that sounds. Where did you learn that?"

"You really want to know?"

"Yeah."

"Are you sure?"

"Yes, I'm sure."

"I learned it from Donna! She was taking French in school. It was the first thing that she taught me and just about the only thing that I remember. Anyway, I gave her this giant birthday card and she cried like a baby. I guess she decided then not to be a virgin when she got married because that night, she let me do it. For the next two years we did it every chance we got. About two months after her 17th birthday she told me that she was pregnant. I had just graduated and was about to go to college in September, but that changed everything. Together, we told her parents and of course they were very disappointed with us. I expected her dad to kick my ass, but instead he took me outside and we walked through the projects talking. I thought he was going to start punching me or start strangling me, but he was more concerned about our future that he was angry. He let me know without a doubt that he expected me to do the right thing, which meant marriage. College was out for the moment. When I agreed to get married, he smiled and put his arm around me and called me son. It was a great feeling because I respected him, and he always treated me like a part of the family.

"He had just started his own business and he was looking for someone that he could trust to work with him. He promised me that if I married Donna and went to work for him that in a year, I would have enough money to take care of my family and go on to college too!"

"But baby, wasn't he living in the projects? How was he going to do that?" Diana curiously asked.

"That's the same thing that I thought, but what I didn't know was that for the past five or six years he had been going to night school at Pitt after work and he got his degree. He had started out just like me. His girlfriend, now his wife, was pregnant and they got married young. They didn't believe in abortions. He had dreams but his dreams were sidetracked because of an unplanned pregnancy, but he never gave up on his dream. He did what he had to do but he vowed to get his college degree and start his own business. It took years, but he did it!

"As he laid out his plan, I could see that it was well thought out and planned very well. It wasn't just a pipe dream; it was really going to work. I agreed and went to work for him. Donna and I got married in September and she was due to deliver in March, but she had complications and she lost the baby. Both of us were devastated because we were looking forward to being parents. She went back to school and finished. By the time she graduated, her father's business was moving right along, and we were all doing okay. Everybody thought he was going to move out of the projects right away, but he didn't. He stayed and saved his money because he didn't want to move out and pay rent to someone, he wanted to move into his own house.

"Donna and I had our own place, but we had our problems. She wanted to get pregnant again, but she couldn't, and she blamed me because I was working all the time. I wanted her to go on to college and get that degree that she always wanted, but she got depressed and just stayed at home doing nothing. That caused more problems. We started to grow apart but we didn't separate. We were like two people living in the same house but had nothing in common. She just refused to talk or try to make things work.

"Her father and I became like father and son. We had the business working just as he had planned it to be. A year after I went to work for him, I was financially able to take care of my family and go to college too, just as he had promised. But I didn't go. I wanted her to go and finish her education, but she refused. So, I kept working and banking the money. Dad made me overseer of just about everything. He spent most of his time doing the books and all of the executive work. I handle production, employees, payroll, hiring and firing.

"When Donna turned 19 things really got ugly. Her dad had a house out in Avalon by then and we used to all go out there for special occasions and family gatherings. On Donna's birthday, we had a party for her at her parents' house and all of her family and friends were there, but she didn't show up. She knew about the party, and she led me to believe that she was going to be there. When I got off work and went home to get her, she wasn't there. She left no note, no message or anything. I called her on her cell phone and heard it ringing in the bedroom. She had stuffed it in her underwear drawer. She always kept it with her so I couldn't understand why she left it there. I told her parents and we spent the bulk of the evening trying to locate her. She didn't want to be found. The party was a bust without her.

"The next morning, she called me just as I was getting ready to go out the door for work. She said that she needed some time alone to think. I was furious because she left us all there worrying about her. When I questioned her about her behavior, she wouldn't answer me. I asked where she was, and she said that she was at a friend's house, but she wouldn't say where or who the friend was. I knew all of her friends and they all were at the party waiting for her. Who was this friend? She wouldn't tell me. I later found out that she had gotten hooked up with some people who had convinced her that she would never be happy until she left me and her family and joined up with them. It was a cult! They wanted her and my money and send her back to me to clean out my savings account. She borrowed money from her father and gave it to them. She constantly asked me for large sums of money for this, or for that, but never had anything to show for it. One day I was talking with her dad about her and he asked why I didn't come directly to him for the $5000.

"What $5000?"

"The 5000 you sent Donna to get from me!" He said.

"I didn't send her for any money!" I told him.

"That's not what she told me! She said you needed cash right away and you wanted her to pick it up."

"Dad, I didn't send her! This is the first time I've heard of this. I don't need money. Thanks to you, I've got plenty. I don't know what's going on, but I'm going to get to the bottom of this!"

"When I questioned Donna, I found out absolutely nothing. She acted strange but she told me nothing. I let it go but I was transformed from a loving husband to snooping detective. The next time she asked for money, I didn't question her; I just gave it to her and then I followed her. When

I discovered where she was going, I told her father. He hired a detective agency to find out who they were. They were called The Real Brotherhood! The next time she left with money, her father, her brother Jerry, Ramon and I went to the building. It was in Lawrenceville on Penn Avenue. I saw two men taking Donna into the building. She was going willingly, at least that's what it looked like, but the detectives had said that they brainwash people with the help of drugs. When I followed her the first time and watched her, she walked into the building alone. She walked straight and unencumbered, totally different from what I was seeing this time. I rushed up and grabbed Donna. I got into a shouting match with one of the guys in the foyer of the building. That's when several members of the cult came rushing out and the fight started. Pop knocked two guys out with one punch each. He was vicious! I held onto Donna with one hand and elbowed the guy trying to wrestle her way from my grip. He let go and almost fell to the ground. The cops showed up and were about to arrest us, but I told them that I wanted all of the members of the brotherhood arrested for kidnapping and drugging my wife!

"Your wife?" One of the guys said. "She's not your wife, she's our sister!"

"You're a damned liar!" I shouted. "He's the only brother she has!" I pointed to Jerry who was still in the mood for a fight. "And that's her father, so how can all of you be her brothers?"

The cops turned to me. After assessing the situation, he asked. "How do I know that she is your wife? Maybe I should ask her!"

"Look at her!" I said. "She's drugged. She probably doesn't even know who she is."

"He's lying." One of the guys said. "He doesn't have any claim on her. I want these guys arrested for trespassing. I WANT THEM OUT OF HERE! NOW! Get them off of our property!"

I was so angry that I wanted to punch him right in his nose, but I didn't. Instead I said, "so she's your sister? Well tell me something. What does it say on the inside of her wedding ring?"

They froze like statues. They weren't sure if I was bluffing or not. They probably didn't even look to see if she was wearing a wedding ring, but at that moment, they all simultaneously looked at her ring finger. They saw the ring.

"There's nothing there." One of the guys finally said.

Now it was my turn. "You're wrong! There is something written there, and I'll tell you exactly what it says because I had it inscribed before I put it on her finger!"

The cops took her hand and worked to get the ring off of her finger. Donna was definitely drugged. She was docile and compliant and offered no resistance as the ring was taken off. The cop took a good look and said, "Yep! There's something written there all right. But I can't read it."

"That's because it's written in French! It says, Je' Teime'! It means, I love you!" I said.

Donna came alive for a moment when she heard me say, "Je Teime." Donna looked at me and repeated what I said.

"Now do you believe that she is my wife? These guys are criminals and tried to kidnap her. I want them arrested!" The officer placed the ring in my hand, and I took Donna out of there. I wanted to take her to the hospital, but the police had called for backup and for an ambulance. We sat on the steps until the ambulance arrived and watched the way the police stormed into the building past us. The ambulance took Donna to St. Francis Hospital. They kept her for a few days while they countered the effects of the drugs that were in her system.

If we hadn't shown up when we did, we wouldn't have seen Donna again. They were planning to take her to the commune along with several other women that day. The commune was called THE REAL BROTHERHOOD and it was run by this guy who called himself Brother Love. His real name is Sam Halstead. He's from East St. Louis. He used to pastor a church there until he was caught with the wife of one of his parishioners. The husband killed his wife, shot Brother Love, and then killed himself. Brother love survived although he now wears a metal plate in his head. He moved from there to Pittsburgh about 10 years ago and started a church that later grew into the commune. The word is that all of the women that they recruit, he marries in a ceremony that he performs himself. He has sex with all of the women in a harem-like setting. Drugs are the way of life there and they grow their own marijuana, but they also use cocaine and heroin. Up until dad and I stop them from taking Donna, there was no proof of any of that, just the reports from people who had managed to escape. But Brother Love and the men there kept them so drugged up that none of them could tell a convincing enough story to get a judge to authorize a search warrant.

"In the Lawrenceville building, the cops found several other girls drugged with the same drugs that they gave Donna. They put the pressure on the brothers, and they talked which led to a raid on the commune and the arrest of Brother Love! He's in a federal prison right now.

"But Donna didn't recover as I thought she would. She had a taste of what drugs could do and she started using methamphetamines. Then she went to cocaine and that's where all hell broke loose. I'd come home from work and the TV would be gone, then the VCR and the microwave. It just got so crazy! At the time I didn't understand anything about addiction. I thought I could help her by giving her the money that she needed. I didn't know. Eventually it got so bad that her mom and dad banned her from their house and told me that I should do the same. They said that she needed tough love! What the hell kind of love was that? I asked. She was my wife and she needed me. I wasn't going to put her out. No way! I loved her.

"She tried to stop, but she couldn't. She stayed clean for a few days, sometimes a few weeks, but it never lasted. Finally, she said that she could do it if she left Pittsburgh. She swore that things would be different somewhere else, and I believed her. I talked her father into giving me a short leave of absence and in return I would spend my time exploring the market in hopes of opening a branch of his business there. Donna and I then moved away. I had relatives who lived in Harrisburg, but I didn't want to live there so we settled in York. It's about 20 miles from Harrisburg. That didn't work either because she didn't reach out for help. She tried to do it alone. Even though she didn't know anyone there, she found the drugs and it started all over again. Then I did the stupidest thing ever! I let her talk me into trying it!"

"She got you started on cocaine?" Diana asked.

"Unfortunately, yes! She showed me how to smoke it, and the very first time I did it I was hooked on it. I didn't know it at the time but looking back, I was hooked!"

"Damn!" She exclaimed. "I never would have thought that she was the one that got you started. I just thought you did it on your own."

"Well, I did. She didn't twist my arm or put a gun to my head. I had the option to say no, I just didn't. It's not her fault, it's mine. But that's where my addiction kicked off. She and I got high together for a while and we stayed home most of the time smoking crack. That went on for months and I never did start the business that I intended to start for her father. Instead I spent most of my time sitting around the house getting high with her.

"Donna got so bad that she started turning tricks. She didn't have to do it because we had plenty of money, but I guess turning tricks goes along with the lifestyle. She would disappear for days at a time and then come home smelling really bad. She would take a bath, change her clothes, and go right back out again. One day she came home, pack up a few things and told me that she was leaving. That day she left and didn't come back. I didn't see her again for months. I heard that she was staying with this dealer. It hurt to hear it, but I dulled my pain by staying high all the time. I started having get high parties of my house. Before long people that I didn't even know were coming there to get high. I didn't really mind it at first because there were a lot of women who came by that I got to know and spend a lot of time with. I didn't like getting high alone so when I kicked everybody out and still want to get high, I kept a woman or two around to keep me company. I hardly ever went outside. But all of that got really old really quick and the fun was gone leaving me with the burden of addiction.

"I know I was one of the fortunate ones because I didn't have to steal or do anything like that to get high because of all of the money that I had in the bank. Before I sunk too low, I took a good look at myself and decided to do something about it. I put myself into treatment, then got connected with NA and I've been clean ever since."

"What happened to Donna?" Diana asked.

"She and her dealer friend were arrested, and she went to jail. I went to see her while she was in. I thought that she was finished with it because she talked about leaving it alone and I believed her, but as soon as she got out, she started using again. She came by the house trying to get money from me and tried to entice me into get high again. By that time, I had learned about addiction, enabling and even tough love. I told her that as long as she was using I would do absolutely nothing for her, but if she got clean, I would help her out in any way that I could. She left my house in a rage and cursing at me.

"I came home from work about a week later and found my house broken into. I knew that she had something to do with it because certain things were missing that only she knew about. Like my spare key, my extra bank card that I kept hidden. I had the locks changed, an alarm system installed, and my bank card canceled.

The next time I heard from her, she was in treatment. I went to see her faithfully and we made plans to get back together. She stayed there for four months came out looking and acting like her old self again. Things were going great for a while. We went to church together and to meetings. We talked of trying to have a baby again. We came to Pittsburgh and spent time with her parents, and I smooth out the relationship between her father and I and everything was good.

We went back to York with a new attitude, a new perspective and a new outlook for our marriage and our future. I put everything that I had to making a future secure, but she had other plans. Plans that she didn't share with me. Plans that were selfish and didn't include me. She had learned from the people at The Real Brotherhood how to extract money from trusting relatives and friends. Although she no longer was a part of it, she still thought the way they did. I guess the brainwashing job they put on her really worked. We had a joint account and a savings account that she could access at any time that she wanted to, but the bulk of our money was in an account that only I could access. In order for her to access it I had to be there, or she had to have my signature.

"She devised a plan to trick me into signing over the account to her, then she was going to clean me out and leave, but I found out about it before she could put it into effect. She was going to open her own account and transfer all of the money from our joint account into it. When she got my signature then she was going to transfer all the rest of it too. I found papers that she had gotten from the bank that she had hidden from me. When I found out I was devastated. My first thought was to kill her, but I couldn't do that. I called her father instead and told him about what I had discovered. He cried on the phone. He was hurt but I didn't expect him to cry. Then he told me that she had already done to her mother and brother what she was planning to do to me. I couldn't believe it! How could she do that to her own mother? To her brother who would kill or die for her? When I hung up the phone, I went straight to the bank to put a stop to any plans that she had to take any money out of our account, and I discovered that our joint savings account had mysteriously multiplied itself. She had transferred all of her mothers and brother's money into it, but she had yet to take it out. She had to make one final deposit first! I called her dad from the bank and told him of my discovery. I asked him how much money they had lost. I immediately closed the accounts and opened another one that only I could access. I had a bank cashier's check made out to her mother and another to her brother in the amount that dad said Donna had stolen from them. I had a check prepared for Donna and left the bank.

"When I got home, the phone rang. It was a gentleman from the real estate office that we had spoken to months ago. Donna wanted a house of our own and so we went looking for one. All that we had seen, we couldn't agree on. What I liked; she didn't like. The ones that she wanted were in neighborhoods that were infested with drugs or right on the fringes. I couldn't understand why she wanted to move there, but as I thought about it, it became clear.

"The real estate guy told me that the house that we had looked at on the previous Sunday was now available. I hadn't seen any house with Donna on Sunday! She had left that day and said that she was going to an NA meeting and was going to hang out with a few of her friends afterward. I didn't see her again until late that evening. Through the conversation with the guy, I learned that she had taken someone with her and because the broker didn't really know me and had only seen me once months ago, he didn't remember my face. But he did see the six digits in my bank account!

"It all became clear. Donna was about to take all of the money, just as she had done with her mother and brother. Whether she had actually planned to buy the house or not, I didn't know, but her plans whatever they were, didn't include me. I waited for her to come home and while I waited, I packed my things. She came in around seven just as I was getting off of the phone was my landlord. I called him to let him know that I would be leaving, she would be staying and that I would continue to pay the rent to the end of the lease if she didn't. He agreed and after understanding my plight, he offered me an apartment on Duke Street, but the problem was that I didn't want to live in York anymore. And he offered me a two-bedroom apartment on Susquehanna Street in Harrisburg on a month-to-month lease. I agreed to that sight unseen.

"I sat down and told her everything that I knew about her plan and what she had done to her mother and brother. She tried validly not to show emotion but when I told her about the money and what I had done she went ballistic. When she finally calmed down, she tried to sweet talk me. It didn't work! Then she said that she was pregnant again, that didn't work either! Then she turned cold and said that she never loved me and that she wished that I were dead. I told her to have a good life, I gave her the check and I started to leave. She began to cry and beg me to stay. That didn't work either. The treachery within her was unbelievable. She was clean and sober, and she did all of that. If she had been using drugs I could've understood, but she couldn't use that as an excuse. She was doing evil simply because she wanted to. I moved to Harrisburg and tried to forget Donna. I divorced her about a year later and vowed never to get married again!"

"But you did!" Diana said with a smile.

"Yes, I did!"

"Aren't you afraid that I'll do the same thing?"

"That was my fear at one time, but no, I don't think that way about you at all. You and I have been through hell together. There's a bond between us that can't be broken. What you did for me and what I did for you makes us lovers from the soul! I know that I can put everything that I have into your hands and never worry about it at all. I know from my heart and soul that you, Mrs. Diana Diamond, would never betray me!"

"Ooooo! You said those words again!" She squirmed in the bed.

"Watch it! Baby boy is watching you!"

"You know something baby? If you don't mind me saying so, Donna was a fool! She had the best man she ever could have had but she let money hungry idiots convince her that you weren't worth her time. And where she now? What is she doing? Is she still in York? Is she still using drugs again? What happened to her?"

"Donna stayed in York and I stayed in Harrisburg. I knew that she had started using drugs again when my landlord called me and told me that she wasn't paying the rent. He had gone there to see her and when she opened the door and saw him, she slammed the door in his face. The next time he went back with an eviction notice. She wasn't there or she wasn't answering the door, so he put the notice on the door and called me. I was upset with him because I had told him that if she didn't pay that he was to contact me, and I would pay it. There was no need for an eviction notice.

"But, anyway, I went down there to see her. The place had become a crack house. As soon as I walked up on the porch the door opened and this young girl around eighteen years old, motioned me in. The place was a mess. The girl tried to proposition me while she was waiting for Diana to return with the drugs. She was tired of waiting and she wanted to get high right then. She felt that I would pay her for sex and buy cocaine for her. Donna wasn't there, I decided to leave. I didn't like being there because of the smell, and the way the place was all torn up and allowed to deteriorate. I had begun to remember the feelings that I had when I got high and that was making me uncomfortable. I started for the door and then I heard the back door open and shut. Donna came into the living room with a guy and another girl. She stopped when she saw me."

"What are you doing in my house?" She shouted.

"I need to talk to you." I said.

"I don't want to talk to you! Now get out before I call the police!" She began to shout at me.

"I held out my cell phone for her to use. She didn't say anything else. They didn't want the police there and neither did Donna. I told her that I would leave after I talked to her and not a moment before. We went out on the front porch and once we were alone, I really didn't know what to say or even why I was there. I couldn't change her! She lived the life she wanted to live, but it hurt to see her that way. She had so much to live for and so much potential and she was throwing it all away. So, I just told her that she had two months left on the lease and then the landlord would put her out. I told her that I would pay the balance of the rent and the last thing I said was that I will always be there for her if she ever decided to leave drugs along.

"She looked at me with hatred in her eyes and then she asked me for $100. I couldn't believe it!

"What about the money that I put in the bank for you?" I asked her. She replied. "It's all gone!"

I almost asked how, but I knew how. It went up in smoke in a crack pipe! I was so disgusted and upset that I just peeled off five $20 bills and gave them to her. Then I felt bad because I knew that she would spend it all on drugs. She smiled and kissed me on the cheek. I could smell the cocaine smell on her that I always hated!

"I'm going to get myself together, you'll see! Then I'll call you! Thanks Donn! Je Teime! Then she disappeared back into the house.

"The next time I saw her was about six months later. She had been evicted after the lease ran out and I had no idea where she was until I got a call on my cell phone from the girl that I had met at her house. Her name was Robin. Robin had gone into treatment and was reaching out to me for help. She told me that Donna had gotten busted and was back in the York County prison awaiting trial for possession of cocaine and possession with intent to deliver. I went to see her, but she refused to talk to me. I left and got her lawyer. I told her dad what was going on so he could keep in contact with her, but I never went back to see her. She was convicted and sent to Muncy woman's prison. She got out about a year before I moved back to Pittsburgh, but she was arrested again for the same thing, but she also had several stolen guns. She's in Muncy right now."

Diana was silent for a while. She was taking it all in and digesting it all. Then she spoke. "Baby, you still love her, don't you?" Her voice was soft and mellow and almost apologetic. I could tell that she was asking because she felt the pain as I spoke.

"Maybe I do a little. I used to think that I didn't love her anymore, but pain will make you go straight to denial. I still feel the pain of knowing that she either can't get it right or that she just doesn't want to. Either way, she's become less than she should be, and I know what she's capable of. I know what she could become. Why is it that I stopped using, but she didn't? I find it hard to understand. I just made up my mind and I took advice and listened to people who knew how to quit and stay that way. She did that too, but something happened."

"She wasn't honest with herself." Diana said. "That's why she couldn't be honest with you. That's why she went back. You can't stay clean and sober if you're not honest with yourself first, then with others. Remember when I used to fall all the time? Remember when I refuse to take my medication? Remember when I would get mad at you about nothing? Remember when I kept going back to drinking and getting high? I wasn't honest with myself at all! I wanted to blame everyone for my troubles. I blamed my father because he went to prison and left me alone with an evil mother. I blamed my mother because she abused me. I blamed James because he used me. I blamed his wife for trying to kill me. I blamed Carl for cheating on me, and I blamed the doctors for not making me normal. But once I took the responsibility for my problems and got honest with myself, then things began to change for me!" She continued. "She just isn't honest with herself, and things won't change for her until she gets honest and faces herself for who she really is!"

"You're right sweetheart. I know that. I know that there's nothing that I can do for her, she has to help herself. But…"

"I know baby, but just be there for her when she needs your help, when she has her spiritual awakening." She said sympathetically.

"You don't have a problem with that?" I asked.

"No. Why should I? I'm not afraid of her. I'm not insecure or worried about you. Nobody can take you from me. Nobody can come between us. You said it yourself, we've been through hell together! Were joined at the hip!" She patted me there. "Now that you've told me about her, I understand how you feel. She needs help just like we did, just like we still do! No baby, I don't have a problem with that because I trust you, just like you trust me!"

She continually surprised me with her wisdom and insight. Maybe I was slow in noticing the real womanly qualities of my new wife. Maybe she had been that way all along and it was my oversight. But I was being pleasantly surprised all the time because of it. My decision to marry her had turned out to be one of the best decisions that I had ever made.

"Diana, I haven't been in contact with Donna in years, but I always reserve the thought of helping her again if she asked, but only if she asked, only if she remained off drugs."

"Baby, you've got so much money now that if you sent her a few thousand it wouldn't hurt us at all, and it would probably really help her. You know, just to let her know that she still has friends, and family!" She said.

"I don't know Diana, it's not the money. I just don't want to get anything started again. You just don't know her! She can get really selfish and evil. She ripped off her own mother! She wasn't drinking, and she wasn't using drugs. But she did it just the same. She tried to get me too and it's hard to forget that!" I sighed. "I'll wait until she gets out and contact me."

"But baby, remember when I told you that Carl came out to see me at the hospital? He could have waited, but if he had, I might not be here now. I was in bad shape and his forgiveness helped me to go on. I guess it helped me to get past my loathing of myself for what I had done. I didn't know it at the time, but I needed his forgiveness. Maybe you can help her by writing her a letter and letting her know that you're still her friend and you still care." Diana was very, very serious.

"I've done that. I've always let her know that I cared. I've always let her know that I'd be there as long as she was clean and sober. She knows that, I don't need to tell her that again, she already knows."

Baby, I know you have and that's good," I braced myself for the line that always begins with 'but'! "But sometimes that just isn't enough. Sometimes when you're kicking yourself for screwing up again, what someone said to you the last time just isn't enough. You need to hear it again. You need to be reassured again! Do you understand?"

I understood and I saw her point. I remembered my own failures and my repeated attempts to succeed that ended in defeat. "I see your point." I said. "I'll write her a letter and send her some money but if she comes after me, thinking we're going to get back together, then it will be your fault. I'll let you handle it."

"Ha!" She laughed, "if she tries that, I'll handle it all right! You won't have to worry about it. I'll give her a little woman to woman, leave my husband alone, or die talk! She began to laugh again. At first, I thought she was kidding, but after I saw her face, and especially her eyes, I wasn't so sure!

CHAPTER 23

Meet the Carvers

We crossed the Mississippi River and entered St. Louis. When we exited the train, we were greeted by Diana's Aunt Peggy. Aunt Peggy was Diana's father's sister, as was her Aunt Ruby. Diana had told me about Aunt Ruby when we were still dating, but she never mentioned Aunt Peggy or any of her family in St. Louis until we were on the train.

Aunt Peggy, Diana said, had a falling out with her father when he started getting serious about her mother. Aunt Peggy didn't like her mother at all! She, and other members of the family, felt that she would be great trouble for Diana's father. When he decided to marry her mother, Aunt Peggy stopped speaking to him and that went on for years. Aunt Peggy moved back to the family home in St. Louis, met her husband, got married, had kids and from time to time came back to Pittsburgh to visit her brother and his daughter until he went to jail. After that, Diana said she never saw her again.

Aunt Peggy and her husband Arthur, greeted us with hugs, smiles, laughter and a lot of talking. When they saw Donnte' they couldn't keep their hands off of him.

"Oh! He's just the cutest little thing!" Aunt Peggy said as she lightly pinched his cheek. She kissed him over and over all across his face and head. He didn't seem to mind at all. He loved the attention.

Uncle Arthur gave me a hearty handshake, a strong and manly hug. There was something about him that made me like him right away.

"I'm Arthur." He said. "Good to meet you, Donn!"

"Hi Arthur. Do you know me?" I was surprised that he knew my name.

"Sure." He replied with a smile.

"How?" Diana hadn't mentioned my name when she spoke to them on the phone.

"Ruby told us all about you!"

"Aunt Ruby?" Diana heard that name and spoke. "Aunt Ruby is here?" She was so excited that she started fidgeting.

"Yes! She's here!" Aunt Peggy replied. "Your Aunt Martha and Aunt Betty are here too, and so is Uncle Floyd and a whole bunch of relatives that you've never met. Don't you know? It's your grandmother's 80th birthday! Everybody's here!"

"IT'S GRANDMA ETTA'S BIRTHDAY? I didn't know that!" Diana almost fainted from the excitement. "I haven't seen her since I was little. I didn't know it was her birthday. I remember how she always used to sing me to sleep. She used to sneak me cookies when my mom would beat me. She called me her "Baby Bunny"!"

She could hardly contain herself. Her excitement was bubbling over.

We left the station in Uncle Arthur's brand-new Cadillac and arrived at the family house 20 minutes later to a throng of smiling, happy faces. The entire family was standing on the front lawn, steps, and porch of Grandma Etta's three-story house. The adults stood in line from the front gate to the porch along both sides of the walkway and greeted us with handshakes and hugs and warm welcoming smiles. The small children were too busy running around to pay any attention to us; the older children stood alongside of their parents looking curiously to see who we were. It seemed that Aunt Ruby had told everyone about us because, as we made our way through the gauntlet of relatives, they greeted us by name.

We climbed the wooden stairs to the porch and just outside of the front door sat an old woman and an old wicker rocking chair. There was no doubt in my mind that she was Grandma Etta. The shock had a visible effect on me as I took a double take. That face, I had seen it before! She slowly rose from her chair, refused help from her relatives, but carefully placed her hands on the arms of the chair and pushed herself up. Once she was up, a smile as bright as I've ever seen took control of her face. She stretched out her arms to Diana.

"My baby Bunny!" She said.

Immediately Diana was reduced to tears. She ran into the waiting arms of her grandmother and sobbed like a baby.

"There, there, my child. You're okay now. Grandma Etta's got you! Everything will be all right!" She hugged Diana and kissed her forehead.

It was a heart wrenching scene. Diana was 25 years old, but not at that moment. She had become a little girl again, safe from the world in her grandmother's arms. It touched me and tears tried to well up in my eyes but the manly side of me fought them off.

Diana reached down from her embrace for my hand. I gave it to her, and she stopped crying long enough to introduce us.

"Grandma, this is my husband, Donn! Donn, this is my grandma Etta!" The tears started again.

"It's a pleasure to meet you ma'am!" I said.

"Come here son!" She held out one arm to me while the other was securely holding Diana. I stepped in and felt the love of generations enfold me as I pressed against her wrinkled face.

"Welcome, son! Welcome to the family!"

Dinner had been delayed because they were awaiting our arrival, but once we got there, it commenced. There were tables set up in the huge yard outback. The largest table was about 25 feet long and set closest to the rear of the house. It was shaded by two large oak trees.

From the trees hung several lamps, citronella candles and decorations. Other lamps were set in various places around the yard to light the area when darkness arrived. The tables were covered with red and white checkered tablecloths. An assortment of covered dishes bursting with macaroni & cheese, collard greens, green beans & ham, and much more. There were open platters of fried chicken, baked ham, turkey, hamburgers, hot dogs, meatloaf, and fish. There were cakes, pies, cookies, and an assortment of sweet things placed on each table. The small tables, for the children and young adults, were set in a line adjacent to the large table, but with space so that seating could be had on all four sides of each. They also were covered with red and white checkered tablecloths.

Grandma Etta came out and took her seat at the head of the large table and immediately everyone found their assigned seats around the various tables. It was clear to me that Grandma Etta, although she was full of love and compassion, was no one to trifle with. She had strict rules, and everyone knew what was expected of them. From the eldest to the youngest, all gave respect and attention to Grandma Etta!

Diana and I were directed to sit at the big table in the seats that were reserved for her parents. I felt honored. I knew absolutely no one there, and I had just met Aunt Peggy and Uncle Arthur and Grandma Etta, but they allowed me to relax and feel welcomed as a family member. I had no idea where Donnte' was, for he had been whisked away and passed around from one relative to the next. But I wasn't concerned, I knew that he was in good hands because he was with the family!

Diana and I sat side-by-side with her Aunt Peggy and Uncle Arthur on one side and Aunt Ruby and her husband on the other. We sat in the seats where Diana's mother and father were to sit if he were not in prison, and she were not estranged from the family.

Grandma Etta stood up and said not a word. She looked across the length of the table, and as each one of us noticed her standing, we stopped the talking and silence prevailed.

"Everyone please stand." She said. It wasn't a request as it might have seemed, but it was in order. Everyone stood at once and bowed their heads. They knew what was coming next. I assumed from observing them that a prayer of thanks was coming.

I bowed my head, but my eyes remained open as I snuck a peek to my left and then my right. Diana's eyes were tightly clasped together in anticipation of the prayer. To my right, I looked down the table at the three couples standing between me and where Grandma Etta stood. Aunt Ruby and her husband John were to my immediate right. I had not been introduced to them yet, but Diana had pointed out her Aunt Ruby to me with excitement just before we came to the table. Aunt Ruby and Uncle John also stood with their eyes closed, head bowed, and hands clasped together. Everyone at the table also held the same position. My eyes made their way down the table until they rested upon Grandma Etta. Other than myself, she was the only one who still had open eyes and hers were staring straight at me! The intensity of her stare startled me, and I shook involuntarily. I felt like a kid again, a kid who had been caught doing something wrong. She cleared her throat and I slammed my eyes shut and prayed that she wouldn't wrap me on the knuckles with a ruler or some other object as my own grandmother used to do.

(That's it!) I thought. (She looks almost exactly like my grandmother!)

It was uncanny how much she looked like her. I wanted to open my eyes and take another look, but I wasn't going to mess with her. If she was anything like the woman that she resembled, that would be like a suicide mission.

"Now that ALL heads are bowed, and ALL eyes are closed, we will have the blessing! Donn? Would you pray over the food please?" It was Grandma Etta. The shock of hearing my name locked my brain and didn't immediately allow me to accept that she was talking to me.

"Donn?"

"Yes ma'am?" My eyes opened involuntarily for a split second and then slammed shut again, but tighter than the first time. "Yes! Yes, ma'am!"

I heard chuckles as everyone who knew Grandma Etta, knew that she had called on me because I was the one who got caught with their eyes open.

"Dear Lord," I began, "we ask for your blessings over this family gathering and over each and every one here. We ask that you bless and protect everyone here from the eldest to the unborn and everyone in between. Bless this food in the name of Jesus Christ, sanctify it and make us worthy to receive it. Make us worthy in Jesus name. Bless those who have prepared it, bless those who have labored for it, and bless those of us who will consume it. Amen!"

"AMEN!"

The air reverberated as the entire family responded collectively. Then everyone sat down and began to pass the food. Everyone filled their plates preparing to eat.

Before she took a bite of her food, Diana came around me and hugged Aunt Ruby. That's when she introduced us. She was radiant with exuberance for she hadn't seen her favorite aunt in years. After they finished hugging and talking, and after Diana sat back down and started to eat, Aunt Ruby turned to me and tapped me on the shoulder and asked.

"Donn? How did you ever meet Diana?" She came straight out with her question. She looked at me inquisitively and I sensed that she was trying to discover if I knew all that she knew about Diana's mental health.

I answered her question and we entered into a conversation between mouthfuls of food. It became evident to me that she was very concerned about my welfare as well as Diana's. I assured her that I was well aware of the problems that Diana had and that she need not worry. She knew about the incident at my store and the arrest and exoneration of Diana, but she had grave misgivings over Diana's newfound stability and then I assured her that her state of mind was stable and had been that way for some time. She looked deep into my eyes as if she could extract some secret information from them with just a look. Finally, she relaxed and began to eat.

Uncle Arthur and Aunt Peggy sat to my left just on the other side of Diana. Uncle Arthur and I spoke to each other across Diana, while Diana and Aunt Ruby spoke to each other across me. To make things easier for all of us, I switched seats with Diana. Uncle Arthur began to point out 'who was who' in the family. It began with the five children of Grandma Etta and her deceased husband Floyd Carver the first!

"He died several years ago, and Mama almost died too from a broken heart. She really loved that man! She lived for him and when he died, she laid in bed hoping that God would take her too. But he didn't. She finally got up and started being grandma again."

"How did he die?" I asked.

"He had diabetes. Had it from childhood. It just caught up to him and took him away. The good thing was that he didn't have to have feet and legs cut off like so many others have had to do." He paused for a moment, obviously thinking pleasant thoughts of his deceased father-in-law. "That's Martha over there." He pointed in her direction. She was sitting next to Grandma Etta. "She's the eldest so she always sits next to Mama. Her name is Franklin now. Harvey, sitting beside her is her husband. They have two children, Linda and Harvey Junior. That's them sitting on the other side of the table across from their parents. Linda's husband is Vernon Crawford and Harvey Junior's wife beside him is Trudy.

"Then there's Floyd Junior, but he likes to be called Floyd the second, or little Floyd, but don't call him Junior! He doesn't like that at all, but everyone calls him Junior when he's not around. He and his wife Betty, sitting next to Ruby, have three children. They are across the table sitting next to Harvey and Trudy. Floyd the third and his wife Sharon, Tammy and her husband Howard Brown, and Bimini! Bimini is the only one who isn't married."

"BIMINI?" I said. I knew that name. I looked and sure enough, it was her. She was in St. Louis. I turned to Diana who was busily engrossed in a conversation with her aunt.

"Sweetheart, did you know that Bimini was here?"

"Where?" She turned abruptly to look as I directed her attention across the table. As soon as she saw her, she got up and fast walked around the table. Then I wished that I hadn't said anything because I became afraid that this was going to turn out to be a disaster.

"Diana!" I shouted.

She looked back at me with a smile replied. "Don't worry." She winked and kept walking.

But I was worried. I wanted to stop her before she reached Bimini because I was afraid of what she would do. But there was nothing that I could do to stop her short of running across the table. That was out of the question! So, I sent up a quick prayer. I watched as Diana approached Bimini. Bimini had seen her coming and she wasn't sure what to expect, but she had the presence of mind to stand up and face her. Diana walked right up on her and stopped only inches before her face touched Bimini's. Bimini cringed and tried to prepare for the worst, but Diana lifted her arms and circled Bimini with them and hugged her. I breathed a sigh of relief and sent a thank you skyward and I'm sure Bimini did too!

"I love you Bimini!" Diana said as she released her grip. "I forgive you for what you did. You're family and you will always be family! Nothing will ever change that. Okay?"

Bimini began to weep. "Diana, I'm so sorry for what I did to you. Please forgive me!"

"I already have. It's over. " She hugged her again. This time Bimini hugged back.

I sat back down and waited for Uncle Arthur to finish. "Mama was right." He said.

"She was right about what?" I asked.

"We were all worried about what would happen once those two came together. We heard about what happened in Pittsburgh and we thought that Diana would tear her apart, but Mama said no! She said Diana would do just what she did!"

"Yeah. I was worried too!" I said as I picked up a piece of fried chicken and took a bite. I know I was taught not to speak with food in my mouth, but I did it anyway. "So, what's Aunt Ruby's husband's name?"

"Oh!" He came back to the conversation. "John, …John Young. They have three children. There's John Junior and his wife Linda. He doesn't mind being called Junior. Then there's Marcel and his wife Shirley, and Iris and her husband David Sharp. They're sitting right across from us. Then there's Lonnie and Diana, your wife's parents, but of course you know that neither one of them are here. Lonnie is…."

"In prison. I know. Why isn't Diana's mother here?"

"A long story, but the short version is that she is responsible for Lonnie being in prison, and she probably harbors a lot of guilt and shame about it. Actually, nobody really liked her anyway!"

"I heard he killed a man!"

"That's right." He leaned close to whisper. "He killed his wife's lover!" He took a look in Diana's direction and decided against saying anything further. "We'll talk about that later." He smiled. "Then, you know Arthur, yours truly, and his extremely beautiful wife Peggy. Peggy is the youngest of the five but as you can see, she's the prettiest!" He beamed with pride. "We have two children, Arthur Junior and Dorothy. Arthur Junior is married to Janice there," he pointed across the table without using his finger. He just lifted his arm in the direction. "They have three children, Janet, Art the third and Elisha. Dorothy is married to Burt Ward right there, and they have two children. Leroy and Lincoln!"

He seemed to be exhausted once he finished and he hadn't even been to all of Grandma Etta's great-grand and great-great-grands. But I was satisfied with that information. For the time being, it was enough to digest.

I looked across the table to where Bimini sat and saw Diana with Donnte' in her arms holding him up so Bimini could see him. He was all smiles and laughter. Bimini reached out and Diana handed him to her. I looked down the table to where Grandma Etta was, and she looked at me with a wide smile and nodded her approval.

All in all, the gathering was a great success. I got to know the family pretty well in one day and I learned a lot about Grandma Etta that gave me a lot of respect for her. I have to say that the food was very delicious, some of the best that I've ever had. By the time evening came, I had mingled and talked to several members of the family and felt like I was a part of it. I was accepted and treated just as if they had known me all of my life. The Carvers were a great bunch of people.

That night Diana and I stayed at Grandma Etta's house. The family house. The big house, as they called it. Our room was on the third floor in the rear. Grandma Etta directed us to the room by words alone. She didn't attempt to climb the stairs.

"That room was your father's room when he was a boy!" She said to Diana. "You'll be away from all of the young children up there. You will have some privacy. Your cousin Iris and her husband David will be in the room next to you. Harvey Junior and Trudy will take the front room. All of the children, the noisemakers, will be down on the first floor so they won't disturb you."

"Good night grandma. I love you." Diana said.

"Good night, Baby Bunny." Grandma said it was so much love that it was felt by me.

"Good night grandma." I said. It was the first time I called her grandma and it felt good and natural.

"Good night son." She spoke. It felt even better.

She hugged us both and wished us a peaceful night's sleep before she retreated into the family room where there were an abundance of children preparing to bed down wherever they could.

We climbed the stairs to the third floor and entered our room. The room was well-kept. There were definite signs that the room was still occupied by a male, a young male. The clothes in the closet, the colors and patterns of the walls, furniture and accessories. The bed had a blue and yellow striped cover that matched the pattern on the curtains, sheets and pillowcases.

On one wall there were two triangular high school banners. The points faced each other and in the middle was a 9 x 12 picture of an athlete in football gear posing for the camera. It wasn't Diana's father, but she said it was probably Floyd the third. She directed my attention to a faded green and white banner and a football jersey, number 22, on the opposite wall. There was a black and white photo of her father there too. He was also in uniform and posing with a football tucked under his arm and his free hand was extended forward and his right knee was high in the air.

Floyd the third didn't live there anymore either. He had his own family and home, but the evidence of him living there as well as Diana's father, still remained on the walls. In time, the boy who occupied the room presently would probably have his pictures on the wall too!

Diana and I prepared ourselves and Donnte' for bed. Once we were cozy and snuggling together, I asked the question that had been on my mind all day.

"Sweetheart?"

"Yes baby?"

"When was the last time you went to visit your father?"

She began to tense.

"What?"

"Come on, you know what I mean. Your father has been in prison for what, 10, 11 years? Have you ever been out to see it?"

"No! NEVER!" She was upset with me for asking, but what I had to say had to be said. I thought about how she treated Bimini. I saw firsthand how she forgave her and how she welcomed her back into her life with her most treasured possession, Donnte'. She had given up the grudge and had taken the steps necessary to bury the hatchet. If she could do that with Bimini, then she could do it with her father too.

"Why not? He's still your father. Don't you think he'd want to hear from his only daughter?"

She pulled away from me and climbed out of bed.

"I don't want to talk about this!" Her tone of voice was agitated, bordering on angry but I didn't care. She needed to let go of her animosity and forgive him just as she had done for Bimini.

I got up and walked up behind her.

"Diana, you have to move on from your childhood disappointments and pain. This is a perfect time to do that. Don't you see that? You're here in St. Louis for the first time in years and you're with your family. Most of whom you haven't met, some of them you didn't even know existed, but they all knew about you. They knew what you've been through and what you've done but are any of them treating you badly? Are they holding grudges against you?"

"DONN! Please! Not now!" She began to retreat into a different part of the room and away from me. I reached out and grabbed her around her waist and held onto her. "DONN, LEAVE ME ALONE!"

"No. I won't leave you alone." I said.

"I don't want to deal with this right now!"

"Now is the perfect time. Why do you think you're here, at this particular time? On your grandmother's 80th birthday? We didn't plan this. We didn't even know it was her birthday. We had no idea everyone would be here, so do you think this is just a coincidence? We are in the same room that your father grew up in. He's all around in here. Some people call it, 'karma', but I say it's God at work.

"Stop! STOP! STOP!" She tried to pull away. "My dad deserted me and left me with, that, …that woman! I needed him and he wasn't there. He left me!" She struggled to get away, but I held on.

"Do you really believe that he WANTED to leave you? huh?"

"Yes!... No!... I don't know! STOP IT! I told you that I don't want to talk about this!"

"You're going to talk about it. You can't keep this inside. You've got to let it out and move on. Your father did what he did, and it may not have been right but until that time, he was the best father he could have been,… Right?"

"Uh-huh!"

"He took care of you and he taught you and loved you. He did all of the things that a father would do for his daughter, but he messed up and killed a man. Do you know why he killed that man?" I knew that I was treading on thin ice, but I also knew that this was the right time for her to realize that she had to forgive him and renew the lines of communication.

Just for second, she looked at me with those dead eyes, those scary eyes that I hadn't seen in a long time. Those eyes that I never wanted to see again, but they softened and disappeared.

"What do you know?" She asked.

"It's not what I know, it's not about that at all. What do you know? Remember our vows? I ask, you tell the truth, you ask, I told the truth! Right now, I'm asking."

"Let me go!" She said. Her eyes had softened, and she was thinking so I let her go. She went back to the bed and sat cross-legged on it with her hands folded between them. She stayed quiet for approximately five minutes and I took a seat beside her and waited.

"My mother was cheating on him. She was messing around with this guy who came over when my dad was at work. My dad wanted us to have everything that we wanted so he worked hard. He worked a lot of overtime just to buy my mother things that she wanted, but she didn't really love him. I think he knew it, but he still did everything he could for us. My mother used to talk about him all the time and call him soft, and 'marshmallow man', a punk and stuff like that because he was loving and gentle. She never talked about him to his face, but she talked to her friends like that when he wasn't around. I hear her all the time.

"One day when my dad was at work, my mother called her boyfriend over. When they were going to mom's room, I would go downstairs and turn up the television really loud so I couldn't hear them. I was 13 then. I had just gotten my baby boobs he used to look at me the way guys do when they want you. He came downstairs and approach me. I was sitting on the couch, kind of like the way I am now, with my legs crossed Indian style and he reached straight between my legs and grabbed me there. He tried to stick his finger and me, but I jumped up and screamed. My mother heard it and came downstairs. I told her what he had done but he denied it! He lied and said that I came on to him because I wanted some of what he was given her. He told her that I said that I was going to tell her that he had molested me if he didn't do what I said. That was a damn lie! She looked at me and then at him, and then she slapped me with the back of her hand so hard that it knocked me over the back of the couch. I was lying on the floor crying and she stood over me calling me a lying bitch and a whore! She believed him! She didn't believe me!"

Diana began to cry. She fell over into my lap and curled up in the fetal position. I stroked her hair and waited. I knew where the story was going but I wanted her to tell it.

"I'm sorry baby." She said between tears.

"It's okay sweetheart. Let it out."

She began to talk again after she wiped her eyes on my T-shirt.

"They went back upstairs but not together. Mom went up first while he went into the kitchen to get a beer. He came back to the living room and I was still on the floor crying and he said, 'you're mine now little girl! I'm gonna break you in really good first chance I get!' Then he grabbed at my leg. I moved out of the way and he laughed again and then went upstairs.

I was really scared then because my mother didn't protect me. He could do whatever he wanted to me, and she wasn't going to lift a finger because she believed him and not me. I didn't want to tell my father, but I was scared that he was going to rape me! I was scared, baby! What else could I do?"

She broke down again. I didn't know the right words to say. There were several thoughts that came to mind, but they all seem so trite. I waited and comforted her by continually stroking her hair and softly rubbing her neck and shoulders.

"Everybody thinks that my dad killed him because he found out that mom was having an affair with him, but that's not why he did it. He killed him because I told him that he had molested me. Baby I didn't know he was going to kill him! I just wanted to feel safe again. I just wanted someone to protect me from him! I didn't want my dad to kill him, but he did, and he went away to prison and left me with,… Her! I was all alone again. He didn't have to kill him! He didn't have to…."

Again, she sobbed but this time I did have something to say.

"Diana, your father acted just like most fathers would when they been told that someone had molested their daughter. We're men! We're protectors! It's our job to make our wives and children feel safe and secure. That's what we do. That's who we are.

"You've got to stop blaming yourself for what happened, because that's what you're doing. You're blaming him for leaving you but you're blaming yourself for telling him what happened. You can't change any of that. What is done, is done. He did what he felt was right at the time but now 11 years later, I'm sure he's thought about it more times and he can count, and he's kicked himself about it over and over. But Diana, he did what he did to protect you! Maybe he didn't plan to kill him, maybe it was an accident. Maybe he just wanted to talk to him or to scare him or something like that and things got out of control. Diana he's probably stuck in that prison worried about you and wondering what's going on with you. Don't you think that he still loves you?"

"I… I… I guess so. I, (sniff-sniff) could write him, but I'm not going to no prison to see him. That's out!" She said sternly.

"Okay, don't go! We're going to be in California anyway but write him! I'll write Donna, and you write your father! Deal?"

"Okay! Deal!"

CHAPTER 24

Fun with the Family

October the 5th was the date. You might think that there would be an abundance of snow on the ground or falling from the skies at that time of the year in St. Louis, but that wasn't the case. It was one of those gorgeous autumn days. Probably the most gorgeous day I had ever experienced at that time of year. It was Grandma Etta's 80th birthday! I thought of my own grandmother and how perfect a lady she was. I remember how she always gave me the right advice and always showed me love when I felt unloved. It was uncanny that this woman looked so much like my grandmother. It made me miss her all the more.

I opened my eyes to the sound of hammering out in the backyard. It was almost 7 AM and Diana was still asleep. She was curled up in the fetal position with an angelic face. At the very least, she had agreed to write a letter to her father, but I had a suspicion that once she did and he answered her, she would want to visit him.

Donnte was missing in action. His cousin Sasha, the 15-year-old granddaughter of Uncle Floyd the second, (not Junior) decided that she absolutely adored him and wanted to keep him with her all night. Why not? She was family, and I had been told that she was the preferred and regular babysitter for Uncle Arthur and Aunt Martha's great grandchildren.

I eased out of bed as not to disturb Diana and tiptoed over to the window. Outback, I saw Uncle Arthur and, Uncle John and several of the men getting things set up for the birthday party. They were stringing a banner between the two trees that shaded the large table. I strained to read the banner, but it was on an angle that made it difficult to read from where I stood. I watched for a few minutes until the thought came to me that I should go down and help them out. I grabbed my clothes and tiptoed toward the door. Before I reached the door, I heard Diana's voice.

"You're just going to sneak off? You're not even going to kiss your pregnant wife good morning? I want a divorce!" She spoke.

"You want a divorce? You'll get one just as soon as pigs fly south for the winter!"

"Come here and kiss me." She purred. "How's Big Al?"

I started back to the bed. "He's fine, and lonely! He's beginning to think that Jennifer doesn't like him anymore. You know he's overly sensitive!"

"Jennifer was thinking the same thing about him." She spoke. She threw the sheets off revealing her body. She was clothed only in her mint green panties. "She's sensitive too! Extremely sensitive!"

"I can't. Really, I can't! You don't know how bad I want to, but I've got to go down and helped the guys." I pointed to the window. She got up and looked out. "We've waited this long; we can wait a little while longer." I couldn't believe those words were mine.

"Maybe later, okay?" She purred again.

"Sure." I kissed her and went outside.

"Hey Uncle Arthur, Uncle John." I called out as I exited the back door.

"Hey Donn! You come to give us a hand?" Uncle Arthur greeted me with a smile.

"Yes. What do you need for me to do?"

"Actually, all that we have left to do is to string this banner and we're finished until the food is ready. That's going to be a little time from now. Sometime this afternoon."

We worked for about five minutes before we got the thing hanging straight. We sat down at the big table with cups of steaming coffee that Aunt Martha had made. Aunt Martha was the eldest of Grandma Etta's children. She was about 60 years old and had several great grandchildren of her own. She was the perfect likeness to her mother. Her daughter Linda was the spitting image of her.

Uncle John put seven spoons of sugar in his coffee, tasted it and declared that it wasn't sweet enough. He then added two more. My instincts told me that I wasn't going to have a good relationship with him. There was just something about him that rubbed me the wrong way. Unlike the other men there, he didn't smile, and he didn't try to be friendly with me. He looked at me in a way that made me feel very uncomfortable.

"It's a miracle that you're not diabetic!" Uncle Arthur said as Uncle John added the final two spoons of sugar. "How can you drink that stuff so sweet? You kill the taste of the coffee!"

"That's why I do it!" Uncle John said. He added the cream to the coffee and stirred. "I don't really like the taste of coffee that much."

"Then why do you drink it?" I asked.

He looked at me and his look said that I was intruding. He tried to intimidate me with his stare, but it didn't work.

"You drink coffee?" He asked.

"Yes, I do."

"What do you put in it?"

"Cream and sugar, just not that much." I took the spoon and put one level spoonful of sugar in it, then a dash of cream and I stirred it. "That's all I use. I like the taste of coffee."

He didn't like what I said, and he didn't like the way that I said it. We were about to enter a confrontational dialogue.

"Donn? That is your name, isn't it?" He asked sarcastically. "Or is it really, Donald?"

"It's Donn!"

"Oh, so it's a Don... like John, ...not Donald... like Johnald!" He chuckled and looked to Uncle Arthur for support. Uncle Arthur didn't respond, neither did the other men at the table. I thought his remark and plea for support was very juvenile.

"What's your point?" I asked. I tried to give him respect because he was 57 years old, 26 years my senior, and his son John Junior was just a year older than me. So, for that fact alone, I tried to respect him.

"My point is this. Stay the hell out of my business! Stay out of my conversation!" He was truly angry.

"What are you talking about? You are saying that no one can ask you any questions?"

"No! Not everyone,... Just you!" He snapped.

"What your problem?" Right then, I had lost respect for him, and I had made a mental note not to call him UNCLE John anymore. From that moment on, he was just John. "What do you have against me? What have I done to you?"

"This is a FAMILY affair! You're just a guy passing through. You don't live here, and you don't know anything about us, but you're here trying to fit in. Well, let me tell you something. There is a place for you to fit in, but it's not here!"

"Well, that's your opinion…. JOHN! I'm sure that you're the only one with that opinion. I'm just as much a part of this family as you are. And you're right, I am just passing through, but while I'm here, I'm going to take my place beside my wife, just as you have. You married into this family just like I did, so don't think that you're any better or different than I am just because you've been here longer! Your name isn't Carver, and neither is mine, so you can hate me or dislike me as much as you care to, but it's not going to change anything except my opinion of you!"

I took my coffee cup and placed it to my lips to taste the hot liquid. I took my time before I removed it. It was partially to enjoy the flavor and partially to aggravate John. He watched me and I watched him. Finally, he got up and stormed off, cursing under his breath.

"Don't mind him. He's going through a mid-life crisis, and he feels he should be running things, but he can't even control his own wife!" Uncle Arthur said.

"Aunt Ruby runs things?" I asked.

"Always has, and always will."

"Well, that explains a little. He's miserable and he wants company. But he won't get it from me. Besides, Diana knows who the boss is in our family!"

"Yeah,… You are!" He said flippantly.

I took a sip of my coffee. "Uncle Arthur, why does he have a problem with me? We've just met. He doesn't know a thing about me." I asked.

"That's just the way he is. I think he doesn't like the attention you and Diana are getting. He's always been a selfish kind of guy that always wanted things his way. He throws a tantrum when he doesn't get it."

"A long time ago, Lonnie, Diana's dad, beat him up and he never forgot it. Lonnie never liked John because John always felt that he was better than everyone else. Personally, I don't see what Ruby sees in him, but that's just her. She's always bringing stray dogs home! Ha ha ha! Anyway, Lonnie was only about 15 or 16 and John was 20. He tried to tell Lonnie what to do. Lonnie told him that he already had a dad and didn't need another one. John got mad and slapped him. Before anyone could react, Lonnie punched him in the face. John was stunned. He took off his shirt and told Lonnie that he was going to beat him within an inch of his life, but it didn't work out that way. John only hit Lonnie once. Lonnie beat John all over the street and would have hurt him really bad but Big Daddy stepped in. Big Daddy, that's what we called Papa Floyd.

John never forgot that. We used to tease him about it when we could get away with it. I was fifteen at the time. When we heard that Lonnie had killed a man over his wife, John seemed very happy with the news knowing that Lonnie was going to jail. He's always talked as if he wants Lonnie to spend the rest of his life in prison. To this day he holds a grudge against Lonnie. But that fight has been over 30 years ago!"

I was thinking of what Diana had told me about why her father had killed that man. The family really didn't know the truth. At least Uncle Arthur still thought that it was about Diana's mother. How would they react if they knew the truth?

Uncle Arthur continued. "Ruby and your wife have always been close, and John didn't like that either. Probably only because she's Lonnie's daughter. Now that you're here with her, maybe he's transferring his anger for her father to you!"

"Maybe. I'll try to talk to him." I said.

"Negative! He will just make you want to punch him in the nose. He's held a grudge against Lonnie for 30 years, do you think you can change him in a few days? Just tolerate him for a day or two, that's the best course of action."

"Maybe you're right." I said. I noticed the two other guys nodding their heads in agreement.

"I know I'm right. He's really harmless but he thinks he's a fire-breathing dragon!"

We all laughed. We sipped our coffee and the three of them recounted stories of incidents in the family that had happened over the years. Most of them were witty, humorous, and funny. I listened and occasionally chuckled and laughed. All that I heard I absorbed and kept like a family heirloom. They were telling me these things because to them, I was part of the family and I listened and absorbed because I felt that same way.

Breakfast was served at 8:00 AM. The seating arrangement was the same as the night before. The tablecloth had been changed from the red and white checkered pattern to a solid deep ocean blue. While the men were outback preparing the yard for the day's activities, the women were busy in the kitchen preparing breakfast that consisted of scrambled eggs, fried eggs, cheese omelets, hash brown potatoes, sausage patties, sausage links, bacon, ham, fried ham chunks, French toast, pancakes, grits and waffles.

The same ritual was observed as was held the previous evening. Some of us had already been out in the backyard long before the women began setting the tables and bringing out the food. The rest of the family, including Diana, either came out as Grandma Etta appeared or shortly after her. Those that came out behind her, who were mostly the young children, scrambled for the seats before she reached hers. She had reached her 80th birthday, but by no means was she old and decrepit. Once she got herself moving, she moved with surprising agility and speed. Once everyone was at their place, Grandma Etta spoke after she delivered a warm smile.

"Good morning. Who would like to bless the food for us?" Grandma Etta asked.

Immediately the hands of most of the children shot straight up. They began waving frantically to secure her attention and to be the one selected. Grandma Etta looked along the tables where the children were. She began to decide which one to choose.

"Lisa, how about you?" She said in her loving grandmother tone.

"Yes ma'am!" Lisa was excited to be picked. She was the granddaughter of Floyd the second (not Junior), and the daughter of Howard and Tammy Brown. She was seven years old.

Lisa took control with authority. "Everyone please bow your head." She said it and everyone did. My eyes were shut, and I assumed that everyone else's were too because I didn't hear Grandma Etta clear her throat. I wasn't about to take a chance to look, not this time!

"Heavenly father, thank you for all of this food that you have provided for us. Bless it in Jesus's name. Bless our family, bless those that are here and those that aren't here. Bless Grandma Etta and thank you for her. Today is her birthday you know, and we love her a lot and I know that you love her too and might want her with you in Heaven, but we will be grateful if you would leave her here for a while longer! Thank you! Amen!"

"AMEN!"

Just as everyone began to settle in and sit down, Uncle Floyd the second (not Junior) spoke. "MAY I HAVE YOUR ATTENTION"! He paused and then said it again before the area became quiet. "MAY I HAVE YOUR ATTENTION! All of you children, come and join us around the big table," he motioned to them to come, "come on over here kids and gather around. Come on!"

The kids gathered around. They push and began to jockey for position closest to where Uncle Floyd and Grandma Etta stood.

Floyd was a big guy. Tall and healthy. He weighed about 250 pounds, but he was quick and agile and loved to play with the children. I had witnessed him playing the monster role, walking and growling like Frankenstein, and he had all the children laughing and screaming and running all over the yard. He seemed to be having more fun than the children were. It was obvious that he was very well loved among them all.

"This day is a great day in the city of St. Louis. One of the greatest women that this city has ever seen is celebrating her 80th birthday. I'm not just saying that because she's my mother, but every word of it is true! Don't you agree?"

"YES!" Was the response of everyone there.

"She's the greatest!"

"Love you grandma!"

"Best grandma in the world!"

Uncle Floyd put up his hands for silence and received it.

"If anyone doubts how great she is, just let them look around. Look around and see all who are here because of her. Some of us are here because we were born to her, others have married into the Carver family and therefore are just as much a part of her as anyone else. We are ALL family! We all owe a debt of gratitude to her. She is mother to some, grandmother to others, great grandmother and even great-great grandmother!

Because she is a praying, God loving woman, there has not been one who has been lost to Hell among us! Not one! We are here because of her, so let's make this day one of the best days in her life. Starting with the singing of happy birthday!" He started singing and everyone joined in. "HAPPY BIRTHDAY TO YOU! HAPPY BIRTHDAY TO YOU! HAPPY BIRTHDAY GRANDMA ETTA! HAPPY BIRTHDAY TO YOU!"

Everyone clapped and cheered. The children, who had been given noisemakers, blew them, turned them, and shook them. After the air was filled with joyful noise and after a few minutes of revelry, we sat down to breakfast.

I looked around and saw a family united by love. A family that prayed together and shared their time with each other. I was glad to be a part of it. Diana sat beside me with glassy eyes. I could tell that she was thinking similar thoughts and becoming overcome with emotion. I leaned close to her and whispered into her ear.

"Je Teime!"

Her eyes filled with tears, and she threw her arms around my neck and hugged me.

"Je Teime! Je Teime! Je Teime!" She repeated. "Thank you for bringing me here!"

"You're welcome!" I kissed her and gazed into her beautiful eyes. "Thank you for having such a wonderful family." I said.

"You're welcome, but I wish I had come here more often when I was younger. My life would have been so much better and different."

"Baby, you're just fine the way you are. You are exactly what I need. I love you just the way you are, and I wouldn't change a thing about you!"

For a moment or two we were lost in each other, and I could only see her face and only hear her voice. Everyone else had suddenly disappeared and only she and I were there, until Aunt Ruby said.

"Okay you two! There are kids around! Get a room!" Her laughter became infectious and sped from her to us like a plague.

Aunt Ruby, Uncle Arthur, and John, (formerly known as Uncle John), also heard her comment and two of the three of them laughed along with us. John looked at us with a cruel, sinister face. My first thought was to say something that probably would ignite his anger, but I decided against it and gave him a simple smile before I turned away to enjoy the laughter and camaraderie of my family.

During the breakfast meal, Vernon, Aunt Martha's son-in-law, announced that the men were going to the court to play a game of basketball. Diana's ears perked up when she heard the word basketball.

"Cousin Vernon?" She inquired. "What about us women who can play? Are you afraid of us?"

Tammy and Bimini chimed in, in support of a game involving the women. Linda and Shirley, Aunt Ruby's daughter-in-law along with Dorothy, Uncle Arthur's daughter put their two cents in.

The discussion lasted about five minutes before it was decided that after the men's game, we would play the women.

"But we'll take it easy on you!" Floyd the third said.

"What?" Diana was now standing up and excited. "You guys better be ready for the whippin' of your life! Don't take it easy on us because we don't want any excuses when you lose! And when that's over," she looked straight at me, "I've got a score to settle with you!"

"Oh, you remembered?" I was grinning wildly when I said it. "Do you also remember what the terms are?"

"Sure, I remember. Do you?"

"What are you two talking about?" Aunt Ruby asked.

"We've got a bet. We're going to play one-on-one, and the loser has to do whatever the winners, ...that's me, ...says...all day!" Diana boasted. She put her hand on her hips as women do and moved her head the way no straight man can.

"Will see!" I said. "We'll see!"

CHAPTER 25

The Game

We left the house at 10:30 that morning crammed in a caravan of cars and vans carrying the entire Carver clan. Grandma Etta told her son Floyd the second, (not Junior), to make room for her in his van.

"I wouldn't miss this for all the tea in China!" She said as Uncle Arthur and I helped her up into the front passenger seat. I rode with Uncle Arthur while Diana rode with Aunt Ruby. Donnte' was again being held captive by his relatives.

We went to an outside court on the campus of a local college. Once there, we picked the teams on site and tried to make it as even as possible according to height, weight, and age. There were 10 men who wanted to play. Most were third-and fourth generation Carvers. The second-generation men, Uncle Arthur, Uncle Harvey, Uncle Floyd the second, (not Junior), and John (formerly known as Uncle John) all took on the roles of officials. Vernon Junior and Walter, both fourth-generation Carvers in their 20s, became our coaches. My team consisted of cousins Art Junior, John Junior, Floyd the third, Vernon and myself. The opposing team had cousins Bert, Marcel, David, Howard and Harvey Junior.

The first game began with my team defended the north goal and their team defendant the south. John Junior was our Center. Marcel played center for the other team. Floyd the third and Vernon Junior were forwards, Art and I were the guards.

John Junior tipped the ball from tip-off right into my hands. On the first run, I felt myself swell with confidence. Not only Diana, but the entire family was watching, so I had to show off! Of course!

Harvey Junior and Howard were opposing forwards. They took their place in zones on either side of the paint. Bert and David came out as guards to stop us, but they were not able to. I passed the ball over to Art Junior and made my way to the edge of the paint at the foul line. He passed the ball back and I took my first shot. Nothing but net! The cheering began and I smiled, took a bow, and winked at Diana. She acted as if she didn't see me, but I knew that she did.

When they came at us, David pulled up in front of me and took the long jump shot. It swished through the net. It wasn't quite at the three-point range, but it was close. The cheers rose again, and David trotted back down the court smiling.

The teams were pretty evenly matched by ability too, so no one pulled away with the score in the beginning. David and I guarded each other and traded shot for shot. The difference was he only had one shot that he was able to make and that was the long jump shot and he would shoot it before I got close to him. He hit it almost every time before I got a chance to pressure him, but I knew that if I could get to him quicker, than he would begin to miss more often.

Everyone there could play the game with skill. Harvey Junior was 40 years old and Vernon 41, but they had skills that couldn't be denied. Their game was a little slower than the rest of us, but it didn't matter. They play the game against each other and moved the crowd with their antics.

At halftime, the score was 33 to 30 in our favor, but by no means did we get big headed and think that we were going to crush them. I sat on the bench and wiped the sweat from my face and neck. I looked around to where Diana was sitting and when she saw me, she tried to hide her smile of pride and show me nothing but disdain. I knew she was proud of her husband's ability on the course. She tried to act as if she was not impressed. She was impressed! I made sure of that!

She was sitting side-by-side with Bimini chatting away and acting like two young girls. It was as if they never had any history of bad blood between them. I got up and walked over to them. Bimini saw me first.

"Hi Donn!" She said.

"Hi Bimini! I would hug you but I'm all sweaty from… Showing off!" I laughed as I spoke to her, but I looked at Diana.

"You ain't 'all that'!" Diana said.

"Oh, yes I am, and you know it! Doesn't she Bimini? She was talking about me the whole time I was playing, wasn't she?" I grinned. "You don't have to answer that, I already know!"

Then I spoke to Diana. "Hey Sheryl, get you're 'A' game ready!"

"Don't need it! My 'B' game is good enough for what I've seen, Reggie!"

"Reggie? Cheryl? What gives?" Bimini asked. "You guys are weird!"

"Explain it to her baby. I've got to get back to the game. You haven't seen half of what I can do! But you will! I blew her a kiss and she returned.

The second half went much better than the first for us. That's when we started to pull away. David brought the ball down and tried his usual pull-up jump shot, but this time I was in his face. His shot didn't make it to the rim. Air ball. I had broken him, and he knew it. The look in his eyes said so, but I didn't try to overwhelm him. It was just a family game. We were there to have fun, so I didn't dominate but I never stopped showing off!

We won the game. The final score was 69 to 54. I scored 32 points. Then the women played. It was Diana, Bimini, Iris, Dorothy and Tammy against Janice, Shirley, Linda, Sharon, and Trudy! The game started off slowly but a few minutes into it, Bimini and Diana got into a groove and moved the ball up and down the court like they had been playing together all of their lives.

They were so much better than any of the rest of the team. The best player on the other team was Janice, but she was not nearly as good as Diana or even Bimini. There was no doubt that Diana was the best player out there. She was really good! It surprised me how good she was. I thought she was just talking trash when she bragged about her skills, but she backed up every word that she said with action. I thought that when she and I played that it would be a breeze, a walk in the park, but I could plainly see that she wasn't going to go down easy. She was better than some of the guys there, but she still had to go a long way to catch me.

Their game ended with Diana's team winning 47 to 38. Of course, Diana scored the most points. She came and sat next to me and leaned against me sweating and still breathing heavily from her last 'coast to coast' run.

"How do you like me now?" She asked between breaths and smiles.

"Oh, I like you fine. I really thought you were kidding when you said that you could play, but you're really good! Really good!"

"Thank you, baby. You know, I didn't think that you could play either. But sweetheart, you are definitely the best player out here! Your fantastic!" She looked up and kissed my cheek.

"Thank you. You know something?" I played with her hair; it was something I naturally did when we were close. It was all wet with her sweat and not at all set in the way that she usually put it. It drooped and laid across her back and chest.

"What?"

"You're all sweaty and tired and… Un-fresh, but I'm so turned on right now that if the family wasn't here, I'd tear your clothes off and…."

"AND WHAT?" The voice wasn't Diana's. It came from over my shoulder.

I looked to see who it was, and it was Aunt Ruby.

"Ah…I'd…ah…um…" I couldn't say what I wanted to say, and I couldn't think of anything else that would fit the G rating.

"That's the first time since I've met you that you have been at a loss for words!" Aunt Ruby smiled and chuckled when she spoke.

"I want to know. What were you going to do?" It was Diana speaking this time.

I looked and Aunt Ruby was listening with high intensity.

"You can't hear this, Aunt Ruby," I said. "You're too young. Your ears are still tender and virgin!"

"Sweetheart, ain't nothing on me been virgin for over 35 years!" She let out a hearty laugh.

"Is it all about Jennifer and Big Al?" Diana's face was alive with smiles.

"Who's Jennifer, and who's Big Al?" Aunt Ruby was puzzled but it didn't take long for her to figure out what we were talking about. "OH, OH! Jennifer and Big Al! I get it. You two! You've got names for your stuff?" She shook her head and then changed the subject.

"Are you two going to play a one-on-one? That's what everyone is waiting to see!"

"Yeah, were going to play, but she's got to catch her breath first."

"Okay, take your time." She walked over to where her mother sat and began talking to Grandma Etta.

I turned to Diana because I sensed that something was bothering her. "Is there something wrong?"

"No…. Well…. Yes!"

"What?"

"Well I didn't know that you were really that good. I can't beat you and I don't want you to take it easy on me either. I don't want you to embarrass me."

"Then why don't you just challenge me to a shooting contest. You can shoot just as good as I can, maybe better. That way it will be even!"

"You'd do that for me?"

"Of course. I love you!"

She hugged against me. "I love you too!"

The first game was 10 shots from the free-throw line. She went first and made all 10. I stepped up to the line and prepared myself for my first shot. Diana whispered in my ear.

"Jennifer is tingling, baby! She's waiting for Big Al! What are you going to do about it?" She placed the palm of her hand on my chest trying to distract me.

"I'll take care of Jennifer right after I take care of you.... Mrs. Diamond!" I switched to my Barry White baritone voice when I said it. She trembled. "So, you want to play dirty, Mrs. Diamond?" She chuckled again. "Then," I rubbed the tip of my fingers along her neck to her throat. "we'll play dirty!"

She gasped for air and her eyes were almost closed when I took my hand away.

"Come on Donn! Quit stalling!" Shouted Bimini. "Shoot the ball!" She grinned my way. Her words allowed Diana to recover.

"You can come out here too! I'll beat the both of you!" I shouted back.

Bimini smiled at me. "No. You don't want any part of that. We'll embarrass you!"

"Embarrass me? You must be kidding! I'll play you two on two! You pick my partner!" I bragged.

She got up and strolled out onto the court where Diana and I were standing. She sashayed up to me and said. "Donn, you're good, but we'll beat you. Are you sure you want to embarrass yourself like that? Huh?"

"Just pick someone! Anyone! Just as long as they're over 16 and male." My ego rose up and took over my senses. It shouted loudly that I was the best and I couldn't be beaten. I was out of control.

"Okay. I will!" She turned to confer with Diana. They put their heads together and looked up at me. "How about Uncle Harvey?" They both giggled again.

Uncle Harvey was 61 years old. I was about to protest, but I hesitated too long.

"Uncle Harvey, you want to play? You used to be pretty good, right?" Bimini went straight for his ego.

"USE to be?" He stood up and motioned as if he were shooting the ball. "I'm still good! Good enough to whip you two smart alec kids!"

He stepped down from the rises and started toward the court to where we were standing. Everyone started cheering and whistling. Harvey threw his hands up, did a 360° spin, grinned widely at the crowd and bowed to them. Uncle Harvey was the family clown. He had a flair that was unique to him. He stood next to me and stuck his tongue out at Diana and Bimini. They in turn stuck their tongues out at him, so I joined him.

My enjoyment level was at its peak! I was in the midst of the kind of family that I always wanted to be a part of. It was the kind of family that spent most of their time enjoying each other instead of being in conflict. I was surrounded by so many people with so many different personalities but the harmony and unity and love that came forth to me and hit me just where I lived. I knew nothing of a large family. I grew up in a different world, but this large family world was awesome!

Aunt Martha came out onto the court. She was displeased with the decision that Uncle Harvey had made. Suddenly, everyone became quiet. The cheers stopped, the laughter too. The talking also stopped leaving me to assume that a confrontation was about to bloom, and no one wanted to miss it.

Martha had that sternness that she inherited from her mother. Her look of determination demand respect and intimidated everyone in the same way as Grandma Etta does when she assumed control of family. But, Uncle Harvey, the only one that still smiled, wasn't intimidated in the least.

"Harvey! You know you're too old to be playing with these young kids!" She turned to Diana and Bimini. "How old are you? 24, 25?"

"25!" They said together, neither of the other symbol.

"And you, Donn! How old are you? 26, 27?"

"31." I said and silently thanked her.

She turned her attention straight back to Uncle Harvey. "You've got 30 years on them at least! 30 YEARS, HARVEY! You're going to hurt yourself out here. You can't keep up with them, so come on back and sit down!"

"No can do, sweetie pie! I've been challenged. Called out. Put on 'front Street'! I must defend my honor!" He pretended to be drawing a sword from his belt and in a mock gesture, he stabbed Bimini and then Diana. Then he returned the invisible sword to its original position in its imaginary sheath.

"Harvey! Stop playing around! You know you can't keep up with them, so come on and sit down!" She was still determined not to give in.

Uncle Harvey leaned close to Aunt Martha and whispered something into her ear which brought a beam of joy that erased the look of scorn that she carried out onto the court. She giggled as he whispered, and she twisted as if he were tickling her, but his hands were firmly cupped around her ear so that only she could hear what he had to say. When he backed away, she stood quivering like a bowl of Jell-O, and if she had died at that moment it would have taken the undertaker a week to get the smile off her face.

"One game! That's all!" She conceded. She didn't walk off the court, she floated. Whatever he had said certainly changed her attitude.

The talking resumed. The laughter rose from the chuckles, and the chuckles from the whispers, and the whisper from silence.

"Yes dear." He said smiling as she walked away. When she had just about reached the court's edge, he stuck out his tongue at her. Everyone broke out in hilarious laughter. She spun around, knowing what he was up to, but not quickly enough to catch it.

"You better keep that tongue in your mouth, Harvey Franklin!"

He winked. She tried not to smile but she couldn't help it. She returned to her seat.

———◇———

Diana and I finished our game. It was quick. I shot and made all 10. That meant Diana and I were tied.

"One more, okay?" Diana was determined to beat me.

"Okay! This time I'll go first."

I made the first six shots with ease, but on the seventh, I came up short and missed.

"Oooooo!" The crowd reacted.

"Diana said. "You're finished now!" Her confidence level had risen.

I paid no attention to her and concentrated on my shot. Numbers eight, nine and 10 went in like a hot knife through soft butter. I only missed one shot, but Diana was deadly from the foul line. She took the ball and bounced a few times before she set herself for the first shot. It swished through touching only the bottom of the net. She smiled at me. I wanted to distract her, but I didn't. The second shot went through like the first, and so did the third and fourth. Before she took the fifth shot, she blew me a kiss and winked. I licked my lips as I looked at the spot where Jennifer resided. The thought that was placed into her head was enough to throw off her shot. She missed!

"Oooooo!" The collective gasp rose again. I couldn't lose! I could only win, at the worst, tie. Either way, I could live with it.

Diana was upset with herself. If she had just left me alone and continued to shoot, she might have gotten all 10 and she would have beaten me. Now she could only tie. She composed herself and took the next shot. Number six, seven and eight went through easily but number nine hit the ram and rolled around several times. Everyone gasped again. The ball stopped and fell through the rim. All she had left to do was sink the final shot for a tie. She looked at me but didn't say a word. She didn't offer any gesture either. Although I was her opponent, I was rooting for her to make the shot. She turned to the basket, bounce the ball as she normally does, looked up at the rim, set herself and let the ball fly. It seemed to be moving in slow motion. It rose in the air as it spun in reverse from the English that she had put on it. As it came down, there was quiet all around me. I heard nothing! Not a sound! The whole area erupted with cheers when the ball swished through the net.

I ran and hugged her. I picked her up and spun around in the air.

"I knew you could do it!" I said.

"You really, really love me, don't you?" She asked. "You didn't want me to lose?"

"Yes, and no! Yes, I really, really love you, and no, I NEVER want you to lose!"

"Je Teime'!"

"Je Teime'!"

The game with Bimini and Uncle Harvey started about 15 minutes later. It was just a half-court game with the winner being the first team to reach 15 points, counting by ones.

Uncle Harvey and I gave the ball to Diana and Bimini first.

"Donn, do you know that I can't move as fast or as long as you, so I'm going to stay close to the paint and feed you. You do your thing but remember that I still CAN play the game!"

"Okay, Uncle Harvey. We'll work it out. There's no way they're going to beat us!"

He smiled and said, "Let's go!"

We started to play. Bimini dribbled close to Uncle Harvey and faked a move to the left, but it didn't faze him. He stood his ground and watched her eyes. When I saw his movements and concentration, I knew that he could play. I stopped worrying about him. Bimini passed the ball to Diana who was just in front of me in the wing. Diana dribbled the ball between her legs and switched from her right hand to her left. Her eyes were steadfast as they peered into mine waiting for that moment. She switched her dribble again and faked to the left, but I didn't go for it. I waited, never removing my eyes from hers.

"What you gonna do, babe?" I questioned. "You have to do something. But, don't do the wrong thing!"

"I love you, baby!" She said. "We're going to have such a great life together!" She smiled and kept dribbling.

"Yeah, I know. I know how you feel, but right now everybody's watching for you to make a move!"

"Okay!" She passed the ball back to Bimini and then ran past me to the basket. I knew what she was doing, but I let it happen anyway. Bimini returned the ball to her and she went up for a layup. Everyone cheered. She retrieved the ball and gave it to me.

"Don't do that again!" Her eyes told me that she wasn't pleased with me.

"Do what?" I acted dumb.

"You know what I'm talking about!"

"No, I don't. Tell me."

"Don't take it easy on me."

"I don't know what you're talking about." I tried to keep a straight face. I don't think that I did a very good job of it.

"Do that again, and Jennifer will go on strike!" She grinned as she walked past.

"You can't do that!"

"Why can't I?" She questioned me.

"Because I know the secret!"

"What secret?"

"I'm not telling you, but I'll show you later!"

"You're incorrigible!"

I took the ball and passed it to Uncle Harvey.

"Yeah, I am, but we're still going to beat your brains out!"

Uncle Harvey surprised me when he began to move the ball. He showed off too. He dribbled straight at Bimini and she took up position and waited. He started to break right and when she committed to his move he spun backwards and to the left and then past her, leaving her standing still while he made an easy layup. The thing about it was that he really looked good doing it. Even Bimini gave him his props when everyone whistled and cheered for him. She smiled and bowed in reverence. He bowed back to her, and then to the crowd which had now grown beyond the family by way of groups of guys who had come to play ball. There were also students that had been passing by who stopped to see what was happening. The crowd swelled and everyone was enjoying what 'old man', Uncle Harvey was doing.

The game continued as Diana and Bimini showed off too. They weren't going to be outdone by their sixty-one-year-old Uncle. Before they brought the ball back into play, they huddled together to formulate a plan. They knew that they were younger and faster than us, especially younger than Uncle Harvey, so they use that to their advantage. Diana took the ball out at half-court. She passed to Bimini who was just 10 feet in front of her and off to the left of center. Diana made a quick move straight at me. Bimini dribbled to the left to draw Uncle Harvey away from center, and then she passed the ball back to Diana. Bimini then sprinted across the court to the right edge of the court near the back-court line, leaving Uncle Harvey in her dust. Diana passed the ball quickly to Bimini and she sprinted to the basket. Uncle Harvey tried to catch her but by the time he had gotten there she had passed the ball to Diana. Diana instead of trying to shoot the ball passed it off to Bimini again who had blown past Uncle

Harvey and was standing at the foul line. She shot the ball. It swished through the net. They expended a lot of energy to gain that point and I knew that we could get it back, but we couldn't afford to let them run around us like that. Uncle Harvey just didn't have the energy to keep up.

The next time they got the ball we guarded them with a zone defense. Uncle Harvey stayed to the left and I stayed to the right, and everything out above the foul line was left alone. They tried to draw us out as they had done previously, but it didn't work. I did what Diana had asked, …no… what she had threatened, and I didn't lighten up on her. She proved to be a better defensive player than I thought, the final result was that I could not be stopped. The game ended with Uncle Harvey showing off again. I passed him the ball and he motioned to Bimini to come to get the ball. He taunted her. She tried to steal the ball while he stood stationary dribbling the ball out in front of him. As soon as he saw her eyes move, he moved the ball before she lunged for it. Around his back it went, and he sprinted to the basket left-handed. Bimini try to recover but it was too late. Uncle Harvey called upon all of the strength and dunked the ball… Left-handed!

Everyone went wild! Cheers, clapping, whistling, and above all I heard Aunt Martha scream with delight. Uncle Harvey bowed to the crowd and then removed his invisible sword and ran Bimini through again.

Silliness ran deep in the Carver clan. Bimini clutched her gut and pretended to be mortally wounded as Uncle Harvey removed his invisible his sword from her stomach. She dropped to her knees and then rolled over on the ground faking death. A few seconds later, she coughed and kicked her feet. Then stillness. Another kick and then stillness again. Uncle Harvey stood over her and returned his sword to its place. Another rumble of laughter swept through the family crowd.

"And let that be a lesson to all of you! I'm sixty-one,…..but I'm not done!" Laughter rose louder and hardier.

"And Martha?" He said.

"Yes dear?" She replied from the risers. There were stars of adoration in her eyes.

"I'll see you later!" He sat down on the ground. "……. Right after my nap!" He laid down and pretended to be asleep. Everyone found it hilarious and we began to laugh.

The final score was 15 to 13. We wanted to play another game, and but Aunt Martha was dead set against it. Grandma Etta also was against it. There was discussion about it between us until Grandma Etta spoke.

"Harvey! I've never had the opportunity to turn you across my me!" She spoke as she walked out on the court with several other family members. "But if you try to play another game, I'm going to tan your hide!"

That was the end of our basketball game. We left the court shortly after that with the whole family in tow. We said our goodbyes to the students that were gracious enough to wait for us to finish. We thanked them for the use of the court, and they thanked us for the chance to witness the family fun.

CHAPTER 26

St Louis or Malibu

The Carver family was 62 souls strong. It began with the matriarch, Grandma Etta, who was the eldest and trickled down to the youngest, my son, at four months old. Only three family members were missing that day, Floyd Carver senior, Grandma Etta's deceased husband, and Lonnie and Diana Carver. Diana's father and mother. Whether Diana's mother and father knew about the family gathering was really unclear to me. Lonnie was in prison and couldn't make it even if he didn't know. Where Diana's mother was, no one knew! Or if they did, they weren't saying.

I learned that John, formerly Uncle John, was the one that was responsible for making the contacts with the out-of-town family members. Knowing now what I knew about how he hated his brother; I assume that he didn't contact either of them. He also made no attempt to contact Diana because she also knew nothing about the celebration.

There were four generations that carried the Carver name. The first of course was Grandma Etta and her late husband Floyd Carver senior. Then came Floyd the second, not Junior, Floyd the third and his son Floyd the fourth was 14 years old. But there were actually five generations there, but they didn't carry the Carver name. They came down through Martha and Uncle Harvey Franklin. Three generations followed them carrying the last name, Crawford. Their daughter Linda was the third generation. She was 41. She married Cousin Vernon Crawford. Their son Vernon Junior was 22. His brother Walter was 21. They were the fourth generation. Vernon Junior and his wife Holly were the parents of Vernon the third, and Heather. Walter and his wife Bridget were the parents of Bridget, Belinda and Bonnie. They were the fifth generation and Grandma Etta knew each and every one of us by name.

"How can you remember everyone's name and who they belong to?" I asked her.

"Son, I've been around here a long time. I've been there when most of them were born. I've changed their diapers and watched them take their first step. How in the world could I ever forget?" She smiled warmly. "Besides, I have a mind like a steel trap!"

Diana and I went into town with Aunt Ruby to pick out something that Grandma Etta would like for her birthday. We returned at 3:30 PM just before the party began at 4 o'clock. We assembled in the backyard and there were a lot more people at the party that there was the day before. Neighbors came, friends from across town, as well as people from out of town and of course her living relatives and friends from the town of Joplin Missouri where she was born. We presented her with presents, and she showed each of us the same consideration and thoughtfulness regardless of how she really felt about the present itself.

Aunt Ruby told us that Grandma Etta was a coffee addict. She drank it religiously every morning and at almost every meal. She insisted that a Mr. Coffee automatic coffee maker was the ideal gift for her. Grandma Etta had one that she bought years ago, but it no longer woke her up with the fresh smell of brewed coffee. Instead of waking her up with that tantalizing aroma, it only beeped the time, but didn't automatically produce coffee the way it was designed to. So, we bought her a new one!

It was a fact that Grandma Etta loved her coffee and drank it religiously. I thought back to the days when Diana and I would rendezvous at 1 o'clock in the morning and drink coffee from the coffee pot that she always kept filled. I realized that coffee, like beauty, was an inherited thing for Diana.

Grandma Etta loved the coffee pot. She had this ear to ear grin when she tore open the wrapper and saw the box. She said that she would use it every day and I believed her!

The day was winding down and I, as well as most of the family, begin to fade with fatigue. I enjoyed the family and the fun, but I was looking forward to being back on the train with my wife and son. She and I hadn't had sex at all since we had been in St. Louis and I was beginning to feel the strain. From the look in Diana's eyes, I believed that she was feeling it too!

For most of the time up to that point, Sasha had control of Donnte', and she did not want to let him out of her sight. She held onto him as if he were her own. I was concerned about the effect it would have on her once we left. Diana and I enjoyed our time away from him, but we also missed him terribly. I missed his smiles, his giggles and his baby talk. I missed seeing his bright eyes follow me as I moved around him. I missed holding him and I missed his unique smell. (Not that one!)

The party went on until long after dark. The young children ran throughout the yard playing with each other and making noises as young children do. The teenagers took control of a corner of the yard away from the tables and away from the watchful eyes of the grown-ups. They set up their CD player and turned up the volume to create the atmosphere that they were familiar with. The corner became their dance floor, their private place for their generation. The rest of us sat like old people talking and munching on the tidbits of leftover ham, turkey and fried chicken. Uncle Harvey and Aunt Martha were still there, although some of their generation had left before it got too dark and were probably in the house sound asleep!

There had been so much food when we sat down to eat that it was hard to believe that most of it was gone. There were 60+ family members and at least 30 friends and neighbors who had stopped by. Most of the neighbors brought some type of covered dish with them, which made the food even more plentiful. So were the mouths that devoured it.

As I looked around, I could see that I wasn't the only one that had been worn out by the day's activities. Most of the grown-ups were just sitting and talking. Some were already asleep.

Uncle Harvey and Aunt Martha had gotten up just after the cake was cut and served. We were busy with Grandma Etta when they made their exit. They waited until most of us were engrossed before they snuck off like two hormone crazed teenagers! Uncle Harvey was about to pay his debt to Aunt Martha for his opportunity to play ball. From the look on his face as they crept away, I knew that paying her was going to be just as much a pleasure for him as it was going to be for her.

Uncle Floyd the second, (not Junior), and Aunt Betty were sitting side-by-side propping each other up. They were only inches from sleep. Aunt Betty didn't talk much, and she was usually very silent when Uncle Floyd talked. In the beginning I thought that she didn't like me because she didn't say anything other than 'hi.' But later I discovered that she didn't talk much to anyone, not even to Uncle Floyd! It was just the way she was. She was a very good person and she loved everyone. She was the one that made sure that the house was clean and straight. She was the one that cleaned our room while Diana and I were out buying Grandma Etta's present. She did the behind the scenes work and expected no praise or thanks for it. When I learned that she had cleaned our room, I sought her out to thank her.

"It's nothing, brother Donn. Don't thank me. Thank the Lord! He gave me the desire and the will to do it. It's not about me, it's all about him!" With every word, her face was aglow. She said it and she meant it.

Aunt Ruby and Diana were chatting away as usual, but this time Aunt Peggy, Bimini's sister Tammy, Iris, Janice, and Dorothy were all involved too. John, (formerly Uncle John), was sitting next to me and it seemed that no one wanted to talk to him. More than likely, it was the evil look that he wore. Uncle Arthur approach as I watched John.

"Donn, Art Junior and I are leaving for a while. A friend is stranded out on the interstate. We'll be back in a couple hours."

"Do you want me to go with you?" I asked.

"No! We've got it covered. You stay here and get to know the family a little bit better. Maybe you can talk to John there." He motioned with his eyes.

I looked over at John. "Okay. I'll see you when you return."

He disappeared quickly and I turned my attention to John.

"Are you okay?"

"Leave me the hell alone!" He snapped at me.

"Why do you work so hard to make people dislike you? Why do you push your family away?" His attitude was uncalled for and I felt I didn't deserve it.

"Who do you think you are?.... My psychiatrist? You're just a young punk trying to move into this family. What's your angle? Do you think there's money here? Huh? You're just one of those inner-city boys trying to shake down a good black family? Who are you? What are you up to?"

His tone was full of harsh words and his words were full of acid. I wanted to drive my fist through his face!

"I'll answer that, but before I do, you think about this. I just came here yesterday, and I get along with everyone except you! You've been here probably longer than I've been alive, but who likes you? Who wants to be around you? Nobody! Even your own wife over there doesn't want to be bothered with you!" I pointed in her direction. She was busy chatting and laughing with Diana and others.

"Your son, John Junior? Where is he? He's not sitting here with you and it's not because he doesn't love you and not because he doesn't want to sit and talk with you. It's because you bring everyone down. This is a party! Your mother-in-law is celebrating 80 years of life and everybody's happy about it but you! This family love you but they don't like you! Where is Marcel? Where is Iris? Where are your grandchildren? They're not here with you! Why? It's because of your attitude. It stinks! What happened to you years ago is something that you need to let go. You should be enjoying life, but you are as sour as a lemon! Pretty soon you'll be 80 and who do you think will be there at your party?

"Now, to answer your question about who I am, I'm the husband of your niece. The father of her child. I'm just a guy from Pittsburgh that happened to be passing through and found a little happiness and pleasure among a loving family that is mine in the same way that it is yours. Am I looking for money? No! I don't need to! I've got plenty of it. Tomorrow I will be gone, and I'll remember all of the fun that I had and all of the love that I felt and all of the good food that I ate. I'll remember everything good about being here and it will be a pleasurable memory. Something I can smile about when I'm old, alone and thinking about my life. That's who I am. Just a guy who loves life and loves people who love life, but you'll never understand that! I pray that one day you'll change. It would be a shame if no one showed up at your funeral, but you!"

I finished and he glared at me. His eyes were like burning coals. His forehead and nose oozed with sweat. He was angry but he still said nothing. I expected harsh words, but they never came. He got up and briskly walked into the house through the back door.

"Well, at least he didn't cuss you out!" I heard a voice over my shoulder. It was Linda, John Junior's wife. "Maybe you penetrated that thick skull of his. Usually he spits fire!" She sat in his seat.

"I wanted to punch his lights out!" I said.

"I know the feeling. I've tried to talk to him too. Everybody has at one time or another, but he's stuck in his ways. He's been that way so long that it's really hard for him to change. He's really a good guy. He'll give the shirt off his back if you need it, but he has a hard time forgiving and it's hard for him to trust. He hasn't figured that out yet."

"Well, I hope he gets it right soon. Life is too short to be miserable all of the time!"

"Amen! So, when are you guys leaving?"

"Tonight, on the 1:07 AM train." I was missing my son and I began to look around for him.

"Don't you think you ought to be getting some sleep?"

"No! We'll sleep once we get on the train. We've got a sleeper berth."

"Oh, that's good. What made you decide to leave Pittsburgh and head West?"

"Several things, but the main thing was the attitude of our so-called friends and customers after the incident and fire in my building."

I waited for her comments. "We heard about that. Thank God Diana was there. He would have killed you!"

I felt a stab of pain in my chest again. It had nothing to do with this scar or what produced it. It was that feeling that said I didn't function as a man. It said, 'if not for Diana, you'd be dead!' … 'If Diana hadn't showed up when she did…' All of it hit me when she uttered those words. I was thankful, but with it came the feeling of worthlessness. She meant nothing by it, nothing negative, and I knew that, but it still tore the scab off of my emotional wound that probably would never heal.

"I'm thankful too!" I said trying hard to believe my own words.

"So, you're going to Malibu California, I heard. Why Malibu? I've heard that the homes there are really expensive. A lot of movie stars have beach houses there!"

"We inherited a beach house and property. I don't know if we're actually going to live there but were going to check it out." I told her.

"They must have been filthy rich! You're very lucky!" She said while smiling at me. "If you ever want to get rid of it, or even rent it out, let us know!"

I didn't think that she was serious but her look and her next words told me that she was.

"I'm very serious! I'm ready to get the hell out of St. Louis! John and I have talked about it many times. The only reason we're still here is

Grandma Etta, but she's got so many people here who love her and want to take care of her that she really doesn't need us anymore. I'm tired of being here. Don't get me wrong, St. Louis is a great place to live, and it's really nice here, but a beach house in Malibu? What could be better than that?"

"That's what I thought too. That's why we're going to check it out. There aren't many things better than living next to the ocean. When I was with my first wife, we took a vacation to Charleston South Carolina and stayed in a hotel right on the beach. The sounds of the ocean and the smell of the sea water was something that I fell in love with. From that day, I wanted to live by the ocean."

"So, you're probably going to stay there, if you feel that way."

"Probably! But it's really up to Diana. Whatever she wants, that's what we'll do."

"Oh! A REAL MAN!" She smiled. "You must really, really love her to say that!"

"I do!" I smiled this time, purely involuntarily. "She's the part of me that has been missing all of these years." I didn't notice Diana coming up behind me.

"Ooooo, that's so sweet." Diana kissed me on the neck from behind.

"Hey Diana!" Linda spoke.

"Hey Linda!"

"Diana, you're one lucky girl. This is a real man!"

"No, I'm not lucky, I'm blessed! He's a Godsend! He's the other part of me that I have been missing too!" Diana kissed my neck again and whispered in my ear. "Don't be too long baby. Jennifer is ready and waiting!"

She quickly turned to Linda to see if she had heard. Linda gave no indication that she did. Satisfied, Diana left.

"Don't keep him too long, Linda!"

"I won't!" Linda replied.

My eyes followed Diana's rear until she disappeared through the back door. I envisioned Jennifer squeezing Big Al in that death grip that we loved so much.

"Donn?"

I heard but it didn't register. My mind was still with Diana.

"DONN?" She said again. This time it took effect.

"Oh, yeah…. Yeah!"

I shook the image of Jennifer from my mind, but I didn't let it go too far.

"Sorry Linda. It's just that she's such an amazing woman that sometimes I get mesmerized by her!"

"John Junior used to talk that way about me. He used to look at me like that, but now…" She stopped. The subject was changed. "Who's Jennifer?"

"Oh, you heard?"

"Yes, I did. She doesn't whisper too well. Jennifer is a friend?"

"Oh, yeah. She's my best friend!"

"But I thought Diana was… OH! OH! Jennifer!" She laughed, slightly embarrassed.

I nodded.

"Well, I don't want to keep you from 'Jennifer', so I'll let you go." She stood up when she spoke. "Donn, you have a copy of all of the family information, don't you?"

"Yes. Aunt Betty gave it to me a while ago." I stood up with her.

"Once you get to California and get settled, call me. Let's keep in touch."

"I'll do that!" I hugged her.

"Jennifer, huh?"

"Yeah!"

"If she's Jennifer, then you, are you?"

"Big Al!"

"Big Al?" She blushed as much as a light-skinned black woman could. "Go on! Give that woman what she wants!"

Diana was waiting in the room when I got there. Donnte' was lying in bed with her. He wasn't asleep, but he was close to being there. He had her left breast firmly gripped between his lips and his tiny hands. He looked up at me as I came into his view.

"Hey, baby boy!" I sat down and watched him feed. "I missed you! Goo-go- Gaga!" His eyes lit up. A smile broke across his face and his lips loosened on the nipple sending breastmilk shooting my way. Of course, it was funny to him and he gave me a hearty laugh.

10 minutes later, Donnte' was asleep and content. I laid him in the crib. Diana looked at me and she tried to convince me that she was still ready and willing to have sex, but she didn't have that fire there any longer. I understood. I didn't like it, but I understood. Big Al always protested

in situations like that. He still possessed that one-track mind. He didn't care about how she felt. He didn't care that breast-feeding our son was her primary job now and that it occasionally took something out of her. He was the same as he always was. The difference was not with him, the difference in how I responded to Diana, and Jennifer, was that I now listen to the big head more, and the little head!

"Come on baby!" Diana said. "I'm ready." She was willing, but she wasn't ready. She held out her arms to me and I laid beside her. She turned over onto me and kissed me. I wrapped my arms around her and returned the kiss. Her lips were soft and sweet, and her body was firm and luscious, but she needed rest.

She wasn't some woman that I had picked up for a one-night stand. She wasn't someone that just happened along and wound up in my bed. She wasn't even the Diana that I had met two years ago, the one that called for sex at one in the morning. The one that I didn't care how she felt just as long as Big Al and I were satisfied. No, she wasn't any of that. She was my wife! She was the one that I loved!

"Diana, let's just lay here and I'll hold you." I said. "You need rest."

She wasn't too disappointed, she was relieved.

"Baby, I told you I'd never deny you." It was halfhearted, but she tried.

"I know. When I see that you are willing but not ready, it's up to me to make the decision."

"But I'm ready!" She said it, but there was no excitement in her voice. She was trying hard to convince me, but I knew my wife. She needed rest.

"No, you're not! We'll wait. Right now, we'll just cuddle and rest. You rest, I'll wait!"

"But baby, you need me. I'm your wife and I'm supposed to give it to you!"

"And I'm your husband, and I'm supposed to take care of you. We'll wait!"

She looked me in the eye. "Are you sure?"

"Yes. I'm sure!"

"Is Big Al sure?" She reached for him, but I stopped her.

"Diana, please! Don't do that! He'll just rise up and make it that much harder for me."

"Okay. I love you."

"I love you too! Je Teime'!"

We cuddled and laid in silence. I heard Aunt Martha's voice coming from the next room. She seemed to be calm, relaxed and happy. I didn't hear Uncle Harvey's, so I assumed that he was taking another nap.

All of the sounds coming through the window from the family in the yard made me long for the comfort and security of a huge family. I never had it that way growing up, but I listened to the sounds and I realized that I liked it. I have always enjoyed the solitude of being alone and I preferred it, but that was changing. The feeling of belonging overcame me as I mingled with the Carver family. The feeling of belonging, the feeling of purpose. There was that feeling of responsibility and accountability for each person, and that felt good.

After Donna, I decided to be responsible for, and accountable to, no one! Then Diana and Donnte' came into my life. I didn't want to be alone anymore. I wanted to trust and be trustworthy. I wanted to belong to something greater than myself. I wanted to be a part of something special.

I thought about California and the beach house and I tried to compare that to living in St. Louis with the Carvers. Would I long to be in St. Louis once we settled in Malibu? Would I get that feeling of loneliness as I thought about the fun I had with the Carvers?

"Baby?" Diana spoke softly. "What's on your mind?"

"Oh. Nothing. Just listening to what's going on outside."

"I was listening too. It makes me feel good about being here and I don't want to leave."

"I understand. I love being here too and I love our family!"

"Really?" She perked up.

"Yes, because we've had so much fun here."

"That, and the fact that everybody loves us, except, …. Uncle John!" I replied. "Yeah, everybody except John!"

She gave me an odd look. "Why did you call him John, and not Uncle John?"

"He doesn't deserve it!" I said dryly and quickly.

There were a lot of things that I wanted to say about him, but I decided to let it go.

"Huumm." She mumbled and then changed the subject. "What if we get to Malibu and don't like it? What if we really don't want to live on the beach?"

"What? We'll love it! We'll love it and you know we'll love it!"

"You don't know that. We might get some really bad neighbors, or we might not like the house!"

"Diana that's ridiculous. That beach house has a ½ acres around it. Our neighbors aren't even going to be close, and who can hate a beach house? It's a beach house, a BEACH house! AT THE BEACH, BABY. We'll love it even if it's a shack!"

"I don't know!"

"Diana, we were living over top of the store in a cramped apartment, on a busy street full of people who didn't like us and didn't want us around because we were black. Trolleys rumbling by at all hours of the day and night. We had no family living there and few friends, but we were okay because we were happy and content together. Do you really think that we won't want to stay on the beach? We've got each other and Baby Boy there. We've got love! We'll be fine!" I wasn't just saying it to convince her, I needed to hear those words too. "And if by chance we don't love it, we've got enough money to move wherever we want to!"

"Yeah, I guess so, but did you ever want to live with a large family? Don't you enjoy the crowd?" She asked. She involuntarily rubbed my thigh. It felt good.

"Sure. I love it but what are you getting at? Do you want to stay here?"

"No. I don't know." She thought before she spoke again. "I guess I really don't want to stay here. I just want my family around. I'm just getting to know them and it's too soon to leave."

"Do you want to stay? We'll stay if that's what you want." I was hoping that she would say yes, because I didn't have a problem with that at all.

"Yes and no. I do, but we need to get to California and take care of our business. We need to stick to our plans."

"Plans were made to change." I said. "If you want to stay, then we'll stay. It's not a problem. It's okay with me."

She gave it thought again but she stuck to her guns. "No baby, we need to go on with what we planned. We can always come back and visit later. I love my family, but my life and heart are with you!"

It was settled. We would continue on to Malibu.

"Do you still want to leave tonight or wait until tomorrow?" I asked.

"Tonight. If we stay one day, we'll wind up staying two, or three, or four. No, let's leave tonight as planned."

"We laid in silence. Again, we listen to the sounds of the family filtering through the window glass. We wanted to stay but we knew we should do the right thing and stick to our schedule. We wanted to continue in our fun activities, but we also knew that we had to act as the responsible adults that we said that we were and take care of business first.

I thought of lessons learned. My addiction to fun and good feelings was at the core of my unmanageability. I had spent a great deal of time chasing a good feeling and not living on life's terms. So, I refused to utter the words that could, and probably would, open the door again to our combined unmanageability. Although I wanted to, I didn't say we were staying another day.

CHAPTER 27

I Love You, Daddy

There was a knock on the door. We didn't respond. The knock came again. I got up and opened the door. It was Sasha wearing the face of sadness, and she had tears in her eyes.

"What's wrong Sasha?" I asked.

"Come on in, honey!" Diana said from the bed. "Come here!"

She held out her arms and Sasha fell into them. She began to cry. Diana looked at me and her eyes told me that it was something that she wanted to manage alone. I grabbed my shoes and pulled the door closed behind me as I entered the hallway.

It was 9:30 PM and I returned to the yard. Most of the children were inside but the teenagers were still outside in the corner with their music playing. The music wasn't quite as loud as before and the adults were scattered all around. Some had left for their homes or went inside to escape the chill that was falling with the creeping darkness. The ones that remained were scattered here and there. Grandma Etta wasn't outside, and I assumed that she was in her room resting. I wanted to talk to her before I left but I didn't want to disturb her. After all, she was 80 years old!

Linda and I began to talk and when I told her why I wasn't going to disturb Grandma Etta, she said, "Oh, she won't mind. She really wants to see you before you leave. Right now, would be a good time to talk to her because she's waiting for Diana's father to call her. He calls her every Sunday evening, but even though today isn't Sunday, he will be calling. It's her birthday! She'd love it if you would stop in!"

"I don't know Linda. She looked awfully tired earlier."

"She'll be very disappointed if she doesn't get to see you, Diana and Donnte' before you leave. Why don't you stay until tomorrow?"

"I thought about it and I probably would if there was a train leaving in the morning, but there isn't. There's nothing going my way until tomorrow evening."

"Well, whatever you do, I think you ought to talk to her before you leave." She said.

"You're right. I'll go knock on her door. If Diana comes down, please tell her where I am. Sasha is up there with her now, and she's crying."

Linda started to speak but she hesitated when I mentioned Sasha.

"I know it's none of my business, but what's wrong with her?" I asked.

"Oh, it's nothing. One of Otis's friends…...."

"Otis?" I tried to place him in the family structure. "Oh! He's cousin Harvey Junior's son?"

"That's right. One of his friends got fresh with her outback. He touched her where he shouldn't have."

Rage began to overtake me. I had just met her, but within the short period of time, she had become family. Stirring deep inside was the desire to protect family. "Who is this guy? What's his name? How old is he?"

"Calm down, Donn. It's okay. His name is Simeon, he's 16th and he's gone home. Cousin Floyd and Cousin Harvey Junior spoke to him and sent him home. Tomorrow he'll be back to apologize, and everything will be okay."

"Okay." I relaxed.

"Don't forget Grandma Etta." She said.

"I won't. I'm going to see her right now. Don't forget to tell Diana where I am. Okay?"

"Okay."

I found my way to Grandma Etta's room in the front, on the first floor. She had converted the den into her bedroom because it was too difficult for her to climb the steps. I knocked on the door.

"Come in! Whoever you are!" She said through the closed door.

I opened it and entered. She was sitting in the same wicker chair that she sat in when we arrived. Her face brightened when she saw me.

"Donn, come on in! I've been wondering when you were going to come and talk to me. Sit down!" She pointed to a chair that matched her chair, the difference was that it wasn't a rocker. "Where's your wife?"

"She's upstairs talking to Sasha. She kicked me out!" I smiled and approached.

She giggled and then she asked. "How is Sasha?"

"She was crying when I left. Something about Simeon touching her." I sat down.

"Well, she'll be okay. She's an extremely sensitive child. She was more embarrassed than anything else." She seemed totally unconcerned.

"Grandma, we're going to be leaving tonight about midnight. Our train pulls out at 1:07 AM. I thought about staying another day, but I feel the right thing to do is stick to our plans. I really enjoyed myself and I wanted to thank you for everything!"

"Thank me? I should be thanking you! It was a pleasant to have you here, if only for a day. I should thank you for bringing Diana, my Baby Bunny, back to me. Yes! I should be thanking you. So, thank you! Diana said that you two bought a beach house in Malibu California. That must be exciting. I've never been to California. I 've spent most of my life right here in St. Louis."

"We didn't buy the house, grandma, it was a gift from a lady that we helped take care of. She left it to us after her death."

"Yes, you're right. Diana did say that. I guess I must have gotten it mixed up. When you get to be my age, sometimes the gears slip a little, like an old transmission. You know what I mean?" She chuckled as she spoke.

"Yes ma'am." I didn't really know, but I tried to understand.

"Donn, let me ask you something."

"Yes ma'am?"

"How long have you known Diana?"

"Two years, almost three."

"So, you know a little about her, yes?"

"A little, but I'm learning more and more, day by day. I know that she is the most beautiful woman I have ever known, inside and out! She has her problems, but so do I." I offered.

"Yes." She hesitated and thought before she spoke again. "She seems much, much better, but I haven't seen her in over 10 years."

"Yes. She is like a new person."

"So, you've seen her at her worst?" She was concerned and she wanted to know how much I really knew.

"Oh yes! I've seen her at her worst. I'm aware of her problems and I know about her mental illness. But I also know that she has transformed, and the demons no longer control her, she controls them. She has accepted her illness and has taken the steps and responsibility to keep it under control." I felt as if I were Diana's lawyer, pleading her case.

"How much do you know about her mother and father?" She asked. Obviously, there was much more to the family story than what I knew.

"Not much. She hasn't talked about them that much."

"Son, I'm going to tell you some things that you need to know about this family. You have a son with her and a child on the way. They may be affected by their heritage and family bloodlines."

I tried to relax as I listened to what she told me about Diana's ancestry, but I couldn't relax. I remained tense as I listened. I was hearing things that Diana herself didn't know. I wondered why she was telling me without Diana present, but before she finished, I understood. Diana wasn't yet ready to hear it.

"Donn, you are the man of your house and the guardian of your family. You need to know about any and all things that may threaten your home, whether it be external or internal. It's easy to battle with the external things, but not so easy to do battle with the internal. But son, you can't fight against the demons if you don't even know that they exist!"

"I understand, but it's an awful lot to bear!" I said.

"Yes son, but it's your burden. You have to bear it!"

My heart was heavy and sad. What I had heard change things in my life at that moment. I wished I had never heard the truth. But the problem with knowing the truth is that you can't go back to not knowing!

"Grandma?"

"Yes son?"

"Do you want me to keep this from Diana? If so, I don't know if I can!"

"You should tell her, but only at the right time. You choose the time. Don't let her manipulate you because it's too important. Do you understand?"

"Yes ma'am!"

I was sitting in the chair shaking. What I knew might send Diana over the edge again. It might devastate her to the point that she may want to give up on her recovery and start drinking and drugging again. I began to imagine all sorts of scenarios. I thought the worst and my mind was spinning and racing at the same time.

"Son, go get your wife and bring her here to me. I need to talk to her before she leaves."

I agreed, but before I got the chance to leave the room, Diana knocked and came in. Sasha was fine she said. Everything was okay.

After hugging grandma, she sat in the chair where I had been sitting and I stood behind her. There was something that was about to be revealed, she knew it. She was anxious and that was a good thing. She waited for Grandma Etta to begin, and she kept quiet while grandma spoke. From time to time, she turned to look at me. She knew that I knew more than she did. There wasn't a doubt that she was going to pressure me for the information just as soon as she could. But I remembered Grandma Etta words. 'You choose the proper time. Don't let her manipulate you...' Those were great words, but I wasn't sure if I could stand up to them.

When grandma finished speaking, Diana sat silent. My hands were on her shoulders for comfort. She held my hands in hers.

"Grandma, do you know why my dad went to jail?"

"Of course, I do, child."

"No grandma! I mean, do you know why he killed that man? It wasn't about my mother!"

Diana waited with anticipation. She wanted to tell her grandmother the whole truth, but Grandma Etta already knew.

"I know that my son loves you more than he loves life itself. Every letter that I get from him, he asks about you. In every phone conversation that we have, he asked if I've heard from you. What could I tell him? Until recently, I didn't know anything at all. Your mother's ties with us faded around the time he went away. I didn't know where you were or how you were doing. Ruby lost contact. You know your mother and Ruby never got along, and Bimini stopped calling when she started using drugs, but even though I couldn't tell him much, he never stopped asking about you.

"Sweetheart, the reason I wanted you here,... Right now.... Is to give you a chance to talk with your father!"

Diana tensed up. "What do you mean?" She asked, somewhat afraid of the answer.

"He will be calling me in about," She looked at her watch. ".. Five minutes!"

"How,... How do you know, grandma?"

"He always calls me late in the evening at the same time... Usually on Sunday, .Besides,... It's my birthday. He'd better call!"

"Grandma! I.... I.... I don't know if I...."

"Sweetheart, if you don't want to talk with him, that's all right. I won't tell him you're here, but what do you want me to do if he asks? I can't lie!"

"It's okay grandma. You can tell him I'm here. I'll talk to him."

Diana still had her hands on my hands. She squeezed to let me know that she was afraid, but that she was going to do what her grandmother wanted.

"You will? That's wonderful! He'll be so happy to hear your voice."

Grandma Etta was happy. I saw a tear begin to form in the corner of her eye.

"Grandma, did he tell you what REALLY happened?" Diana squeezed harder.

"Yes, . Baby Bunny. He told me everything. I know all about it."

I was silent for just a moment or two which made the sudden ringing of the phone seemed that much louder.

"Hello?" Grandma Etta answered.

Diana's hand gripped mind with authority. She was nervous with anticipation. She wanted to speak to her father, but she also was afraid.

"Baby, I'm right here!" I whispered.

She whispered, "I love...Je Teime!"

"Hi son. How are you?" Grandma spoke. It was Lonnie, Diana's father.

"How much time do you have to talk.... 10 minutes.... Okay.... What?.... That's good. I'm glad to hear it.... Thank you, son! It was a beautiful day. Everyone was here.... Except you and your wife... Did you get the letter I sent you last week?.... Oh, you're welcome. I would've sent more, but I was a little short..... I know I don't have to... Yes, I know you're grown, and you can take care of yourself, but you're still my son and it doesn't matter how old you are...."

There was an abrupt silence as she listened to what he had to say. She looked at Diana and smiled briefly. I thought about what he must be going through after 11 years in prison and with so much more to go. Things must be tough for him to have to rely on his mother to send money to sustain him. I didn't know this man and I had never seen him nor even heard his voice, but he was the father of my wife. By creating her, he was instrumental in creating my happiness and joy. I felt I owed him something and I decided right then and there to send him money to live off of so he wouldn't have to rely on his elderly mother. She didn't mind sending it, but her words let me know that, at times, it was a bit of a strain on her. I had so much money that it would never be a strain on me. Diana had convinced me to send Donna money, so I only thought it fair to send him some too!

Grandma Etta and Diana's father chitchatted for the first five minutes and then she closed down the conversation with these words.

"Lonnie, we've got to end the conversation now…..(Silence)…. I know the 10 minutes aren't up yet, but I have someone that wants to speak to you…. (Silence)…. Well….. I'll just put them on the phone…. Wait a minute!"

She handed Diana the phone. Diana removed her left hand from mine and gripped the phone. She looked back at me and her eyes were wide with fear of anticipation. I nodded and held onto her other hand as she put the phone to her ear.

"Hello daddy?" Her voice was shy, pensive and childlike. When she spoke again, her voice went from being childlike, to the voice of a child. It's your Baby Bunny!"

There was silence as she listened to her father speak to her for the first time in 11 years. I moved to the side of the chair so that I could see her face. Tears found the tracks along both sides of her eyes and down along the side of her nose past her cheeks, around the corners of her mouth to her chin. These were not just a few isolated drops, but streams that flowed continuously. She became choked up when she spoke and almost erupted in boo-hoo tears.

"Daddy, I'm so sorry! I didn't mean for you to go to jail! I…. I…."

He obviously was speaking again, and she remained quiet while he did. I imagined him telling her that it wasn't her fault, and not to blame herself for any of what happened. I imagined him saying that he loved her that he needed her in his life, because she said.

"I love you too daddy. I promise, I'll write you as soon as we get to California ….(Silence)…. Okay daddy….(silence)…. He's right here with me…. Yes Sir!"

She handed me the phone. I was at odds as to why he wanted to talk to me. What would I say? I took the phone.

"Hello?"

"Hello, what's your name? Donald?"

"No Sir. It's a Donn!"

"Okay.... Donn. Look, I don't have much time, but I want you to promise me that you'll make Diana contact me once you get settled in Cali'."

He spoke with authority. He wasn't giving me an order, but it felt like one! His voice was strong and direct.

"Yes sir, I'll do that!"

"Thank you, Donn. And…. Thank you for taking care of her. You must really love her."

"Yes Sir, I do!"

"Okay Donn. Put her back on." I did and they talked for a minute or two before she handed the phone back to Grandma Etta. Grandma Etta was sitting with several tissues from the Kleenex box that she had been using to sop up the tears that were flowing from her own eyes. She handed Diana the box of Kleenex from the nightstand. She spoke for another minute and then said her goodbyes and hung up.

"Thank you, grandma." Diana let go of my hand and got up. She knelt down on the floor, placed her head in her grandmother's lap and began to weep. I wanted to go to her, but Grandma Etta stopped me and motioned me to the door. I understood but I didn't want to leave.

I had never seen Diana cry that way. I felt helpless but I knew that she was in good hands, so I left the room. It was the second time I had been kicked out of a room that evening!

I opened the door to my room. Sasha was sitting on the bed playing with Donnte'.

"Hi uncle Donn." She said cheerfully.

"Hi Sasha. How are you feeling?"

"Okay."

"You were crying when I left. Are you sure you're okay?" I asked. I didn't let on that I knew what had happened.

"Yeah. I feel better now. Aunt Diana talk to me." She looked down at Donnte' lying on the bed and she continued to play with him.

"That's good. I'm glad you're okay." I wanted to lay down and rest, but I found myself sitting with Sasha and playing with Donnte'. I loved to hear his giggly laugh and he was putting it out nonstop as we played with him.

Diana came in the room about 10 minutes later and gave me a weak smile that told me that she needed to rest or talk. I hoped it was rest! Sasha looked in our faces and offered to take Donnte' so that we could be alone, but Diana said no. She and I hugged Sasha before she left the room and then Diana sat down on the bed beside me.

"How are you feeling?" I asked.

"Strange!" She said. "It's hard to explain. I've got all kinds of emotions going on now. I feel like a little girl in a woman's body, but I also feel like a woman who still is in a little girl's body. My emotions are all messed up. Talking to my father took me back to when he was my dad. I can't get back the feeling that I had back then, but I want to feel like his little girl again. I want to BE his little girl again, but I can't be! Too much has happened. I feel like I've missed so much growing up without him. I want that time back! I want to be his Baby Bunny again! Do you understand?" She was near to tears.

"I guess so."

"Baby, I really love being here, but after talking to my father and my grandmother, I know that it's time to go. I'm ready to get on the train with my husband and my son and start looking forward to our new life together!"

"Are you tired of being around your family?" I asked.

"No. Not really. But it's just that everything here is so perfect. But it's really not perfect! My family isn't perfect, but they seemed that way. There's something wrong here. I don't know what it is, but something isn't right. You and I are right, but we've been through hell, and we still have problems. That's the way life is. Life here isn't like that, nobody's upset, nobody's angry, except Uncle John and nobody pays him any attention anyway."

"But Diana, we've only been here a day and a half. People always show their good side to strangers and although we are family, we're still strangers. That's all that it is. You're reading too much into it!"

"Maybe, but I'm still ready to go." Her mind was made up.

"Are you going to write your dad when we get to Malibu?" I switched tracks.

"Yes." That was all she said. She wasn't quite herself and I could see that she had a lot on her mind. My concern level went up a few degrees. I had to keep in mind on what could, and would, happen to her if she allowed depression or some other negative emotion to sink in. Vigilance was key.

"Baby, I think we ought to send your father some money when we send Donna what I decided on." I waited for her response. She was just beginning to feel feelings that she hadn't felt in years. I had never before seen her cry in the way that she did when she fell into her grandmother's lap. This was unfamiliar territory for her, and for me! I just didn't know what to expect.

She didn't disappoint me. She didn't let me down. She remained true to the words that she had spoken some time ago when she decided to go forward and not look back. She didn't let depression stay in her head. It wasn't welcome there anymore.

"How much were you thinking of sending him?" She asked as she brushed back her hair.

"About a thousand dollars."

"That's fine." Her fingers twirled and played in her hair.

"I really think that it should come from you, not from me!"

She thought about it. "No. From both of us. I'll send it with my letter, but I will let him know that it's from both of us. Okay?"

"That's fine."

She picked up Donnte' and kissed him. She was still feeling sad, but she fought against her depression that tried to overtake her.

There was a knock on the door, and I could hear more than one voice in the hallway.

"Donn? Diana? Can we come in?" It was Aunt Ruby and she said 'we', but I hoped that 'we' didn't include her husband, John.

"Come on in!"

With her came Aunt Peggy, Aunt Martha and Uncle Floyd. They all had smiles and endearing looks. They gathered around us. Their attention was on Diana, not me. Aunt Ruby presented herself as the spokesperson for the family.

"Mama told us that you talked to your father. She also told us that you're feeling guilty about him being in jail. Sweetheart don't do that to yourself. What your father did is what any man would do under the circumstances. Some of us have known all along what really happened but it was something we didn't speak about. Some of us didn't know the situation that you were in. I was one of those and I'm so sorry that I wasn't there to protect you! What happened to you was not your fault, you must believe and understand that. What happened to your father was not your fault either. Please don't blame yourself for that. But what we want you to do now is to stay in contact with your father, and with us, because we are family! Family sticks together no matter what and helps each other no matter what! We love you, Diana. We always have, and we always will."

"Diana," it was Uncle Floyd speaking this time. "I was one that didn't know what really happened. I just found out the truth. But let me tell you from a man's point of view, if what happened to you happened to my daughter, I would've done the exact same thing! I would've killed him! So, don't blame yourself for what happened. As men, our job is to protect you and make you feel safe even if we have to suffer! That's what we do because that is part of being a man! Your father is a real man! Just keep that in mind and try to get a relationship going with him now. He loves you very much! We love you!"

Aunt Peggy and Aunt Martha also spoke to her in the same manner. Before they were all finished Diana was crying like a baby again, but this time she was crying as she hugged each one and told them all that she loved them. I had to fight back the tears in my eyes because it was such a touching scene.

CHAPTER 28

The Diary

Even though it was 1 o'clock in the morning, a large portion of the Carver family came to the station to give us a warm and loving sendoff. Grandma Etta was very tired from the day's activities, and it was far past the time that she usually retired to bed, but she stood on the platform waving as our train slowly pulled out of the station at 1:07 AM.

Diana and I waved and watched until we could no longer see them and then we retired to our sleeping compartment. The train was not the same one that we had arrived on, but the compartment was pretty much the same. We wasted no time getting Donnte', as well as ourselves, ready for bed. She and I laid in the arms of the other comfortable, and relaxed.

We were silent for quite some time. I felt a sense of emptiness as we moved away from St. Louis. I had grown to love my new family in just one day and already I missed be around them. I knew that Diana was feeling the same way. She had spoken to her father for the first time in over a decade, so her degree of missing them was far greater than mine. I pulled her closer and held her tightly. She responded by cuddling her body closer to mine. We laid that way, holding onto each other, feeling the warmth generated between us. We listened to the sounds of the train click-clacking over the rails reminding us that we were leaving St. Louis.

"Je Teime'!" She whispered.

"Je Teime'!" I replied.

Talking wasn't necessary. Her thoughts were my thoughts. Her wants were my wants. Jennifer and Big Al were starving for each other. I placed my right hand on her thigh, and she opened to my touch. Big Al woke up immediately. I touched Jennifer and knew that she was ready. I pulled Diana on top of me giving me a clear vision of Donnte'. He was sound asleep.

Diana looked at me with her bedroom eyes. I can't fully explain what happens to me when she looks at me that way. My blood boils with desire and my limbs simultaneously sing the same song of love and I become like a junkie, totally and completely hooked on her. I must, without a doubt, have her in my arms and in my bed. There's only one thing in mind, just one thing! Big Al doesn't need to take control anymore because my whole-body screams with desire for her, and only for her. With big Al in control, it's not necessarily about her. For him, any woman will do! It isn't love that drives him, it's just lust. Lust can be transferred to, and placed upon, any woman. But it was no longer simply the feeling of lust! I was in love with Diana! I was in love with her with every part of me. With everything emotional, spiritual and intellectual. It all manifested itself in the physical, and Big Al was no longer controlling me. He was the main player in the physical game of love, but he was subject to the dictates of my entire being.

"You know, if we keep on like this, we're going to get pregnant all the time!" I said.

"I told you I'd have 15 babies for you! I love you that much."

"I love you too! So does Big Al!" I grinned.

"No, he doesn't! He just loves Jennifer! Donn?.... Baby? Shut up and make love to your wife!"

"Yes, Mrs. diamond!"

"Oooooooo!"

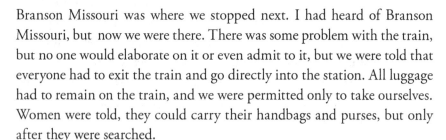

Branson Missouri was where we stopped next. I had heard of Branson Missouri, but now we were there. There was some problem with the train, but no one would elaborate on it or even admit to it, but we were told that everyone had to exit the train and go directly into the station. All luggage had to remain on the train, and we were permitted only to take ourselves. Women were told, they could carry their handbags and purses, but only after they were searched.

"What's going on?" I heard a woman say as she was helped down the steps and onto the platform.

Others made comments that were filled with questions. I myself had questions but I didn't voice them. I took control of my wife and son and exited the train. We were herded from the train by the Missouri State

Police and corralled into the tiny station were there were not enough seats to accommodate us all.

The Branson Police Department along with the County Sheriff and the Missouri State Police checked all of our identification, paying special attention to the women. And then told us to relax. The station was secured and surrounded by troopers and local police. Once they secured us, they boarded the train. I assumed that they were looking for someone, some escaped convict, or convicted killer who had alluded justice by bolting from custody and diving through a window to freedom.

The passengers, including myself, were upset at the disruption and treatment, but none of the law enforcement officers seem to care. They just kept us contained within the station as they were ordered. Through the window I could see a large portion of the train on a slight curve. There were about 10 passenger cars and roughly five or six freight cars. I watched the police move through the train in search of whatever, or whoever they were looking for.

I listened to the talk around me. Everyone had their theory of what was going on. Diana, and a very young, and very blonde, lady was engrossed in conversation. The woman said that when the train stopped in Springfield, they heard about an escape from a state prison. That's why the search was going on.

Others around had different theories and the voiced them continually. There was the one that was based on the possibility of a bomb on the train, another surmised that a gold shipment that was secretly being shipped on the train was about to be hijacked, and still another concern was that a letter bomb was being transported to California in the mail car. But after hearing about the daring prison escape in Springfield, I leaned more towards that theory.

Diana and I had slept while the train was in Springfield. We didn't hear anything because we were exhausted after sex and had fallen off into a deep sleep. I had no recollection of stopping anywhere until Branson.

There was something going on in one of the freight cars. A large number of police were running in that direction. The car was just at the end of the last passenger car. I pressed against the window with several people pressing against me trying desperately to see. Diana and the blonde woman beside me were straining too!

"I bet they trapped those criminals in there!" The blonde said.

Just as she spoke, gunfire broke the silence of the air. The officers outside of our window instinctively ducked their heads and quickly pulled their weapons. All of us that were inside reacted as civilians do by ducking as the instinct for survival took over and then, as curiosity overtook instinct, we raised up again to see what was going on. The officers who were close to the freight car took cover behind anything that they could. Their weapons were drawn and pointed in the direction of the slightly open freight car door. From my vantage point, I couldn't see much, but I knew that whomever the officers were after, were trapped inside the freight car. There was no possible escape!

People inside of the station began to push and shove. Everyone wanted to see. No one wanted to miss a thing. Down at the end of the building, there were windows which allowed for a better view and many of the passengers moved in that direction. There was no way that everyone was going to be able to see from there, but they tried. I stayed where I was and Diana, and the blond woman, stayed by my side.

I looked at my son. His look was a look of curiosity. Diana was calm and unafraid, and her look wasn't the normal look of most of the people waiting. Her look was different, ...Maybe spiritual. Yes, spiritual! She was praying! But, for whom? The police, ...the people on the freight car, ...us, ...or ....everyone?

All of a sudden, the gunfire started again. I could see the smoke from the guns being fired inside of the freight car. The police returned fire, but the thick steel walls of the car allowed for no penetration. Once they saw that, they changed their tactics. Several of the officers in swat gear eased along the side of the car along the tracks. They had tear gas canisters in their hands. They came within 10 feet of the cracked door and then they stopped. An officer who had taken up position behind a sand pile raise his megaphone and began to speak.

"This is Captain Carlo of the Missouri State Police! You are surrounded and you cannot, and will not, escape! Throw down your weapons and surrender with your hands in the air!"

The air became calm and silent as everyone waited for the response from those within the confines of the freight car. Everyone within the station was quiet. You could hear a pin drop! We waited and watched.

Three, or four, minutes past seeming like hours. There still wasn't any response from those inside the freight car. The captain gave the go-ahead and the SWAT team began to advance, slowly and methodically. The first man eased close to the opening of the door. He threw his canister in and ducked under the car. The canister came flying back out a few seconds later, but not before it released some of its toxic smoke inside. Then the second man eased up and threw his canister. He also ducked under the car. The third, fourth and fifth man did the same. The speed of the SWAT team made it impossible for the men inside to throw out all of the teargas canisters before the toxic fumes filled the inside of the car. The remaining canisters came flying out but not before the thick smoke billowed out through the opening. The police force stood ready and alert with weapons pointed directly at the opening of the door. One gun was thrown out. It struck the ground not far from the tracks and then another, and another until seven handguns were lying on the ground. The captain spoke again.

"Open the door all of the way! Jump down and lay face down on the ground with your hands outstretched above your head!"

They did as they were instructed. The door opened and seven of them dressed in tan prison jumpsuits, jumped down coughing and laid face down on the ground. Immediately the swat team from the Missouri State Police, dressed in the appropriate gear and gas masks, surrounded and secured them with handcuffs and then stood guard over them. It was finally over.

The tension inside of the station eased, and the small talk about the incident began. Most of the passengers moved away from the windows happy that the criminals had been caught and subdued. They spoke of the criminals in terms that allow themselves to feel superior and distant. I wondered what the criminals had done, before they had escaped, to have themselves placed in the position that they now found themselves in. I watched as the officers continued to hold them at gun point. They gathered around them so quickly that I could only see them and was no longer able to see the prisoners on the ground. I watched, having seen many instances of police brutality, hoping that this wouldn't be another. I had no reason to believe that these officers would do such a thing, but on the other hand, I had no reason to believe that they wouldn't!

"What's on your mind, baby?" My wife asked.

"Hoping that whomever those people are, that they'll survive."

"I was thinking the same thing. I thought of how angry the cops must be after they spent all that time chasing them down. They must be really pissed off that they were shot at! When cops get pissed off, they retaliate!" She said.

"Yeah, I know!"

We watched together. The blonde lady nodded her head in agreement.

The officers began to holster their weapons and thin out from around the criminals on the ground. They were, one by one, lifted carefully from the ground. There were no kicks or punches thrown which pleased me. Once I could clearly see the captured seven, I realized that they weren't men at all. They were women!

They were paraded past us to an awaiting prison van at the opposite end of the station. They looked at us as they passed by. Some tried to look tough and some did look tough! They were loaded on the van and it pulled away. Only then were the doors to the station unsecured and only then were we allowed to return to the train.

The blonde's name was Felicia. She was 19 from Grand Rapids Michigan and on her way to Fort Worth. She and Diana quickly struck up a friendship and were out in the dining car talking, sharing cheesecake, and drinking coffee. I left them alone and took Donnte' back to our sleeping quarters. When I announced my plan, they gave me the okay with a minimum of concern and then continued their conversation. I was so proud of Diana. She had come a long way from the woman I knew when we met.

Once the train began to move, I sat by the window with Donnte' in my arms, watching a farmer plow through his field. It didn't seem like he was trying to plant anything, it seemed more like he was just furrowing his fields getting ready for winter. The farmer faded from view and was replaced by the scene of rolling hills on which cattle were grazing in multitudes. I held Donnte' up to the window so that he could see out. He focused on the field of cattle and his face lit up with delight.

"COW!" I said. He looked curiously at me. "COW!" I pointed out the window. He looked out. "COW!" I said it again. He looked at me and smiled. He looked out of the window and his eyes again focused on the cows. I wanted to believe that he understood my meaning and being his father, I knew that he would be a genius child, walking and talking in just a few months. But the reality of it was that genius didn't run in my family. I was pretty smart, but far from genius. I just hoped and prayed that he would be smarter than his parents. I would do everything within my power to make that a reality.

We sat together for at least a half an hour with him sitting in my lap and the both of us transfixed on all that was going on outside. Mom was right, the countryside was beautiful, and the scenery was amazing. The colorful blend of trees that changed as autumn took control was breathtaking!

(Mom), I thought, (She wants me to read her Bible and I have yet to open it.)

It was still in my travel bag, so I laid Donnte' on the bed and pulled it out. I opened it to Genesis 18 and started reading to myself and then remembering mom saying that I should read the Bible to my family. I started reading aloud.

"And the Lord appeared unto him in the Plains of Mamry and he sat in the tent door in the heat of the day. He lifted up his eyes and looked, and low, three men stood by him and when he saw them, he ran to meet them from the tent door......"

"What are you doing?" Diana entered the room. "You're reading the Bible? YOU? I can't believe it!" She was pleasantly surprised.

"Yes, I'm reading the Bible! I'm reading to my son!"

She closed the door and then sat cross-legged beside me. She looked at Donnte' and tickled his stomach. He giggled and kicked his feet.

"He's the cutest baby I've ever seen. Everybody just loves him. Wherever we go, people just fall in love with him." She tickled him again and his giggling touch my ears. "I just love him so much! I never thought that I could have a child and feel like this. I'm so grateful to you baby for loving me and not giving up on me!" She leaned over and kissed me on the cheek. "What were you reading?"

"Remember mom talked to us about how God had promised her a son? She said that I was that son and if I read Genesis 17, 18, and 21, I understand how God can do the impossible, so I'm reading it. She also said to read aloud to my family, and we'd be blessed." I explained.

"Read on, Sir!" She picked up Donnte' and the way she held him touched my heart.

I continue to read and when I finished reading chapter 18, I saw a handwritten note on the edge of the page instructing me to go back to chapter 17 and began reading at the 16th verse. I did. Then I read chapter 20 in full and began to understand. God had promised Abraham and Sarah a son of their own in their old age. A son that would be the father of many nations. A son that they had always desired. It seemed impossible because they were far beyond the age and ability to have children, but God was faithful to his word and they did have a son, and they call him Isaac. The same was true with mom, but I was the son she asked for. Maybe not biological, as Isaac was to Abraham and Sarah, by the son nonetheless!

I noticed another notation on the page just where the word of the Bible said that Abraham was 100 years old when Isaac was born. She had written, 'Ecclesiastes 3:7'. I turned to it and read; "a time to rent, and a time to so, a time to keep silent, and a time to speak!"

"What does that have to do with what you read about Abraham, Sarah and Isaac?" Diana asked.

"I don't know. Maybe she was trying to tell us something."

"What's that?" Diana noticed something hidden.

"What?"

"Right there!"

She pointed to a piece of folded paper that was lodged between the page binding and the leather cover. It wasn't visible when the Bible was closed, but the way that the Bible opened at Ecclesiastes, allowed the cover to separate a little from the binding exposing it. I pulled it out. It was folded several times and had something hard inside. I felt it and surmised that it was a key. Was it the key to the locked box? I opened the paper and took the key out. I handed it to Diana. She looked at it and then pushed it back to me.

"I'm too nervous, you open it!" She said. Her hands were shaking so I took the key and she handed me the box. This key fit perfectly and release the catch as soon as I turned it. The lock fell open. She gasped.

"Are you ready?" I took the lock off and prepared to open the lid.

"Yeah. Go ahead."

I opened the lid and looked in. There were several expensive leather-bound notebooks. On top of them was an envelope that was addressed to 'Mr. and Mrs. Donn Diamond'. The envelope was sealed, and I gave it to

Diana. The books were not notebooks or cookbooks, but they were mom's diaries. Diana tore open the envelope and began to read the letter inside. I waited patiently as she silently read.

"Diana? Are you going to share it with me?" My impatience surfaced.

"Oh, I'm sorry baby. Wait a minute. I'm almost finished."

I waited until she finished and then she handed the letter to me. She pulled out the first diary from the metal box and stared at it but didn't open it.

The letter was very short and simple. Mom had a secret life that she wanted to remain secret until after her death. The truth could now be told. "A time to keep silent, a time to speak." She said that she could think of no one else that she'd rather have her diaries than us. She also said that once we got to Malibu that we would find her most precious jewelry and cookbooks in a safety deposit box, along with other valuables. Diana pulled out the rest of the diaries and looked at them never bothering to open or read any of them.

"Aren't you going to read them?" I asked.

"I don't know if I should. A woman's diary is sacred."

"Baby, she wanted us to read them. If she didn't, she wouldn't have left them to us."

"Yeah, I know that, but I've never read anyone's diaries before. It's kind of sacred to women. Someone else reading them without their permission is like, …taboo! Like pulling up a Nun's dress! You just don't do it!"

"Well, I'm not a woman. It's not sacred to me and I've always wondered what you women write about in there, and, you have her permission! Also, ….I thought about looking up a Nun's-dress! I just never tried it!"

"You're nasty!"

She slapped me on the leg.

"So, what's it going to be? You want to read, or shall I?"

"You do it. I just need time to prepare myself, okay?" She said.

I watched her stare at the cover and tremble just a little.

"Okay." I said.

There were six or seven of them. Each one bound and approximately 75 to 100 pages thick. It was a lot to read. She probably had been writing since she was a young girl. There was plenty of history there. A lot of heartaches and pain, a lot of joy and happiness. The life of a great woman.

Diana looked closely at the first, then the second. The third caught my eye because mom had written words from Ecclesiastes 3:7 on the cover, up in the corner. It wasn't large, but it caught my eye immediately. "A time to keep silent and a time to speak." There was something relevant about that Scripture. Was she directing us to that particular diary? And if so, why? What was this particular one the one that she wanted us to read immediately?"

"Baby pull that one out first!" I said.

"Why?"

"Look at what she wrote on the cover. I think there's something there she wants us to know right away."

She pushed the others aside and held that one in her hand. She read the writing up in the corner and agreed with my assessment.

Cautiously and slowly she opened the cover. On the inside page, mom had drawn a happy face and had written the page numbers in it and underlined it.

"I guess this is where she wants us to start." Diana said and turned to the page. She began to silently read, and when she finished, she stopped and handed it to me.

"What's wrong?"

"Read it!" Was all she said.

I began to read but I couldn't I believe what I saw. My brain just wouldn't accept it. How could it be? What I thought was just too far-fetched to be reality.

"Baby, are you thinking of what I'm thinking?" She asked.

"How can I not? But this is...... Crazy!"

"It would explain why she loved you so much and why you always felt so close to her but, you're right, it is hard to believe!

I read the pages again and then closed the book. I began to shake. My whole entire world was thrown in an uproar by two pages and an old woman's diary. Just two pages that didn't actually establish anything, but proposed answers to questions that had plagued me from the day that I found out I was adopted. I only knew that my father was a black man and my mother was white. They had an affair and I was the result. She was married to a prominent man in the city, a white man, and had given me up for adoption and resumed her life. I always wondered who she was. I wondered who my father was. I wondered why they gave me away! Why didn't at least one of them love me enough to keep me and raise me?

"Baby, are you all right? She asked.

I couldn't speak. How could I be all right? It seemed that mom was REALLY my mother!

Her diary said that she had actually had a son, born on the same day as I. In the same hospital. The product of her and a black man. A son that she had given up for adoption. She named her son 'Donn' after his father! It seemed that mom was actually my mother. I sat in shock and barely heard Diana when she called my name.

"Bab?... Baby? ....DONN?"

"Huh?... Yeah,.... Yeah,... I'm okay! I think I'm okay. This is too much for me right now!"

She took all of the diaries and put them back in the metal box. There was more to the story, but I just wasn't ready to read it all at that moment. I had to digest the information that I had already received.

If it were true, if I really was her biological son, why didn't she tell me before she died? Why did it have to be a secret all the way to her grave? I didn't understand. I didn't know if I ever would, but I believe our relationship would have been so much better if I had known. Obviously, she didn't think so. There had to be some very good reason for what she did. She may have thought that if I had known that I would resent her for all of the time we spent apart. Maybe there would have been too many questions for her to answer in her ill state of health. If it were true, she would have put all of the answers to my questions in her diaries, I just had to read them and learn about her that way. I laid back and tried to relax. Diana laid beside me placing Donnte' on my chest.

"It makes sense!" I said. "When I first met her, she seemed to know me already. The first time she came into my store, she looked at me as if she already knew about me. She probably had been keeping tabs on me all through my life. I always felt a special feeling for her and that's why I wouldn't charge her for cleaning her Windows. Wow! This is too much to handle it!"

"You want to read some more?" Diana asked. She stroked my face gently.

I did want to read, but I didn't want to do it just then.

"You know, Donn, we really don't know if it's true or not. It could be a coincidence. All we're doing is assuming and speculating. You should read the rest and find out for sure." She continued to stroke my face and she added a kiss on my cheek.

"You're right, but not now. I'm just going to lay here and try to rest."

"You're not going to rest! How can you rest with that on your mind?" She got up and changed and fed Donnte' until he was full and sleepy. She then disappeared into the hallway. She spoke as she passed through the tiny doorway.

"I'll be right back."

She was gone for about 10 minutes and in that time all that I could think about was mom. I asked myself questions and speculated on the answers, but I refused to pick up the diaries and read. I was torn between wanting, and not wanting, to know. When she came back, she held a covered plate that contained two large and juicy cheeseburgers that were surrounded by so many French fries that some fell off the plate when she removed the cover.

"Here baby. Eat something."

She took Donnte' from my chest and placed him in his crib. She handed me the platter and then she stripped down to her panties and bra. She knew that I loved seeing her clad only in panties and bra, she also knew that I got turned on every time I saw her beautiful body. She knew a lot about me, and how to arouse me sexually because she knew about my fetishes, and she knew that seeing her panties hug her body was one of them!

She sat down with me then she picked up the other cheeseburger and took a bite before she put it back on the plate. There was no doubt as to what she had in mind. She was going to feed me first, then sex me, and finally rock me to sleep. It was fine with me and I couldn't wait! It was one thousand percent better than any sleeping pill!

She watched me as I ate. I guess she was trying to wait for the right moment. She took the plate after I had finished my cheeseburger, but I didn't get a chance to finish the French fries.

"You don't want to get too stuffed! I need you to be flexible!" She began to purr as she always does when she wants to make love. "You can eat the French fries later!" She put the cover tightly back on the plate so that the French fries could stay as warm as possible.

She began to undress me, and I laid back and watched each piece of clothing slowly disappear. I was smiling and Big Al was very happy too! Very happy and very excited. Very happy!

My thoughts of the earth-shattering news that mom dropped on me began to quickly fade away to be replaced by thoughts of Diana and Jennifer. My wife knew exactly how to please me! She wasn't timid or afraid to do anything that gave me pleasure. Sometimes I thought that she got more pleasure out of what she did for me than I did. I was content to lay back and let her work her magic. For the moment, I decided not to worry about who I was or where I had come from, or even who my mother was, etc. I closed my eyes and enjoyed every touch of Diana's body, her hands, and her lips! There was plenty of time later on to ponder all of the questions that plagued me. I put all of that out of my mind and concentrated on the pleasure that my wife was giving me.

I savored every feeling, every touch, every movement and every second of my wife's tenderness, love, and luscious body. I forgot all about my heritage, my mother, my father, and my family as Diana took care of my sexual desires, and our train sped onward to California!

CPSIA information can be obtained
at www.ICGtesting.com
Printed in the USA
BVHW041023090623
665707BV00004B/12